Dr Michèle Serrand

La nouvelle ménopause

Le guide des hormones naturelles après 45 ans

Pour la présente Édition

9, avenue Albert II
MC - 98000 MONACO
Tél.:0037797776210
Fax:0037797776211

Direction :
Christophe Didierlaurent
Responsable éditoriale :
Fabienne Desmarets
Mise en page et infographie :
Pierre Stracquadanio

Dépôt légal : *2015*
ISBN13 : 978-2-35934-352-6

Crédits photos :
Eye Wire, Good Shoot, Photo Alto, Photo Disc, Digital Vision,
Image Source, Copyright © 20 N. Abdallah et
ses concédants: tous droits réservés

Imprimé en Union Européenne

Dr Michèle Serrand

La nouvelle ménopause

Le guide des hormones naturelles après 45 ans

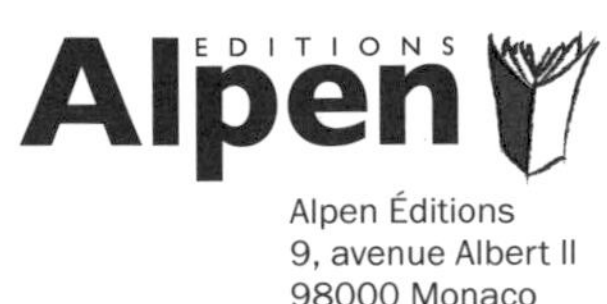

Alpen Éditions
9, avenue Albert II
98000 Monaco

Michèle Serrand est médecin hospitalier et écrivain. Elle pratique l'homéopathie depuis une quinzaine d'années. Présidente d'Homéopathes sans frontières - France, elle enseigne cette discipline à des médecins et des pharmaciens en Afrique et en Asie.

Du même auteur :
Ginseng : mille ans de bienfaits, Alpen éditions.
Bien vivre après un infarctus, Alpen Éditions.

AVERTISSEMENT
Les informations contenues dans ce livre ne peuvent pas remplacer un avis autorisé. Avant toute automédication, consultez un médecin ou un pharmacien qualifié.

Introduction

En France, les femmes abordent le plus souvent la ménopause avec anxiété. Les journaux féminins sont pleins des difficultés de cette période, qu'ils agitent comme autant d'épouvantails. Ces articles ont longtemps conclu presque systématiquement que « tout cela se passe bien lorsque l'on prend le THS : traitement hormonal substitutif », que la grande majorité des gynécologues et des médecins généralistes proposent.

Cependant seules 20 % des femmes prennent un tel traitement. Très souvent, elles l'arrêtent dès la première année. Parmi celles qui prennent un THS, elles ne sont que 10 % à le poursuivre après 5 ans. Et ceci pour au moins deux raisons. Tout d'abord elles se lassent de prendre régulièrement des produits chimiques. Ensuite, elles craignent les cancers que peut favoriser le THS, notamment le cancer du sein. Bien que les propos des laboratoires pharmaceutiques, relayés par la grande majorité des médecins, soient rassurants, les femmes sont prudentes. Ces médecins nous disent que le risque est faible, que les femmes traitées par THS sont mieux suivies. Ce suivi favoriserait la détection et la prise en charge rapide de ces tumeurs. Le pronostic serait meilleur. Malgré tous ces bons arguments, les femmes se méfient. Toutes ont entendu parler de cette grande étude menée aux Etats-Unis, l'étude *Women's Health Initiative (WHI)*, qui montrent les dangers du THS. Certains médecins leur expliquent que ce ne sont pas les mêmes hormones qu'en France et qu'il y aurait beaucoup moins de problèmes chez nous. Ils mettent l'accent sur les mauvais effets de la ménopause : ostéoporose et maladies cardiovasculaires entre autres, arguant que ces mauvais effets seraient prévenus par la prise du THS. Or, cette même étude a montré qu'au contraire, le THS aggravait certains risques vasculaires.

Qu'en est-il exactement ? Et que faire ? Sommes-nous condamnées à choisir entre le risque de cancer du sein et le risque de fracture du col du fémur, ou d'angine de poitrine ?

Y a-t-il d'autres voies possibles ? Aurions-nous quelque chose à apprendre des pays asiatiques, notamment du Japon ? Les femmes japonaises souffrent rarement de bouffées de chaleur. Elles ont beaucoup moins d'ostéoporose que les femmes occidentales. Les chercheurs ont montré que cet avantage est lié à leur alimentation, notamment à la présence du soja à chaque repas.

Ce livre vous propose d'examiner d'un peu plus près toutes ces questions :
- Tout d'abord, qu'est-ce que la ménopause réellement ?
- Quels sont les avantages et les inconvénients des traitements chimiques : le traitement hormonal substitutif que l'on appelle maintenant le Traitement Hormonal de la Ménopause (THM) à la suite des recommandations de l'AFSSAPS, mais aussi les nouveaux traitements avec les SERM *(Selective Estrogen Receptor Modulator)* et les SAS *(Selective Action Steroid)* ?
- Comment être bien dans sa peau, en choisissant des produits naturels pour atteindre ce nouvel équilibre qu'est la ménopause ?

La ménopause peut être une étape formidable dans la vie des femmes. Un certain art de vivre, associant une diététique savoureuse, la redécouverte du mouvement, la pratique des techniques de relaxation et l'utilisation sage des nouveaux alicaments riches en phytohormones comme le soja, aide alors la femme à atteindre son plein épanouissement.

(1) Le terme THM est aujourd'hui choisi par l'Afssaps et les médecins afin de le différencier du traitement hormonal substitutif (THS) destiné aux femmes jeunes précocement ménopausées.

TABLE DES MATIÈRES

Partie I

LA MÉNOPAUSE SANS THM : EST-CE POSSIBLE ?

La ménopause sans THM : est-ce possible?

Depuis quelques mois, Martine ne se sent pas bien. « C'est la ménopause », lui dit sa meilleure amie, Lydia, qui est déjà passée par là.

Martine est irritable. Ses nuits sont devenues insupportables. Elle se réveille plusieurs fois par nuit, couverte de sueur. Ceci l'oblige à se découvrir. Puis elle grelotte. Elle remet la couette, se rendort et cela recommence.

Dans la journée, ce n'est guère mieux. Elle est professeur et au milieu des cours elle sent le rouge lui monter aux joues. Une sensation de chaleur l'envahit. Puis elle se met à transpirer. Elle enlève alors sa veste, ouvre la fenêtre. Dix minutes plus tard, elle la referme.

Martine sait bien ce qui lui arrive : depuis quatre mois, elle n'a pas eu de règles.

« *C'est la ménopause* », lui dit sa meilleure amie, Lydia, qui est déjà passée par là.

En 2002, plus de deux millions de Françaises suivaient un traitement hormonal de la ménopause ce qui représente un taux d'utilisation du THM chez les femmes de plus de 40 ans de 18 % environ. La majorité des utilisatrices a entre 50 et 60 ans.

Une nouvelle façon de manger

Mais comment faire ? Martine, pour des raisons de santé, ne peut pas prendre le THM dont lui parlent plusieurs de ses amies. Du coup, elle s'effraie car on lui promet tout un tas de malheurs : peau sèche, chute de la libido, os fragiles. Tout cela ne cesse de l'inquiéter et accentue son anxiété. Du coup, à la maison, elle est nerveuse et avec son compagnon, ça devient de plus en plus difficile.

« Moi non plus je n'y ai pas droit, dit Lydia, et tu vois, je me porte à merveille. Et je ne prends aucun médicament chimique. Mon médecin m'a proposé une nouvelle façon de manger. Il m'a engagée à changer un peu mon mode de vie, à faire plus de sport, à avoir des activités relaxantes. Et il m'a conseillé également des compléments alimentaires à base de soja. Et depuis, je vais très bien : je n'ai plus de bouffées de chaleur. Je dors mieux. Dans la journée, je ne suis plus irritable. Et j'ai envie de faire plein de choses. »

Oui mais pour le cœur et les os, est-ce que c'est suffisant ?

« Mon médecin m'a bien expliqué qu'en associant cette diététique au sport, en prenant les suppléments nutritionnels, je réduisais aussi les risques d'avoir ces problèmes. Il m'a indiqué de bons sites sur Internet où tout cela est expliqué et où l'on trouve les dernières études sur ces questions. »

Martine reprend confiance. Elle va se documenter et fixer un rendez-vous avec son médecin pour faire le point.

Préparer la consultation avec son médecin

Votre médecin possède une bonne connaissance de la ménopause et de ses traitements, mais il ne pourra pas répondre aux questions que vous ne lui posez pas. C'est la raison pour laquelle il est important de préparer votre entretien en prenant l'avis de vos amies qui ont déjà traversé cette période comme de celles qui sont actuellement traitées. Documentez-vous le plus possible : livres, articles de magazine, et bien sûr Internet si vous y avez accès. Intéressez-vous aux aspects nutritionnels et de phytothérapie, en général moins bien couverts dans une consultation classique. Ce livre vous aidera à préparer les questions indispensables que vous devez poser.

Partie II

MÉNOPAUSE, PRÉMÉNOPAUSE, PÉRIMÉNOPAUSE : PEUT-ON Y VOIR CLAIR ?

Comprendre les femmes

Dans le corps des femmes, tout est mouvance, changement, adaptation. À chaque cycle, le jeu des hormones donne un nouveau sens au mot équilibre.

La ménopause est cette période de la vie des femmes où les règles s'arrêtent. Pour beaucoup de femmes, c'est un soulagement synonyme de liberté. Mais pour d'autres, c'est le signe de l'avancement des jours, de l'approche de la vieillesse. De nombreuses craintes y sont associées avec, notamment, celle de vieillir et de ne plus être séduisante.

Reconnue pour sa sagesse dans certaines civilisations, la femme ménopausée doit auparavant affronter la tempête du déséquilibre hormonal qui souffle pendant la préménopause.

Pour bien comprendre le phénomène de la préménopause et de la ménopause, il faut revenir sur le mécanisme des règles.

À la naissance, la petite fille présente dans ses ovaires un certain nombre de cellules, appelées ovocytes, qui sont au repos.

Un phénomène cyclique

Au moment de la puberté, sous l'action d'hormones fabriquées par l'hypophyse, un fonctionnement cyclique se met en place et tous les 28 jours en moyenne vont apparaître les règles. Les règles correspondent à la desquamation de la muqueuse de l'utérus, desquamation qui se produit seulement en l'absence de fécondation. Le premier jour des règles est le premier jour du cycle. Chaque cycle comprend deux parties : la première partie, ou phase folliculaire, voit le développement, au niveau d'un ovaire, d'un follicule. Ce follicule sécrète des estrogènes. Il contient un ovocyte qui, progressivement, deviendra un ovule.

Puis survient l'ovulation : à ce moment le follicule arrive à maturation. Il éclate et libère l'ovule.

Suit la seconde partie du cycle ou phase lutéinique avec sécrétion de la progestérone qui favorise le développement de la muqueuse de l'utérus. Celle-ci tend à constituer un nid pour un œuf éventuel. L'œuf est un ovule fécondé par un spermatozoïde.

En l'absence de fécondation, les taux hormonaux de progestérone et d'estrogènes chutent et la muqueuse utérine desquame : ceci constitue les règles.

Ce phénomène cyclique est sous l'influence de l'hypophyse, elle-même sous contrôle de l'hypothalamus, qui répond également aux taux dans le sang des deux types d'hormones fabriquées par les ovaires : les estrogènes et la progestérone. Ce fonctionnement est très sensible aux neuromédiateurs comme l'adrénaline.

Or les neuromédiateurs sont fabriqués en fonction de nos émotions. La vie émotionnelle a donc des répercussions sur les cycles.

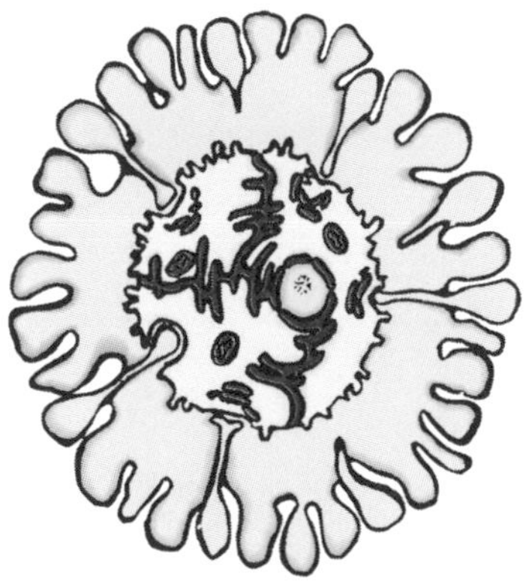

Les ovules sont produits par les ovaires. Ils peuvent être fécondés par les spermatozoïdes.

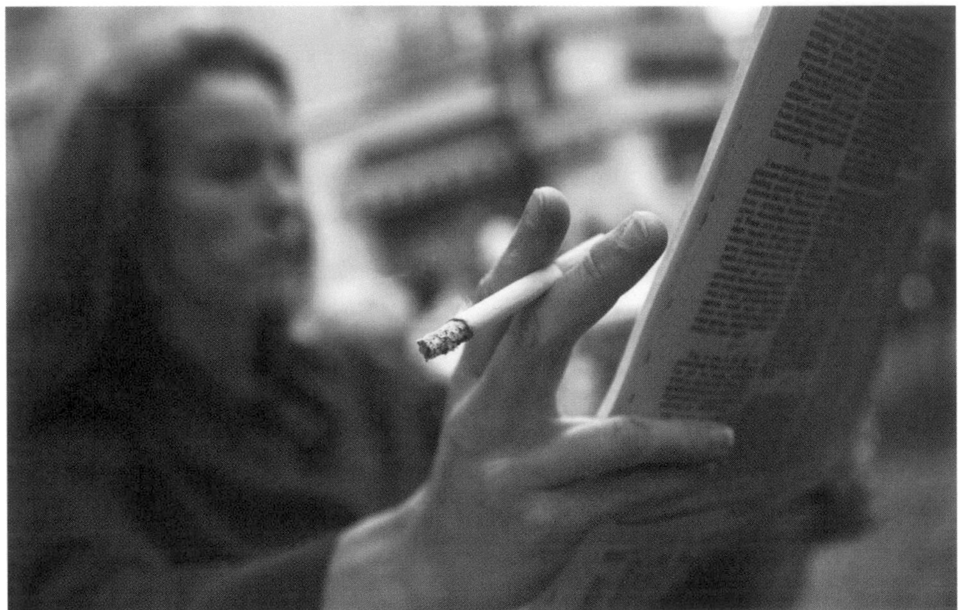

Le tabac, ennemi public numéro 1

Non content de dessécher la peau, d'approfondir les rides, de détruire les poumons, d'abîmer les artères, le tabac s'attaque aux hormones. Il est le seul facteur qui avance avec certitude l'âge de survenue de la ménopause. Dans nos sociétés occidentales, celle-ci survient en moyenne vers 50-51 ans. Avec le tabac, elle arrive 1 à 2 ans plus tôt.

Après la tempête, la sérénité

La préménopause est marquée par une phase de perturbation hormonale. À la ménopause, un nouvel équilibre s'instaure.

Après 45 ans, 80 % des femmes se plaignent de règles irrégulières et de troubles qui annoncent la ménopause

Au moment de la ménopause, il n'y a plus de fonctionnement cyclique mais une sécrétion résiduelle d'estrogènes et de progestérone par les corticosurrénales et les ovaires. Cette sécrétion est très variable d'une femme à l'autre. Voilà pourquoi les femmes n'ont pas toutes les mêmes symptômes.

La période avant l'arrêt définitif des règles s'appelle la préménopause. Au niveau biologique, cela correspond à une diminution de la production de progestérone. Le rapport entre les taux d'estrogènes et de progestérone peut varier d'un cycle à l'autre. Petit à petit, il n'y a plus d'ovulation. Cette période s'accompagne de troubles des règles avec raccourcissement ou, au contraire, allongement de la durée des cycles. Il peut y avoir des saignements plus importants, l'apparition ou l'aggravation d'un syndrome prémenstruel. Lorsqu'il y a espacement des règles, on ne peut pas être sûr qu'il ne s'agisse en fait d'une grossesse débutante. D'autant que la période entre deux cycles peut être de deux, voire trois mois ou plus. Ces doutes peuvent générer beaucoup d'anxiété.

Cette période varie de 6 mois à 10 ans pour certaines femmes et débute en moyenne à 48 ans. Concrètement, 4 à 5 ans avant la ménopause, 80 % des femmes se plaignent de règles irrégulières.

Mini-lexique pour mieux comprendre

Ménopause : arrêt définitif des règles. On ne peut savoir qu'a posteriori que les règles sont définitivement arrêtées. Aussi on parle de ménopause lorsqu'il n'y a pas eu de règles pendant au moins un an.

Préménopause : période avant l'arrêt définitif des règles pendant laquelle on observe des irrégularités menstruelles.

Périménopause : période de préménopause et l'année qui suit l'arrêt des règles.

Le cerveau aux commandes

L'hypothalamus est une petite glande située à la base du cerveau. Elle fabrique des hormones qui régulent les grandes fonctions dirigeant le corps : la faim, la soif, le sommeil, la température du corps, et, bien sûr, la génitalité. Certaines hormones fabriquées par l'hypothalamus sont excrétées directement au niveau de l'hypophyse.
L'hypophyse est située juste en dessous de l'hypothalamus, dans le cerveau, en arrière de la racine du nez. C'est également une glande qui fabrique des hormones qui passent dans le sang. Ces hormones vont stimuler les différentes glandes situées dans le corps : la thyroïde, les surrénales et les ovaires. C'est le « chef d'orchestre » des glandes. Elle est donc sous la dépendance de l'hypothalamus et d'une partie du cerveau. Elle répond ainsi à la vie émotive par le biais des neuromédiateurs. Les hormones hypophysaires qui stimulent les ovaires sont : la FSH (folliculo-stimulating hormone) et la LH (lutéinostimulating hormone). La sécrétion de ces deux hormones est cyclique, avec pour chacune un pic sécrétoire en milieu de cycle favorisant l'ovulation. Au moment de la ménopause, cette sécrétion cyclique s'arrête.

À quoi nous servent ces hormones ?

Estrogènes et progestérone : ces hormones vont partout. Et participent à notre équilibre quotidien.

Les hormones sont des petites molécules qui sont le plus souvent sécrétées par les glandes dans le sang. Elles peuvent ainsi atteindre toutes les parties du corps. Arrivées près de l'organe cible, elles traversent la paroi des vaisseaux sanguins et parviennent jusqu'aux cellules où elles doivent agir.

Les estrogènes sont synthétisés par l'ovaire, le placenta et la corticosurrénale. Ils ont plusieurs organes cibles.
Ils ont un rôle essentiel dans le développement des caractères sexuels féminins.
Leur rôle :

- Au niveau de l'ovaire, ils favorisent la maturation du follicule et de l'ovule.
- Au niveau de l'utérus, ils stimulent la prolifération de la muqueuse utérine et augmentent les contractions musculaires du muscle de l'utérus.
- Au niveau du vagin, ils favorisent un épaississement de la muqueuse et la desquamation des cellules épithéliales. Cette desquamation permet une plus grande production d'acide lactique, ce qui diminue le pH vaginal. Cette action empêche les infections vaginales.
- Les estrogènes augmentent la coagulabilité du sang.
- Au niveau rénal, l'estradiol entraîne une rétention d'eau et de sel. Ceci peut donner un œdème local.
- L'estradiol diminuerait le taux de cholestérol.
- Il amincit la peau et la rend plus souple.

Les progestatifs ont comme rôle principal de favoriser la nidation et le développement de l'œuf fécondé. D'où leur nom : « *pour la gestation* ».

Ils sont synthétisés par le corps jaune, le follicule, le placenta et la corticosurrénale. Pour agir, la progestérone a besoin de l'action simultanée ou préliminaire de l'estradiol.
La progestérone stimule la croissance du muscle utérin, mais réduit son activité.
Elle transforme la muqueuse utérine et la rend apte à la nidation.
Au niveau des seins, elle stimule le développement des canaux galactophores.
Au niveau des reins, elle augmente l'élimination de sel.

Que se passe-t-il en préménopause ?

Les taux de progestérone diminuent. Tout se passe comme s'il y avait un excès d'estrogènes. Les seins sont gonflés, douloureux. Peuvent se développer des kystes au niveau des seins. Les règles deviennent un peu anarchiques : ou plus espacées, ou plus rapprochées. L'écoulement de sang peut être plus important, voire hémorragique. Ce que l'on appelle le syndrome prémenstruel augmente.

La DHEA (déhydroépiandrostérone)

Elle est essentiellement produite par les surrénales. La ménopause ne modifie pas sa sécrétion. Celle-ci diminue régulièrement avec l'âge indépendamment de la ménopause. La baisse est équivalente chez l'homme.

Que se passe-t-il à la ménopause ?

Les ovaires ont épuisé leur stock d'ovocytes. Il n'y a plus de sécrétion cyclique des hormones sexuelles. Les règles s'arrêtent. La sécrétion des estrogènes et de la progestérone est à un niveau très bas. Ce niveau est spécifique pour chaque femme. Ceci explique que chacune aura un ressenti très différent au moment de la ménopause.

La testostérone

Chez la femme préménopausée, la testostérone est synthétisée par les cellules qui entourent les follicules ovariens. Elle sert de point de départ à la synthèse d'estrogènes. La testostérone baisse fortement chez la femme à partir de l'âge de 20-25 ans jusqu'à la ménopause, moins après cette période car si les follicules ont disparu, l'ovaire reste actif et de surcroît la DHEA (déhydroépiandrostérone) produite par les surrénales est transformée en testostérone.

Moins d'hormones : ce qui change

Les symptômes de la ménopause sont dus en partie à la diminution des taux hormonaux en estrogènes. Mais cela n'explique pas tout : le contexte socioculturel est également important. Les recherches scientifiques se poursuivent car la médecine est loin d'avoir tout explicité.

L'apparition de rides à la ménopause n'est pas directement due à la baisse des hormones

Les bouffées de chaleur : un signe fréquent

C'est le désagrément le plus souvent avancé par les femmes. Les bouffées de chaleur commencent parfois pendant la préménopause. Environ 70 % des femmes ménopausées s'en plaignent et 30 % n'en ont jamais.

Il s'agit d'une sensation de chaleur qui survient rapidement, envahissant tout ou une partie du corps, s'accompagnant souvent de transpiration. Elles peuvent survenir dans la journée ou la nuit, et, dans ce cas, elles troublent le sommeil. Parfois, elles sont visibles pour l'entourage, ce qui est fort mal vécu.

Leur survenue est très aléatoire et variable d'une femme à l'autre. Pour certaines, il s'agira d'une ou deux bouffées par semaine. Pour d'autres, elles surviendront plusieurs fois par heure, devenant un véritable handicap.

En moyenne, cela dure 3 ans, puis s'estompe et disparaît en 5 à 8 ans. Malheureusement, certaines femmes vont être gênées pendant plusieurs dizaines d'années.
C'est souvent ce qui motive la première consultation pour ménopause. Le stress, la fatigue, l'énervement aggravent ce phénomène, ainsi que la consommation d'alcool, de café, d'épices, de tabac. La pratique d'un sport et une alimentation riche en vitamine E les diminuent.

Pourquoi les bouffées de chaleur ?

L'hypothalamus, une petite région du cerveau qui contrôle la température corporelle répond à la chute des estrogènes selon un mécanisme mal connu. L'hypothalamus réagit comme si le corps surchauffait : il ordonne au système nerveux central de dissiper la chaleur supposée en excès en dilatant les vaisseaux périphériques et en activant les glandes sébacées. Ces manœuvres peuvent accroître de 2,5 °C la température de la peau. Les bouffées de chaleur persistent 2 à 3 ans en moyenne.

La peau moins souple

Plusieurs facteurs interviennent sur la qualité de la peau. La diminution des estrogènes laisse le champ libre aux hormones masculines secrétées par les surrénales. Ceci explique la chute possible des cheveux sur le front, l'apparition de poils, notamment au niveau de la lèvre supérieure.

La peau elle-même perd de son élasticité. Son épaisseur diminue. Des ridules et des rides se forment. Des taches plus foncées ou blanches apparaissent. Mais ces changements ne sont pas directement liés à la baisse des estrogènes. En effet, ils peuvent survenir avant la ménopause. Ils sont surtout dus au tabac, à l'exposition au soleil, à la prise d'alcool et à des facteurs génétiques. La prise d'estrogènes n'améliore d'ailleurs pas vraiment la qualité de la peau.

La sexualité perturbée

La sexualité est une composante importante du bien-être et de la santé. À la ménopause, il est fréquent d'observer une baisse du désir. Encore une conséquence de la carence hormonale mais pas seulement.

Des muqueuses plus sèches

Les muqueuses sont beaucoup plus sensibles que la peau aux taux hormonaux. Ainsi la ménopause s'accompagne pour une femme sur deux d'une sécheresse vaginale qui peut être très gênante. Elle favorise la survenue des mycoses, qui sont des infections liées à des champignons. Le plus connu est Candida albicans qui provoque des candidoses. De plus, cette sécheresse peut gêner les rapports sexuels qui risquent de devenir douloureux. Au niveau vulvaire, on note également des modifications : raréfaction des poils pubiens, petites et grandes lèvres qui diminuent de volume.

L'utérus diminue de volume. Il s'atrophie. Ce qui est plutôt bénéfique lorsqu'il y a un fibrome, car celui-ci va également diminuer. S'il était à l'origine de saignements, ceux-ci vont s'arrêter.

De nombreuses femmes ménopausées se plaignent d'une baisse de la libido, qui pourrait s'expliquer par un niveau insuffisant d'androgènes (DHEA, testostérone)

Une partie de la muqueuse interne de la vessie est très sensible aux estrogènes. La baisse trop importante de ces hormones, chez certaines femmes, peut induire des modifications qui favoriseront les cystites. Ces cystites se traduisent par des besoins fréquents d'uriner. Il y a des douleurs en urinant, comme des brûlures ou des picotements. Ces cystites ne sont pas toujours dues à des germes et l'analyse des urines ne retrouve parfois aucun microbe.

De nombreuses femmes ménopausées disent avoir moins de désir sexuel. Il n'est pas facile de savoir à quoi est réellement liée cette baisse de libido. Est-ce dû à la baisse hormonale ou à un problème plus complexe de vécu émotionnel concernant la ménopause ? La vieillesse fait peur. Et la ménopause, qui signifie l'avance en âge, est redoutée. La confiance en soi, en son pouvoir de séduction, est mise à mal. Il est probable que la baisse de la libido soit directement liée à ce problème. Or une sexualité épanouie et prolongée est un des meilleurs traitements pour diminuer la sécheresse vaginale.

Des seins douloureux

Dans la période de préménopause, la progestérone ne vient plus lutter contre l'action des estrogènes sur les seins : il s'ensuit des douleurs mammaires dans la deuxième partie du cycle, parfois très invalidantes. Les seins deviennent plus gros, douloureux. Peuvent apparaître des boules ou des kystes, qui vont activer la crainte d'un cancer. Une échographie ou une mammographie permettront de rassurer.

À la ménopause, après quelques années, la glande mammaire va involuer. Les seins seront plus mous et souvent plus petits. Ils seront également plus sensibles à toute modification de poids. Une prise de poids génèrera des vergetures sur les seins. Une perte de poids donnera un aspect flasque aux seins. Et dans notre monde occidental où les seins sont magnifiés en tant que symbole sexuel, cela ne pourra qu'accentuer le malaise. Il ne faudra donc pas imposer de fluctuations brutales au poids.

Une prise de poids génèrera des vergetures sur les seins. Une perte de poids donnera un aspect flasque aux seins.

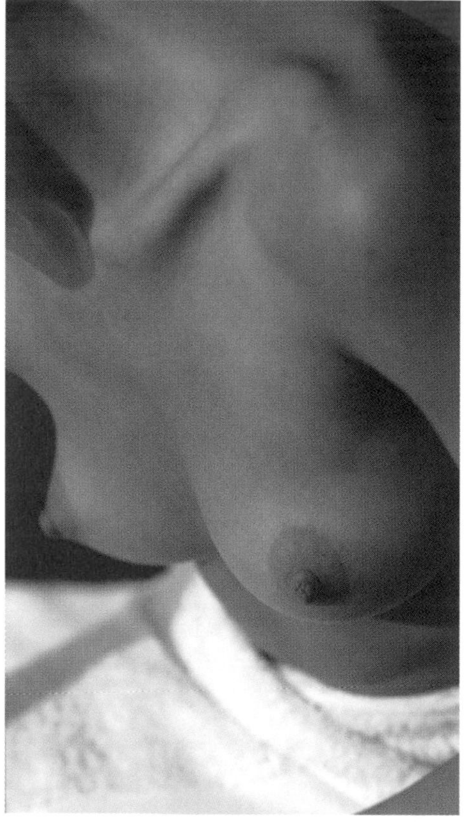

L' humeur se détériore

La période de la périménopause est dans notre civilisation une période difficile car dévalorisée. Il s'ensuit des troubles de l'humeur et du sommeil dont il est difficile de dire s'ils sont liés directement à la baisse des estrogènes ou au contexte social.

Déprime, fatigue et irritabilité

Est-ce lié exclusivement aux hormones ? C'est une période toute particulière de la vie où de nombreux événements interviennent et peuvent, à eux seuls, expliquer les difficultés émotionnelles.

C'est le moment pour les enfants de quitter le nid familial : cet événement est bouleversant même s'il est attendu et souhaité. Parfois, des conflits conjugaux conduisent à une remise en question du couple. Les pressions au sein du travail s'accentuent. Les parents, souvent très âgés, ont des problèmes de santé. La femme de cinquante ans est au milieu du gué, notamment au niveau des générations, entre celle des enfants et celle des parents.

Et également dans sa propre vie : à cinquante ans, elle sait qu'elle a devant elle de nombreuses années qui peuvent être des années d'épanouissement et de bonheur. Mais le discours ambiant fait croire que plus rien n'est possible.

C'est aussi le moment de prises de conscience profondes sur le sens de la vie. La perte des êtres chers favorise cette réflexion. L'investissement mis dans le travail où les pressions sont de plus en plus grandes semble inutile ou tout du moins excessif. Supporter depuis 25 à 30 ans les colères du mari ou son absence de participation au niveau de la vie familiale devient par trop difficile.

Sans oublier ce que l'on pourrait appeler le démon de midi : un compagnon plus tendre, plus attentionné que l'époux qui peut conduire à remettre en question les années de mariage.

Et devant soi de nombreuses années à vivre dont on a envie de profiter à fond.

Quelle est l'influence réelle de la diminution des hormones sur les signes multiples de fragilité psychique et nerveuse ? Elle est difficile à préciser. Ce qui est sûr, c'est que le seul traitement hormonal substitutif est souvent insuffisant pour améliorer les choses.

40 % des femmes ménopausées se plaignent d'insomnie, de fatigue et de stress.

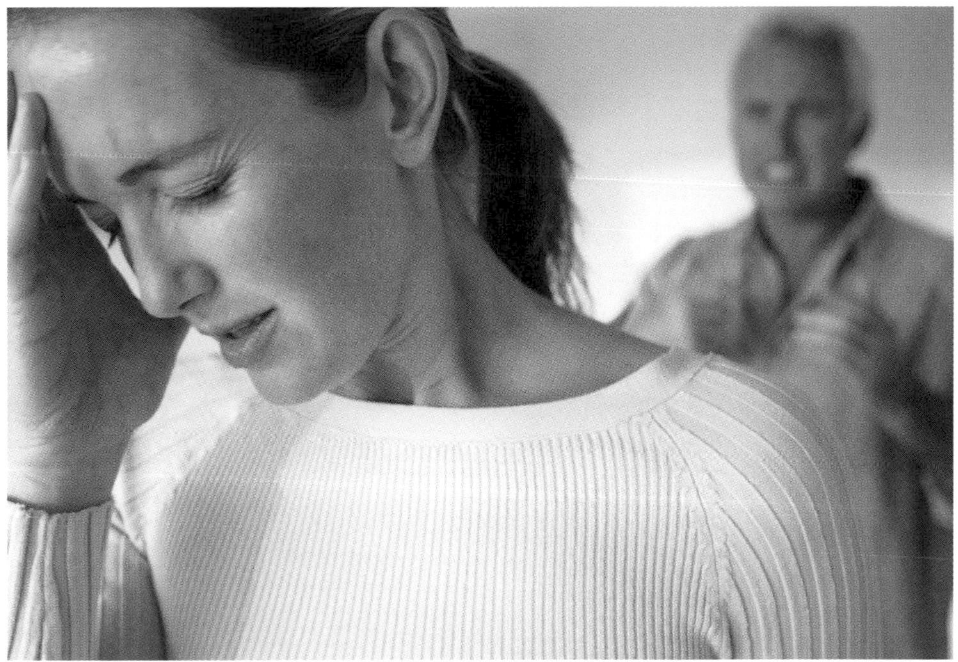

Troubles du sommeil

Les problèmes de sommeil semblent plus fréquents après 50 ans chez l'homme comme chez la femme, mais celle-ci apparaît plus vulnérable. Là encore, le seul traitement hormonal est souvent insuffisant.

Les troubles du sommeil, avec au maximum l'insomnie, génèrent une fatigue qui, au fur et à mesure, va conduire à des modifications de l'humeur dans la journée avec irritabilité, compensation alimentaire, crises de larmes... Pour améliorer tout cela, un nouvel art de vivre est indispensable.

Dans la population générale, environ deux personnes sur dix vont souffrir à un moment donné d'anxiété, de déprime, de fatigue, d'irritabilité, d'insomnie, de stress. Ce sont des moments où l'on se sent particulièrement fragile et vulnérable. Au moment de la ménopause, cela touche quatre femmes sur dix.

Quand le cœur souffre

Les maladies cardiovasculaires constituent en France la première cause de mortalité. Elles concernent environ 30 % des décès. Ces maladies touchent le cœur ou les vaisseaux, notamment les artères, entraînant angine de poitrine, infarctus, artérite, accidents vasculaires cérébraux. La ménopause est une période à risque.

La protection des vaisseaux disparaît

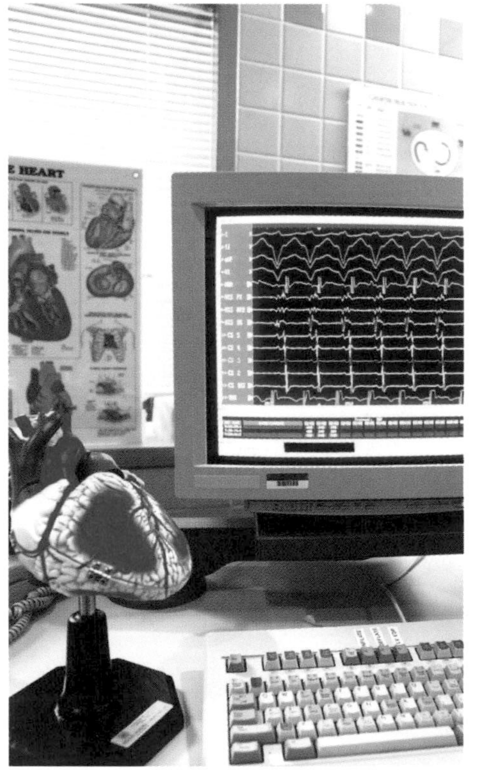

À 40 ans, la maladie coronarienne touche 6 hommes pour 1 femme. Ensuite le rapport entre hommes et femmes diminue.

Sauf cas particuliers, les femmes ne font pas de crise cardiaque avant la ménopause. Les accidents cardiovasculaires sont ensuite de plus en plus fréquents au fur et à mesure que l'âge augmente, et particulièrement après 65 ans. Ceci tend à prouver que les femmes sont protégées avant la ménopause et une dizaine d'années encore après. Cette protection est vraisemblablement liée à la présence des hormones féminines mais pas uniquement.

L'effet bénéfique des estrogènes serait dû en partie à leur action sur les lipides sanguins. Après la ménopause, on constate en effet une augmentation du cholestérol total et du « mauvais » cholestérol et une baisse du « bon » cholestérol. Les estrogènes agiraient, de plus, directement sur la paroi des artères en renforçant ses systèmes de protection contre l'athérosclérose.

Si les hormones jouent vraisemblablement un rôle, d'autres facteurs augmentent à coup sûr la fréquence des maladies cardiovasculaires. Il est de plus en plus évident que le mode de vie joue un rôle majeur.

Les facteurs de risque

Les maladies cardiovasculaires augmentent avec :

- le taux de cholestérol ;
- la tension artérielle ;
- le taux de sucre dans le sang ;
- le taux d'homocystéine ;
- le poids ;
- le tabagisme ;
- la sédentarité ;
- le stress ;
- l'excès de sucres rapides et de graisses.

La différence entre hommes et femmes avant 50 ans s'explique aussi peut-être par la façon de manger, la moindre consommation de tabac, la plus grande attention que les femmes portent à leur poids. De plus, avec les règles, les femmes ont régulièrement une élimination de sang et donc de fer. Ceci est peut-être bénéfique car le fer en excès est à l'origine de troubles cardiovasculaires. Ce qui semble de plus en plus certain, c'est que le traitement hormonal ne protège pas des maladies cardiovasculaires. Il est possible même qu'il en augmente le risque.

La meilleure prévention passe donc par une bonne hygiène de vie, associant une excellente diététique et de la détente (lire page 93).

Les estrogènes ne font pas tout

La maladie coronarienne est une maladie plutôt rare pour les femmes à 40 ans. Toutefois, les femmes qui font un infarctus à cet âge meurent plus souvent que les hommes dans le même cas. Car les estrogènes ne font pas tout. Ils ne peuvent pas protéger contre les autres risques qui augmentent chez la femme depuis une vingtaine d'années : tension artérielle élevée, taux de cholestérol élevé, obésité.

Le poids, ennemi public numéro 2

La crainte de prendre du poids est justifiée car on observe effectivement une prise de poids chez la femme aux environs de 50 ans. Cette prise de poids intervient chez les femmes, qu'elles suivent ou non un traitement hormonal. Il y a deux raisons probables à ces kilos superflus :

- un changement alimentaire avec une augmentation, dans la ration alimentaire, des sucres et des graisses ;
- une activité physique moindre.

Les modifications hormonales de la ménopause conduisent à une répartition différente des graisses chez la femme. Pendant la vie génitale, les graisses sont réparties sur les cuisses et les hanches, constituant ainsi une réserve vite mobilisable pour les grossesses et l'allaitement.

À la ménopause, les graisses se déplacent vers le ventre ! Et en même temps, la masse musculaire diminue

Des os plus fragiles

L'ostéoporose et ses risques de fracture augmentent à la ménopause. Elle touche une femme sur trois après 50 ans.

Ostéoporose signifie porosité des os. La gravité de cette maladie est liée aux fractures qu'elle favorise.

L'os est un tissu qui se renouvelle tout au long de la vie. Ce renouvellement voit se succéder des processus de destruction d'os ancien et de construction d'os nouveau. Ceci se fait sous l'action de deux types de cellules : les ostéoclastes qui sont responsables de la destruction osseuse et les ostéoblastes qui assurent la construction osseuse. Tous ces phénomènes dépendent d'hormones – dont les hormones sexuelles. Petit à petit, avec l'âge, l'équilibre entre les deux types de cellules se modifie.

Les os commencent à se fragiliser à partir de l'âge de 35 ans en moyenne. L'os perd de sa solidité car il fixe moins le calcium. Chez la femme, cette perte osseuse s'accentue encore dans les cinq premières années de la ménopause.

Après 60 ans, la perte osseuse se poursuit. Elle est cependant beaucoup moins rapide. Mais si au fur et à mesure des années la perte osseuse est trop importante, il y a risque de fracture : c'est le cas dans l'ostéoporose. Cette maladie touche une femme sur trois après 50 ans et un homme sur dix.

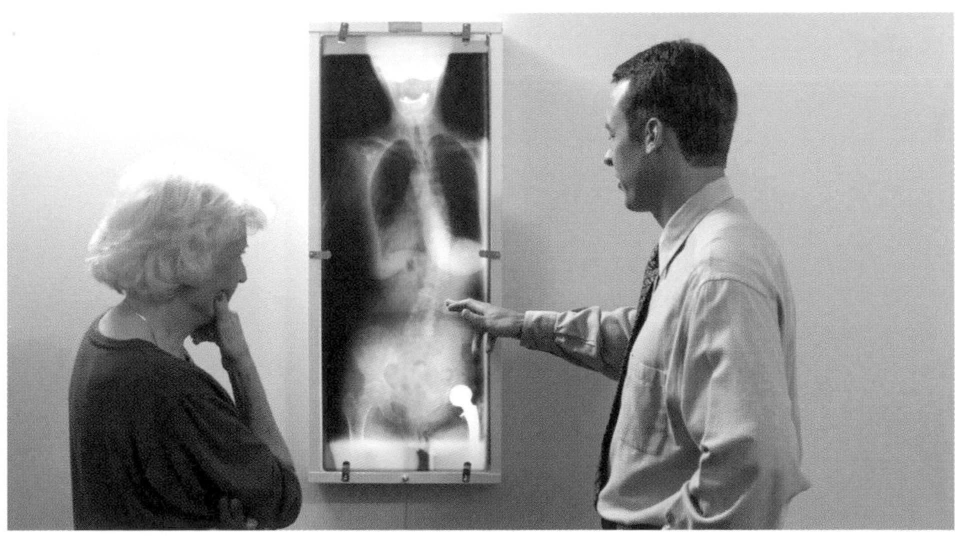

La gravité de l'ostéoporose est liée aux fractures qu'elle favorise.

Redoutable fracture du col du fémur

Le diagnostic précoce est important mais difficile car, au début, cette maladie est indolore. Lorsqu'elle parle, il est souvent déjà tard car c'est une fracture qui en témoigne. Les premières concernent les vertèbres : il peut s'agir de simple déformation d'une ou deux vertèbres. La taille de la personne diminue, mais cela n'est pas forcément très douloureux. Il peut aussi y avoir fracture d'une vertèbre, survenant pour un choc minime ou spontanément.

Ces fractures peuvent occasionner des douleurs aiguës. La personne ne peut plus bouger. Mais parfois on ne s'en rend compte que lors d'une radiographie.

D'autres os peuvent être touchés par l'ostéoporose : poignet et col du fémur. La fracture du col du fémur est la plus dangereuse. Nous ne sommes pas égaux devant ce risque. Un élément très important est le capital osseux constitué par chacun pendant son enfance et son adolescence. Chez la femme, ce capital est constitué deux ans après la survenue des premières règles. Il dépend surtout de l'activité physique, mais aussi des apports en calcium, magnésium, potassium et vitamine D. L'exercice physique doit être suffisant, régulier et énergique. Par la suite, l'agriculture et l'élevage n'allaient plus cesser de se développer, pour finalement exploser au XXe siècle avec l'industrie alimentaire.

En résumé, on peut dire qu'il y a moins de 10 000 ans (soit 5 000 ans avant la construction de la pyramide de Kheops) sont apparus :

- les céréales, jusqu'alors presque inconnues, qui ont dès lors constitué une source majeure de soufre, donc d'acidité ;
- plus de viande, du fait que les animaux étaient élevés, donc prêts à être mangés ;
- du lait animal, puisqu'il devenait facile de traire les mammifères ;
- en contrepartie, moins de produits de la cueillette (fruits, baies, légumes, noix, racines, champignons…) riches en composants basifiants, parce que tout le monde se consacrait à temps plein à l'agriculture et à l'élevage.

Des apports minéraux insuffisants...

À l'adolescence, une consommation de 1 600 mg par jour de calcium augmente la densité osseuse. Or, en moyenne, les adolescentes n'en reçoivent que la moitié. Ce serait sans conséquence si elles étaient physiquement très actives. Hélas, la plupart sont sédentaires. De la même manière, les apports en magnésium et potassium sont souvent insuffisants lorsque les adolescentes évitent les fruits et légumes. Quant à la vitamine D, nous sommes, pour la plupart, en déficit de novembre à mars du fait du faible ensoleillement.

... mais le calcium n'explique pas tout

Les habitants du Burkina Faso consomment peu de calcium (moins de 500 mg par jour) et pratiquement pas de laitages et ne connaissent pas de problèmes osseux. Les Américains et les Suédois en avalent deux fois et demi plus et connaissent eux une épidémie d'ostéoporose. Preuve que si le calcium est important, d'autres facteurs environnementaux entrent en compte.

Comment savoir si l'on court un risque ?

Comment savoir si l'on court le risque de souffrir d'ostéoporose ou si l'on est déjà atteint, puisque cette maladie ne donne les premières années ni signes, ni douleurs ?

L'ostéodensitométrie est un examen sans douleur qui permet de mesurer la densité de l'os

Cet examen donne une indication quant au risque d'ostéoporose. Le radiologue mesure la densité de l'os à deux endroits : les vertèbres lombaires et le col du fémur. Le résultat consiste en deux chiffres pour chacun des points de mesure. Les deux chiffres sont exprimés en fonction d'une moyenne : le T score est donné par rapport à la moyenne des femmes jeunes et le Z score par rapport à la moyenne des femmes du même âge. Une valeur basse du T score signifie qu'il y a une ostéopénie (T score entre – 1 et – 2,5 DS), une valeur très basse une ostéoporose (T score inférieur à – 2,5 DS). L'ostéopénie demande un traitement préventif, l'ostéoporose un traitement curatif. Depuis le 3 juillet 2006, l'ostéodensitométrie est remboursée dans certaines conditions (lire encadré). Cet examen est très intéressant car il permet de prendre les mesures nécessaires pour améliorer la qualité de l'os. Dans le cas d'ostéoporose avérée, un traitement médicamenteux est nécessaire. Dans le cas d'ostéopénie, un certain nombre de facteurs dépendent de vous. Faites le point avec votre médecin.

L'ostéodensitométrie remboursée…

- En cas de signes d'ostéoporose ;
- En cas de maladie ou de traitement potentiellement inducteur d'ostéoporose (corticothérapie) ;
- Après la ménopause, en cas …
  - d'antécédent de fracture du col du fémur sans traumatisme majeur chez un parent au premier degré ;
  - d'indice de masse corporelle <19 ;
  - de ménopause avant l'âge de 40 ans ;
  - d'antécédent de prise de corticoïdes d'une durée d'au moins 3 mois consécutifs, à une dose supérieure à 7,5 mg/jour équivalent prednisone.

Votre risque d'ostéoporose est plus élevé si :

- vous êtes une femme
- vous êtes âgé(e)
- vous êtes ménopausée
- vous êtes maigre ou vous avez une petite ossature
- vous êtes de type caucasien (femme blanche ou asiatique)
- vous avez déjà eu une fracture ostéoporotique.

Ce qui fait du mal aux os

Les facteurs nutritionnels : l'excès de protéines (cet excès conduit à une augmentation des déchets urinaires qui entraînent avec eux le calcium).
Les abus : tabac, alcool, café, excès de sport.
La sédentarité, l'insuffisance de sport.
Certains médicaments comme les corticoïdes, les diurétiques, les antiacides contenant de l'aluminium, les doses excessives d'hormones thyroïdiennes.

Comment renforcer l'os ?

Tout au long de la vie, il est indispensable de :

- conserver une activité physique, fût-elle la marche, qui provoque un « stress » sur la matrice osseuse, l'idéal étant la musculation ;
- consommer suffisamment de calcium (eau minérale, fruits, légumes, laitages, suppléments calciques le cas échéant) ;
- consommer suffisamment de potassium qui permet de combattre l'acidité du corps et épargner le calcium osseux (fruits, légumes, légumineuses, suppléments de bicarbonate de potassium le cas échéant) ;
- veiller à un apport suffisant en vitamine D (soleil modérément, poissons gras toute l'année, supplément de vitamine D3 de novembre à mars).

Partie III

LE TRAITEMENT HORMONAL DE LA MÉNOPAUSE (THM)

Le traitement hormonal de la ménopause (THM)

Les femmes qui suivent un traitement hormonal prennent des médicaments destinés à remplacer leurs hormones dont le taux est devenu trop bas.

En France, les hormones les plus largement prescrites sont proches des hormones naturelles, ce qui n'est pas le cas aux États-Unis

Le principe du traitement est de considérer les phénomènes de la ménopause comme étant dus au manque d'estrogènes. Le traitement consiste donc à apporter à l'organisme des hormones de type estrogènes proches des hormones naturelles qui ne sont plus fabriquées par les ovaires.

Au départ, seuls les estrogènes étaient proposés. Mais on s'est aperçu que cela favorisait des saignements gynécologiques, voire des cancers de l'endomètre – l'endomètre est la muqueuse qui tapisse l'utérus. Les progestatifs ont donc été associés aux estrogènes afin de protéger cette muqueuse.

Les estrogènes utilisés en France

Les estrogènes utilisés en France pour le traitement hormonal substitutif sont différents de ceux que l'on trouve dans la pilule contraceptive. L'estrogène le plus prescrit en France est le 17 bêta-estradiol, une molécule qui ressemble beaucoup à l'estrogène fabriqué naturellement par les femmes. Les estrogènes conjugués équins (Prémarin®) – estrogènes extraits des urines de jument et le valérate de 17 bêta-estradiol (Progynova®) sont également prescrits mais plus rarement.

Bien que synthétisé chimiquement, le 17 bêta-estradiol est une molécule dite naturelle car sa structure est très proche de celle des hormones fabriquées par le corps humain. Ceci permet de le différencier de l'éthinylestradiol qui est la molécule contenue dans les contraceptifs oraux.

Il existe plusieurs voies d'administration. Le plus souvent, l'estrogène est pris soit par voie orale, soit par voie transdermique – les patchs –, ou par voie percutanée – les gels. Une toute nouvelle forme vient d'arriver : la voie per-nasale. Le produit est alors pulvérisé dans chaque narine une fois par jour.

Les femmes ont donc désormais le choix. Patchs et gels sont de plus en plus utilisés. En effet, ces deux modes d'administration offrent une grande souplesse d'utilisation et permettent aux femmes d'ajuster elles-mêmes assez finement le dosage.

La progestérone et les progestatifs utilisés en France

L'association d'un progestatif aux estrogènes est obligatoire chez les femmes n'ayant pas subi d'hystérectomie, ceci afin de prévenir un éventuel cancer de l'endomètre. Le progestatif doit être pris au moins pendant 12 jours chaque mois pour pouvoir contrer les mauvais effets des estrogènes sur la muqueuse utérine. On utilise en France plusieurs types de molécules, mais la principale est la progestérone dite naturelle car proche de la progestérone fabriquée par le corps humain. Elle est donnée par voie orale ou percutanée. Aux États-Unis en revanche, on prescrit plus souvent une molécule de synthèse, la médroxyprogestérone (MPA).

Traitement : avec ou sans règles

Pour conserver les règles, le traitement séquentiel discontinu est le plus fréquent.

Pendant 25 jours, la femme prend des estrogènes. Pendant les douze derniers jours de ce traitement sont associés des progestatifs. Et pendant les 5 derniers jours du mois, elle ne prend rien. C'est à ce moment-là que des règles surviennent suite à l'arrêt de la prise de progestatifs.

Dans le schéma sans règles, estrogènes et progestatifs sont combinés et pris en continu. La quantité de progestatif est en général la moitié de celle utilisée dans les traitements séquentiels.

Le THM inquiète

Principale raison pour laquelle les femmes refusent ou abandonnent le THM : le risque de cancer du sein.

Ce qu'en pensent les gynécologues

Le sein comme l'utérus est une cible privilégiée des hormones. Le cancer du sein est le cancer le plus fréquent chez les femmes. Sa fréquence augmente avec l'âge, que les femmes soient traitées ou non. De nombreux travaux se sont intéressés à la relation entre THM et cancer du sein. En juillet 2002, l'étude américaine WHI a permis de préciser le risque de ce cancer avec un THM peu utilisé en France. D'autres études, menées notamment chez un grand nombre de femmes anglaises (Million Women Study) et françaises (étude E3N) ont ensuite apporté des informations complémentaires.

Bilan en 2007 : les gynécologues français s'accordent pour reconnaître que le THM, en prolongeant l'imprégnation par les estrogènes place la femme traitée à un niveau de risque supérieur à celui d'une femme de même âge non traitée. Le THM qui associe des estrogènes à un progestatif augmente le risque de cancer du sein. Le THM à base d'estrogènes seuls, quant à lui, ne

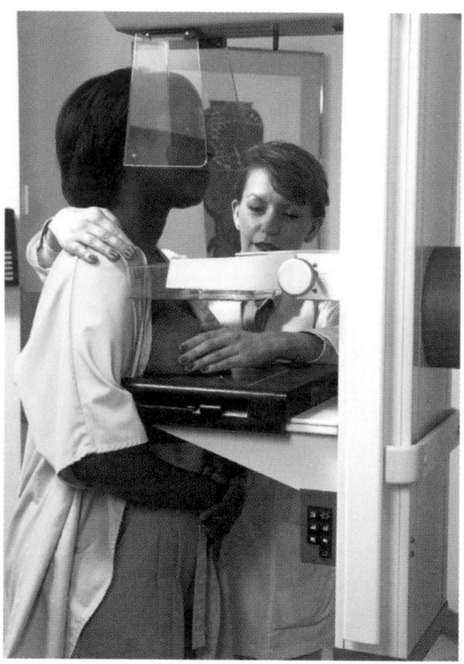

Le risque de cancer du sein augmente :

- avec l'âge
- quand il y a des antécédents familiaux de cancer du sein chez mère, sœur ou fille
- quand il y a des antécédents personnels de pathologie mammaire
- en fonction de certains facteurs hormonaux : premières règles précoces, première grossesse tardive, ménopause tardive, prise d'un THS estrogénique seul

semble pas l'augmenter. On estime que sur 100 000 utilisatrices au pic de l'utilisation du THM (années 2000-2002), entre 35 et 55 cas de cancer du sein sont attribuables au THM.

Remarque : s'il est vrai que le nombre de cancers du sein est en augmentation, il n'y a pas plus de décès chaque année par ce type de cancer. Ceci montre que la maladie est diagnostiquée de plus en plus tôt et mieux soignée.

Le cancer : première cause de mortalité chez les hommes et seconde chez les femmes

Même si on ne connaît pas les causes exactes du cancer en général, certains facteurs de risque ont été clairement identifiés :

- le tabac : le pire de tous et il n'y a plus aucun doute là-dessus
- l'alcool
- le soleil
- les hormones pour les cancers hormono-dépendants comme le cancer du sein, le cancer de l'endomètre chez la femme ou le cancer de la prostate chez l'homme
- l'alimentation mal équilibrée, trop riche en graisses animales et en sucres raffinés.

La progestérone en question

En novembre 2004, le Dr Françoise Clavel-Chapelon (Institut Gustave Roussy, Villejuif) a publié les résultats de la seule grande enquête **française** sur le risque de cancer du sein lié au THM : **l'étude E3N.** D'après cette étude, les femmes qui ont pris l'association estrogènes-progestatif de synthèse ont un risque de cancer du sein augmenté de 40 % par rapport aux non utilisatrices. Celles qui ont pris l'association estrogènes-progestérone naturelle n'ont pas de risque augmenté.

Ce qu'en pensent les femmes

Aujourd'hui, de nombreuses femmes de 50 ans ont dans leur entourage une personne qui a été traitée pour un cancer du sein. En France, chaque année, on recense 35 000 nouveaux cas. Ce cancer fait peur aux femmes. Le fait que le THM augmente le risque de cancer du sein les dissuade de le prendre. Même si le risque est minime ! Le manque de clarté des publications augmente leur méfiance. Il leur semble que le risque est minimisé ou que le rôle du THM est noyé dans d'autres considérations.

Malgré le discours rassurant des gynécologues et des laboratoires pharmaceutiques, les femmes n'ont pas envie de courir le risque et il est vrai que le risque existe.

Le THM prévient-il les maladies cardiovasculaires ?

C'est en tout cas ce que l'on pensait jusqu'à ce qu'une grande étude américaine vienne semer le trouble.

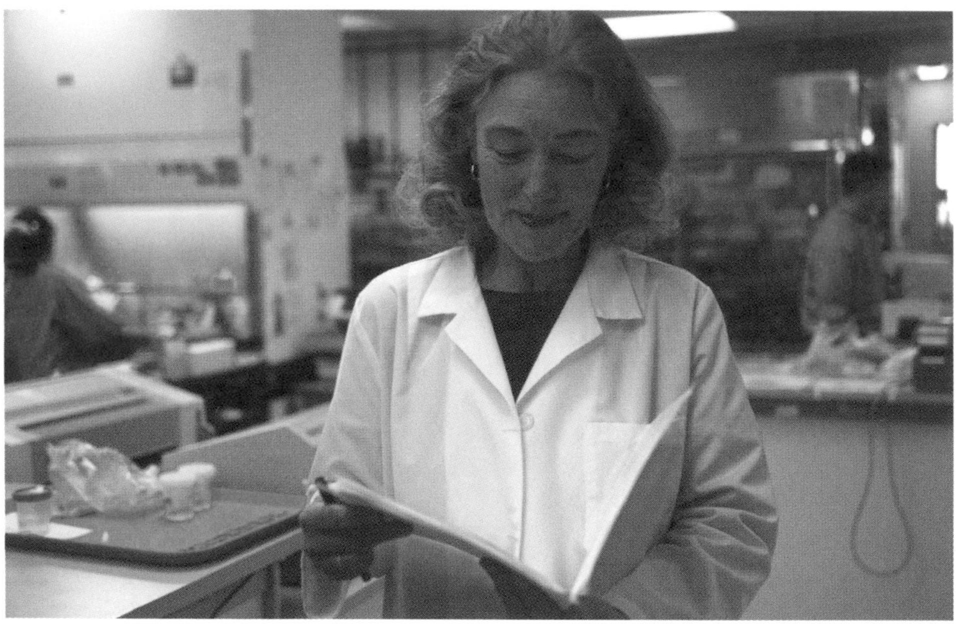

L'étude américaine WHI a été interrompue en juillet 2002 à cause d'un excès de maladies cardiovasculaires chez les femmes qui suivaient un traitement hormonal

S'il est reconnu que le THM augmente le risque de cancer du sein (de façon minime), les médecins affirmaient il y a encore quelques mois que ce risque était compensé par les bénéfices attendus en terme de prévention cardiovasculaire, argument de poids quand on sait que ces maladies sont 2 à 3 fois plus fréquentes chez les femmes après 50 ans.

Les derniers résultats de la recherche sont décevants

La *Women's Health Initiative Study (WHI)* est une étude américaine lancée en 1997 pour évaluer les bénéfices du THM standard donné aux États-Unis sur la santé cardiovasculaire et le risque de cancer. L'étude comparait le THM à un placebo. Et alors que les chercheurs s'attendaient à moins d'infarctus et d'accidents vasculaires cérébraux dans le groupe qui recevait l'association d'estrogènes et de progestérone, c'est le contraire qui s'est produit. Conçue pour aller jusqu'en 2005, l'étude WHI a donc été interrompue en juillet 2002. Il faut préciser cependant que les doses et les molécules utilisées, ainsi que les modes d'administration, sont différents de ceux préconisés pour le THM en France. Ceci n'enlevant rien aux inquiétudes suscitées par l'étude WHI, l'argument évoquant un possible bénéfice cardiovasculaire est donc abandonné jusqu'à preuve du contraire pour le THM français. En 2007, les résultats attendus de la grande étude de cohorte française, l'étude E3N, devraient permettre de trancher.

Hormones et vaisseaux

Selon les données de l'étude américaine WHI, le THM augmente le risque de maladies cardio-vasculaires.

Pour 1 000 femmes traitées pendant dix ans, il y aurait 7 cas supplémentaires d'infarctus du myocarde, 8 cas supplémentaires d'accident vasculaire cérébral, 8 cas supplémentaires d'embolie pulmonaire.

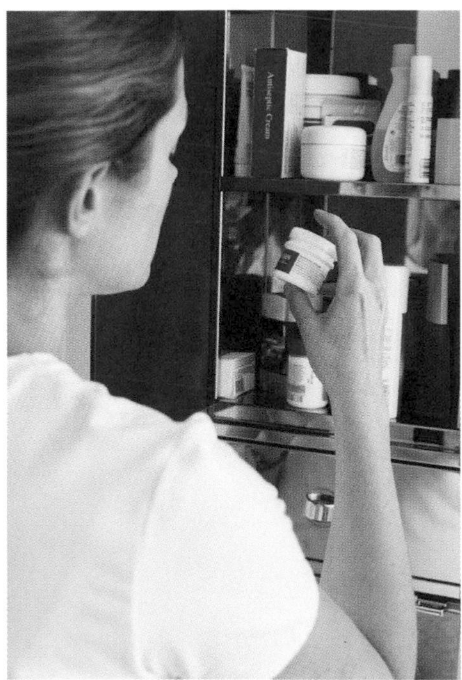

THM : la défiance

D'après l'Association française pour l'étude de la ménopause (AFEM), en 2001, plus de 2 millions de Françaises bénéficient d'un traitement substitutif : elles représentent donc près de 20 % de l'ensemble des femmes ménopausées ou plutôt deux femmes sur cinq entre 50 et 65 ans car le nombre de femmes traitées après 65 ans est très faible (3 % seulement).

Chaque année, 400 000 Françaises « entrent » en ménopause. Mais si le nombre de femmes traitées augmente régulièrement (elles sont 7 fois plus nombreuses qu'il y a 20 ans), les chiffres en matière d'observance sont calamiteux : 8 % des femmes seulement poursuivraient leur traitement au-delà de 2 ans. Elles invoquent généralement la peur de développer un cancer, la crainte de prendre du poids, les problèmes d'adaptation du traitement ou simplement la lassitude.

Le THM rebute, inquiète et l'arrêt anticipé de l'étude américaine WHI a jeté le trouble un peu plus.

Le risque de thrombose veineuse peut augmenter

Après la ménopause, le nombre de thromboses veineuses augmente. L'étude ESTHER, faite entre 1999 et 2004, a tout particulièrement analysé l'impact de la prise du THM sur cette pathologie chez des femmes françaises ménopausées âgées de 45 à 70 ans. Les résultats montrent que tout dépend du type de THM qui est pris. Le risque est augmenté systématiquement quand l'estrogène est pris par voie orale, qu'il y ait ou non un progestatif associé. En revanche, lorsque l'estrogène est pris par voie transdermique (sous forme de patchs), le risque dépend directement du progestatif associé. Il est augmenté lorsque c'est un progestatif de type norprégnane, identique à celui des femmes qui ne prennent pas de THM lorsque c'est de la progestérone naturelle micronisée ou un progestatif de type prégnane. A noter que l'existence d'autres facteurs de risque personnels, comme l'obésité, accroît l'effet délétère des estrogènes oraux.

Quand les hormones sont de retour

Le THM améliore indéniablement la qualité de vie des femmes qui sont très gênées à la ménopause. Il prévient également l'ostéoporose.

Une qualité de vie retrouvée

Le THM agit remarquablement sur tous les désagréments de la ménopause. Il améliore considérablement la vie des femmes :

- disparition des bouffées de chaleurs (dans plus de 85 % des cas), le plus souvent dès le premier mois ;
- diminution des sueurs nocturnes ;
- la peau est plus élastique ;
- la sécheresse vaginale s'amende ;
- les infections urinaires sont moins fréquentes ;
- amélioration des troubles de l'humeur, du sommeil, de l'équilibre mental général, probablement parce que le THM réduit les symptômes de la ménopause.

Au niveau osseux, le THM prévient l'apparition des tassements vertébraux lorsqu'il est donné dès le début de la ménopause. Il ralentit l'évolution de l'ostéoporose vertébrale si elle existe déjà. Concernant le risque de fracture du col fémoral,

Ce que le THM ne fait pas

Il ne prévient pas le vieillissement cutané.

Il n'améliore pas directement la libido !

Il ne fait pas régresser l'incontinence urinaire d'effort et l'impériosité urinaire.

Il ne prévient pas la fonte musculaire.

Il ne fait pas disparaître les graisses en excès.

Il ne prévient pas les troubles cognitifs.

l'intérêt du THM est certain. Il faut suivre le traitement pendant de longues années pour empêcher une fracture du col qui survient le plus souvent au-delà de 80 ans. Le fait de prendre longuement ce traitement en augmente également les effets nocifs. C'est tout le dilem.

Dans l'étude WHI, le THM diminue également le risque de **cancer colorectal.** Pour 1 000 femmes traitées pendant 10 ans, le THM préviendrait 6 cas de cancer côlo-rectal. Les études menées en France ne permettent pas d'affirmer actuellement que le THM « français » protège contre ce cancer.

Le THM fait-il grossir ?

Certaines femmes se plaignent de prendre du poids à la ménopause. Plusieurs explications à cela : la sédentarité, les grignotages de compensation et certainement la baisse des hormones. Avec l'âge, le poids augmente et la masse musculaire (ou masse maigre) diminue au profit de la masse graisseuse. La baisse des estrogènes en est responsable mais pas seulement. L'hormone de croissance (GH), la testostérone, la DHEA qui normalement s'opposent au stockage des graisses baissent elles aussi. Les graisses se répartissent également de manière différente et viennent se localiser préférentiellement au niveau du ventre. On peut alors se demander quels sont les effets d'un remplacement hormonal sur la silhouette ? Les études indiquent que le THM convenablement dosé ne fait pas grossir. Dans l'une d'elles portant sur 671 femmes de 65 à 94 ans, celles qui prenaient des hormones étaient plus minces que celles qui n'en prenaient pas.

Maintenant il est vrai que certaines femmes ont une sensibilité particulière aux hormones et vont se sentir « gonflées ». Il faudra donc réduire les doses d'estrogènes.

THM et maladie d'Alzheimer

Contrairement à ce qui avait été espéré, rien ne prouve aujourd'hui que le THM prévient la maladie d'Alzheimer. C'est même le contraire puisque le THM pourrait accroître le risque de démence chez les femmes de plus de 65 ans.

Shumaker SA : *Estrogen plus progestin and the incidence of dementia and mild cognitive impairment in postmenopausal women : The Women's Health Initiative Memory Study (WHIMS)*. JAMA 2003, 289, 2651-2662.

Contre-indications du THM

Les contre-indications sont liées aux effets secondaires possibles des estrogènes.

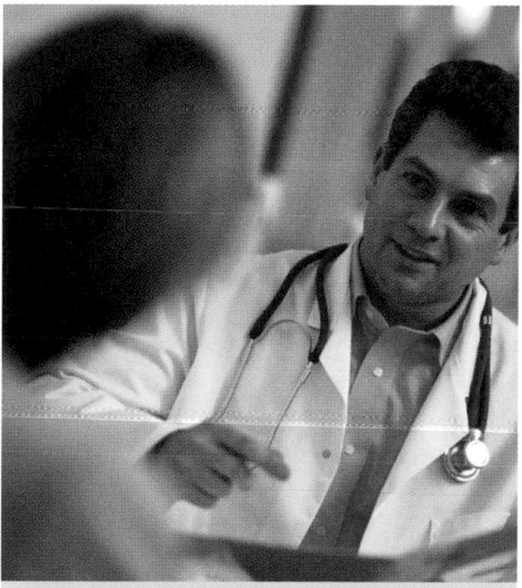

Mesdames, informez-vous !

Il est indispensable que les femmes soient informées du mieux possible afin de choisir en connaissance de cause. Car il s'agit de leur santé. À l'heure où la loi impose d'informer avant tout les patients et de respecter leur choix, il est nécessaire que les femmes insistent auprès de leurs médecins pour que ceux-ci leur présentent les arguments scientifiques qui sont en faveur ou en défaveur de tel ou tel traitement. Aux femmes de choisir ce qui leur convient le mieux en connaissance de cause.

Les contre-indications absolues

Une femme ne devrait pas suivre de traitement hormonal substitutif :

- si elle souffre d'un cancer hormono-dépendant : cancer du sein, cancer de l'endomètre ou cancer endométrioïde de l'ovaire ;
- si elle a des antécédents de thromboses veineuses ou artérielles, ou d'embolie (exemples : embolies pulmonaires, phlébite, angine de poitrine, infarctus du myocarde, accident vasculaire cérébral) ;
- si elle est atteinte d'une maladie cardiaque exposant au risque d'embolie ;
- en cas de pathologie vasculaire oculaire ;
- en cas d'hypertriglycéridémie.

Les contre-indications relatives

Il y a actuellement une polémique concernant les contre-indications relatives qui sont :

- la maladie fibrokystique du sein ;
- les fibromes interstitiels (c'est-à-dire dans la paroi de l'utérus) ou sous-séreux ;
- les fibromes hémorragiques car l'ajout d'estrogènes peut augmenter le saignement ;
- l'endométriose ;
- le diabète non-insulino-dépendant;
- les antécédents de migraines graves.

Pour certains médecins, ces contre-indications proscrivent l'usage du THM. Pour d'autres, le bénéfice du THM en terme de prévention de l'ostéoporose compense les risques encourus.

Précautions

Avant d'instaurer un THM, il faut traiter et équilibrer l'hypertension artérielle ainsi que l'hypercholestérolémie. Les femmes ne doivent pas fumer de manière générale et encore moins pendant un traitement hormonal substitutif car les risques de phlébite et d'embolie pulmonaire seraient alors multipliés.

Il est bien évident qu'aujourd'hui il est très difficile d'avoir des informations définitives sur les effets secondaires des THM. Lorsqu'une étude met en évidence des risques, une autre montre que ces risques ne sont pas les mêmes pour tous les types de THM. De nouvelles études scientifiques sont en cours. En attendant leurs résultats, mettons en avant le principe de précaution.

Une alternative au THM : les SERM et les SAS

Les SERM sont prescrits pour prévenir et traiter l'ostéoporose. Les SAS agissent sur les bouffées de chaleur et d'autres symptômes de la ménopause.

Les estrogènes, fabriqués principalement par les ovaires, passent dans le sang et diffusent ensuite dans tout le corps. Certaines cellules ont une grande affinité pour ces molécules parce qu'elles contiennent un récepteur spécifique aux estrogènes. Il en existe deux types : le type alpha qui est présent dans les cellules du sein, de l'utérus, du foie et le type bêta que l'on trouve surtout dans l'os, le système cardio-vasculaire et les ovaires.

Il existe des médicaments qui agissent spécifiquement sur ces récepteurs : ce sont les *Selective Estrogen Receptor Modulators* ou *SERM*, dont le chef de file est actuellement le raloxifène (Evista®, Optruma®). Ces molécules ont une action à la fois agoniste et antagoniste des estrogènes. C'est-à-dire qu'elles agissent comme les estrogènes – action agoniste, ou qu'elles empêchent l'action des estrogènes en se fixant sur leurs récepteurs – action antagoniste. Cette action est donc variable selon le tissu cible.

Les médicaments de l'os

Des médicaments autres que le raloxifène permettent de renforcer la solidité des os et éviter les fractures.

- Les biphosphonates comme l'alendronate (Fosamax) et le risedronate (Actonel) qui diminuent la résorption osseuse. Leur atout : une seule prise par semaine ;
- Le tériparatide (Forsteo) qui est un analogue de la parathormone, l'hormone qui nous aide à fabriquer de l'os. Il permet une réduction significative du risque de fracture vertébrale ;
- Le ranelate de strontium (Protelos) qui inhibe les ostéoclastes détruisant l'os et stimule les ostéoblastes qui construisent l'os. Il diminue le risque de fractures vertébrales et du col du fémur.

Un effet positif sur l'os

Le raloxifène a un effet positif sur l'os, ce qui conduit à le proposer en prévention et en traitement de l'ostéoporose vertébrale de la femme à risque. Les études montrent une

diminution de l'incidence du cancer du sein, essentiellement pour les tumeurs porteuses de récepteurs aux estrogènes. Il n'a pas d'action délétère sur l'endomètre. Cependant c'est une molécule récente et il faut rester prudent.
C'est pourquoi il présente pour l'instant les mêmes contre-indications que le THM. Il n'a pas d'action sur les bouffées de chaleur.

Les SAS : non il ne s'agit pas d'un roman policier !

Les SAS pour « stéroïdes à activités sélectives » sont représentés par une seule molécule actuellement : la tibolone (Livial®). C'est un stéroïde de synthèse qui a des propriétés estrogénique, progestative et androgénique faibles.

La tibolone agit sur les bouffées de chaleur, la sécheresse vaginale, les troubles du sommeil et les troubles de l'humeur. De plus elle améliore la libido.

Malheureusement, la tibolone augmente le risque de survenue du cancer de l'endomètre, comme le montre l'étude « Million Women ». De plus, elle aggrave aussi le risque de cancers du sein et d'accidents vasculaires cérébraux. Elle a donc les mêmes contre-indications que le THM. Au niveau du squelette, elle diminue la perte osseuse mais les études ne sont pas suffisantes pour la proposer comme traitement préventif ou curatif de l'ostéoporose.

La DHEA : hormone de la jeunesse ?

Voilà un produit très controversé. Alors faut-il en prendre ou non ?

La DHEA (ou déhydroépiandrostérone) est une hormone stéroïde fabriquée par les glandes surrénales. Elle circule dans le sang et l'organisme sous forme de sulfate de DHEA. Elle peut se transformer en estrogènes et en testostérone. On ne connaît pas encore exactement son rôle dans l'organisme. On la retrouve dans le cerveau, les surrénales, les ovaires, les testicules, les tissus graisseux, la peau et le sang. Juste avant la puberté, elle est fabriquée en grande quantité. À partir de 30 ans, sa production diminue régulièrement et à 70 ans, la quantité produite représente 20 % de celle qui était synthétisée à 20 ans.

Le boom de la DHEA aux États-Unis a commencé dans les années 1980. Aujourd'hui, seuls les États-Unis la considèrent comme un complément alimentaire. Elle y est donc en vente libre. En France, elle a le statut de médicament et n'est accessible que sur ordonnance. Cependant, l'Ordre des médecins déconseille sa prescription. Il est donc assez difficile d'en obtenir.

Que dit la recherche ?

Les recherches sur la DHEA sont très nombreuses. En France, le professeur Étienne-Émile Baulieu est le plus actif. Ses recherches ont montré que ce sont les femmes de plus de 70 ans qui en tirent le meilleur bénéfice. La DHEA améliore le métabolisme de l'os et diminue l'ostéoporose. Mais ça n'est pas tout : elle donne un vrai coup de jeune, en améliorant l'hydratation de la peau, la forme physique, l'humeur et la libido.

De nombreuses études ont été menées. Malheureusement presque toutes n'ont concerné qu'un petit nombre de personnes. Et en étendre les conclusions serait très prématuré. Ce sont simplement des pistes intéressantes.

Revue de détail :

- L'application de crème contenant 10 % de DHEA a permis à 14 femmes de 60 ans d'améliorer leur qualité osseuse ; de là à conclure que la DHEA est un traitement de l'ostéoporose : **non !**
- Le faible taux de DHEA dans le sang est corrélé au risque de dépression ; de là à conclure que la DHEA est un traitement de la dépression : **non !**
- La prise de DHEA améliore le moral et la libido des femmes après la ménopause ; de là à conclure que c'est un aphrodisiaque : **non !**

La DHEA peut être prescrite par le médecin et délivrée par le pharmacien. On peut aussi, avec une ordonnance, l'acheter à l'étranger

La DHEA est un médicament

N'oublions pas qu'elle est une hormone semi-synthétique. Elle peut se transformer dans le corps en estrogènes ou en testostérone. Il y a donc de possibles effets secondaires. Comme les estrogènes, elle peut en théorie favoriser le développement des cancers hormono-dépendants : cancer du sein et de l'endomètre. Comme la testostérone, elle peut donner de l'acné et de l'hirsutisme. La voix peut devenir plus grave. Elle peut faire baisser le bon cholestérol, induire une résistance à l'insuline et augmenter la tension artérielle.

Les autres effets secondaires sont moins graves : douleurs abdominales, fatigue, maux de tête, congestion nasale.

La DHEA est donc tout à fait contre-indiquée pour les personnes qui ont ou qui ont eu un cancer hormonodépendant. Elle est également déconseillée aux personnes ayant une insuffisance hépatique ou rénale. Attendons la poursuite des études avant de consommer de la DHEA !

Et la DHEA naturelle ?

Dans le commerce, on trouve de la DHEA « naturelle ». En général, ce sont des extraits d'igname, de soja, de trèfle rouge. Si ces produits sont intéressants en tant que phytoestrogènes ou phytoprogestérone, ils n'augmentent absolument pas le taux de DHEA dans le sang. **Il n'y a pas de DHEA naturelle !**

Partie IV

LES PROMESSES DES PLANTES HORMONO-MODULANTES

Les phytoestrogènes

Les plantes fabriquent naturellement des substances qui, une fois ingérées, miment les estrogènes. On les appelle phytoestrogènes : les estrogènes des plantes. Ces molécules occupent aujourd'hui une place à part entière dans la panoplie thérapeutique de la ménopause.

Histoire d'une découverte

Au début des années 1940, une mystérieuse épidémie d'infertilité chez les brebis manqua de décimer les élevages de moutons du Sud-Est australien. Désespérés, au bord de la ruine, les fermiers mirent successivement en cause des mutations génétiques, les radiations et les pesticides.

Il fallut attendre 1946 pour que le ministère australien de l'Agriculture identifie le responsable : la variété de trèfle *(Trifolium subterraneum)* que les éleveurs avaient plantée quelques années plus tôt. Personne ne se doutait alors que cette plante fabrique naturellement des quantités considérables (5 % de son poids sec) de substances qui, une fois ingérées, miment les hormones femelles. On les appelle phytoestrogènes.

Dans les années 1950, deux de ces substances furent isolées : la génistéine et la daidzéine qui appartiennent à la famille des isoflavones. Elles sont synthétisées par de très nombreuses plantes, dont le trèfle et le soja.

Mais l'intérêt de ces molécules pour la santé et le bien-être des femmes à la ménopause a été pressenti à la suite d'observations épidémiologiques dans les pays asiatiques. En effet, les femmes asiatiques souffrent très peu de bouffées de chaleur. Moins de 25 % des Japonaises et des Chinoises s'en plaignent contre 85 % des Nord-Américaines et 75 % des Européennes. Elles ont en outre beaucoup moins de maladies cardio-vasculaires, de cancers du sein et d'ostéoporose.

Le soja : noble nourriture

Le plus ancien livre de la pharmacopée chinoise, le *Shen Nong Ben Cao*, parle déjà du soja vers 2700 avant J.-C. Le tofu fabriqué à partir du soja est depuis quatre millénaires à la base de la nourriture des Chinois. Il a été introduit au Japon et en Corée par des moines bouddhistes entre les IIe et VIIe siècles. À la cour de l'empereur chinois, le tofu était reconnu comme une noble nourriture.

Dans les pays asiatiques, le soja est une base de l'alimentation depuis plusieurs siècles : les protéines du soja constituent 20 à 60 % des protéines totales consommées.

Les chercheurs ont essayé de trouver ce qui, dans le mode de vie des femmes asiatiques, pouvait expliquer cet avantage. Ils ont remarqué également que lorsque ces femmes émigraient aux États-Unis par exemple, en adoptant le mode de vie occidental, elles étaient touchées petit à petit par les mêmes problèmes que les femmes occidentales.

Les chercheurs en ont conclu que cette différence provenait certainement de l'alimentation des femmes asiatiques et en particulier de leur grande consommation de soja qui est l'aliment le plus riche en phytoestrogènes.

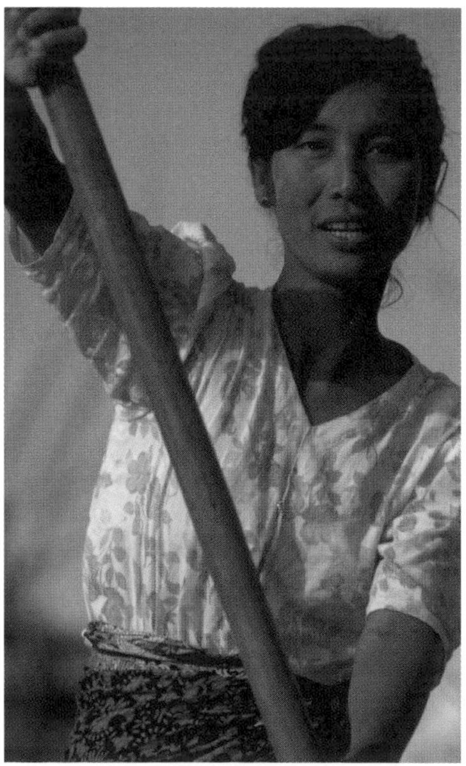

Où trouver les phytoestrogènes

Ils sont présents dans plus de 600 plantes. Ils se répartissent en trois grandes familles :

- les isoflavones : surtout présentes dans les légumineuses, notamment les fèves de soja, mais aussi les pois chiches, les haricots verts, le thé...
- les lignanes dans les graines de céréales complètes, les graines oléagineuses (lin, olive, tournesol), dans les flageolets, les lentilles, les cerises, les pommes, les poires, le pamplemousse, l'ail...
- les coumestans, de structure proche des isoflavones, sont présentes dans la luzerne et particulièrement dans les pousses de soja.

Comment agissent les phytoestrogènes

La majorité des études scientifiques concernant les phytoestrogènes ont été effectuées sur le soja et les isoflavones de soja.

Des substances très actives

Lorsque les isoflavones du soja arrivent dans l'estomac, elles sont hydrolysées. Elles passent ensuite dans l'intestin où elles sont transformées par les bactéries intestinales en génistéine et daidzéine. Ce sont ces substances qui sont actives. De nombreux paramètres influencent cette transformation ce qui explique que l'on observe des taux sanguins différents d'un individu à l'autre. Parmi ces paramètres, il y a la qualité de la flore intestinale, la vitesse du transit, le pH. C'est la génistéine qui a été la plus étudiée à ce jour.

Les deux faces des isoflavones

Les isoflavones ont une structure chimique qui s'apparente à celle des estrogènes. Du fait de cette ressemblance, ces molécules peuvent se lier aux mêmes récepteurs mais elles ont des effets variables selon les organes

Soja : base de l'alimentation asiatique

En Asie, le soja est transformé en lait de soja et en tofu. Mais également en soja fermenté, sous forme de miso, tempeh, sauce soja... Le soja fermenté contient de nombreuses isoflavones. Le tofu et le lait de soja ne contiennent que la génistéine et la daidzéine.

Quelle est la consommation occidentale d'isoflavones ?

On estime qu'elle ne dépasse pas 5 mg d'isoflavones par jour alors que, pour les populations asiatiques, elle serait de 25 à 45 mg par jour. Ce sont les Japonais qui absorbent le plus d'isoflavones avec une consommation quotidienne de produits dérivés du soja estimée à 200 mg par jour.

Enfin, certains experts considèrent que la consommation d'isoflavones peut même atteindre 250 mg par jour pour certaines populations asiatiques.

cibles. Il semble que les isoflavones se comportent en fait comme des SERM (modulateurs sélectifs des récepteurs aux estrogènes).

Explications. Les chercheurs ont découvert récemment qu'il existait deux types de récepteurs estrogéniques : les récepteurs de type alpha et ceux de type bêta dont la répartition varie en fonction des tissus. Les isoflavones ont 6 fois plus d'affinité pour les récepteurs bêta que pour les récepteurs alpha. Ainsi les isoflavones possèdent une action estrogénique sur certains tissus (cerveau, os, poumon, vaisseaux, vessie…) et antiestrogénique sur d'autres (ovaire, sein, utérus…).

Des effets variables

Si la répartition des récepteurs varie en fonction des tissus, la densité de ces récepteurs varie, elle, d'une femme à l'autre. Ceci pourrait expliquer l'efficacité inconstante des isoflavones de soja.

Teneur moyenne en isoflavones en µg/100 g de poids sec

Fèves de soja	40 000 à 200 000
Cacahuètes	120
Pois chiches	80 à 400
Lentilles	10 à 30
Orge	22
Brocoli	15
Chou-fleur	15

Les bénéfices du soja

Depuis la découverte de l'activité estrogénique des isoflavones, la recherche est en effervescence. Pris en complément de l'alimentation, les extraits de soja diminuent les bouffées de chaleur. Et leurs bénéfices ne s'arrêtent pas là.

Les os les plus solides du monde

L'archipel d'Okinawa est un groupe de 44 îles qui s'étend du Japon à Taïwan. Par rapport aux Japonaises, déjà privilégiées, les habitantes d'Okinawa ont 20 % de fractures de la hanche de moins. Des études ont montré qu'à partir de 40 ans chez les femmes, et 50 ans chez les hommes, les Japonais commencent à perdre du calcium, alors que cette baisse intervient beaucoup plus tard à Okinawa. Si Japonais et habitants d'Okinawa consomment sensiblement la même quantité d'isoflavones, les îliens sont physiquement plus actifs et reçoivent aussi beaucoup plus de vitamine D.

Les femmes peuvent se procurer en pharmacie des compléments à base de soja, riches en isoflavones, qui les aideront à surmonter la période chaotique de la ménopause.

Efficacité sur les bouffées de chaleur démontrée

Onze études cliniques en double aveugle ont testé l'efficacité des extraits de soja chez des femmes ménopausées. Cinq prouvent clairement l'efficacité des isoflavones prises en complément de l'alimentation. Une ne montre pas d'effet et les cinq autres trouvent un effet comparable à celui du placebo. Pour le Professeur Mark Messina (Loma Linda University, Etats-Unis), qui est l'un des meilleurs spécialistes de l'action du soja sur la santé, l'action des isoflavones de soja sur les bouffées de chaleur est positive. Il observe, en revanche, qu'elle n'est pas identique pour toutes les femmes et pour tous les produits ; certaines femmes répondent plus rapidement à la prise d'isoflavones que d'autres. Ceci serait lié à deux éléments importants.

Tout d'abord la qualité du produit et la quantité prise chaque jour - il faut 70 mg par jour d'isoflavones dont 2 % au moins de génistéine -, ensuite, la faculté individuelle à transformer les isoflavones en produits actifs dans le sang. L'une des études est française. Chez des femmes souffrant de bouffées de chaleur très invalidantes, les chercheurs ont observé que la prise quotidienne d'un extrait standardisé de soja Phytosoya (soit 70 mg d'isoflavones) permet une diminution de 65 % des troubles contre seulement 28 % dans le groupe ayant reçu le placebo.

Des os plus solides : le secret des Asiatiques

Des études épidémiologiques ont permis de constater que l'incidence des fractures de la hanche est bien plus faible en Asie qu'en Occident. Les Japonaises ont ainsi un risque de fractures inférieur de 40 % à celui des Américaines. Les phytoestrogènes seraient-ils à l'origine de la solidité des os des Asiatiques ? C'est ce que les chercheurs tentent de comprendre.

Après quelques travaux positifs sur le modèle animal (rates ovariectomisées), commencent maintenant les premières études d'intervention chez l'homme. Et elles sont plus nombreuses.

Comment expliquer cela ?

Les isoflavones pourraient intervenir dans le processus de remodelage de l'os par leur action estrogénique. Elles stimuleraient l'activité des ostéoblastes et simultanément inhiberaient la résorption osseuse. Ceci semble confirmé par le fait que ce ralentissement de la perte osseuse est essentiellement observé au niveau de la colonne vertébrale. En effet, les vertèbres sont constituées d'une fraction très importante d'os spongieux, le tissu osseux qui se renouvelle le plus vite et qui est le plus sensible aux estrogènes.

Soja et santé osseuse : une étude encourageante

Une étude en double aveugle faite à Guangzhou (Chine) a étudié l'influence de suppléments d'isoflavones du soja pour prévenir la perte osseuse chez des femmes ménopausées. 90 femmes de 45 à 60 ans ont été suivies pendant 6 mois. Elles étaient réparties en trois groupes : l'un prenait un placebo, l'autre 84 mg d'isoflavones et le troisième 126 mg.

Résultat : l'atténuation de la perte osseuse au niveau de la colonne vertébrale et du col de fémur dépend directement de la dose d'isoflavones utilisée, la dose de 126 mg étant la plus efficace. Une étude multi-centrique, l'Osteoporosis prevention Using Soy (OPUS) est en cours : 400 femmes participent à l'étude qui durera deux ans.

Le soja prévient les maladies chroniques graves

Les femmes qui mangent du soja ou qui le prennent sous la forme de complément alimentaire ont un risque plus faible de maladie cardiovasculaire et de cancer. C'est ce qui ressort de l'ensemble des études menées sur le sujet.

En terme de santé cardiovasculaire, les Asiatiques sont également mieux loties que nous. Certes leur alimentation est riche en fibres d'origine végétale et contient peu de graisses saturées, ce qui constitue déjà un avantage, mais le rôle particulier du soja dans cette protection est également fortement suspecté.

Les études menées chez l'animal et chez l'homme montrent que les isoflavones ont une action sur les lipides sanguins et diminuent ainsi le risque de maladies cardiovasculaires. Elles réduisent significativement le « mauvais cholestérol » (LDL), les triglycérides et augmentent le « bon » cholestérol (HDL).

Antioxydantes, les isoflavones protègent aussi le cholestérol des attaques des radicaux libres. Elles s'opposent à la formation des plaques d'athérome – à l'origine des infarctus – par une action directe sur la paroi vasculaire. Enfin, une étude récente montre que le soja diminue l'homocystéine, un sous-produit des protéines alimentaires toxique pour les artères.

Ces bénéfices apparaissent à partir de 50 mg d'isoflavones soit 25 g de protéines de soja par jour.

La Food and Drug Administration des États-Unis (FDA) a récemment permis aux fabricants d'aliments à base de soja d'indiquer sur leurs emballages qu'un tel régime peut diminuer le risque cardiovasculaire.

Des composés sûrs

Contrairement au THM, les isoflavones apparaissent sans danger pour le sein, l'endomètre, les ovaires dans la mesure où on ne dépasse pas la dose de 1 mg/kg par jour (recommandations de l'AFSSA en mars 2005). Par ailleurs, une étude clinique est en cours. Elle concerne Phyto Soya. Les premiers résultats ont été présentés en décembre 2006. Ils montrent que l'extrait de soja Phytosoya est sûr pour l'utérus. Après un an de traitement, les chercheurs n'ont trouvé aucune lésion suspecte ou cancéreuse. Concernant les effets sur le sein, les premiers résultats sont rassurants. Les résultats définitifs seront communiqués dans le courant de l'année 2007.

Prévention des cancers du sein, des ovaires, de l'endomètre

Les isoflavones ont fait naître beaucoup d'espoirs dans la prévention des cancers hormono-dépendants. Les femmes asiatiques dont l'alimentation est riche en phytoestrogènes ont 6 fois moins de cancer du sein que les Occidentales. Le risque de ces cancers augmente quand elles émigrent aux États-Unis. Les femmes d'origine japonaise nées aux États-Unis ont un risque presque identique à celui des Américaines.

Plusieurs études ont trouvé des concentrations plus faibles de lignanes et d'isoflavones dans l'urine de patientes atteintes d'un cancer du sein par rapport à des femmes en bonne santé. Des études in vitro ont effectivement montré un effet protecteur mais il est trop tôt pour apporter une réponse définitive.

Les chercheurs expliquent cette protection par les effets sélectifs des isoflavones selon les tissus.

Des isoflavones sur la peau

Des études ont montré que l'application d'une crème contenant des isoflavones de soja améliore la protection antioxydante de la peau.

Le soja sous toutes ses formes

Le « lait » de soja : ce sont des fèves de soja que l'on fait bouillir. Puis on broie le mélange et, enfin, on le filtre. Le lait de soja est le filtrat obtenu.
Le tonyu : « lait » de soja certifié par une norme française, fabriqué exclusivement à partir de fèves de soja entières, et non d'isolats ou de farines de soja et ayant une teneur minimale en protéines (36 g/l).
Le tofu : c'est du lait de soja caillé, grâce à un ferment que l'on ajoute. Il est ensuite pressé en bloc. Le goût est fade. Il doit être accommodé et assaisonné.
Le miso : pâte fermentée de soja jaune, très salé. Il est à la base de la soupe de miso japonaise.
Le tempeh : fèves de soja jaune fermentées, avec parfois de la noix de coco.
La sauce soja : soja fermenté. La meilleure sauce soja est fluide, salée, et a besoin de 6 à 7 ans de maturation.
Le tamari : également sauce de soja fermenté et salé.
Mais on peut également utiliser les graines de soja, comme l'on utilise les lentilles ou les pois.

Les isoflavones protègent-elles des autres cancers ?

Les recherches se multiplient. On a trouvé plusieurs actions très intéressantes.

Au bout des études, l'espoir

Les études in vitro sont réalisées en laboratoire sur des cellules animales ou humaines. Elles montrent que :

- les phytohormones sont antioxydantes ;
- elles inhibent la vascularisation des tumeurs, donc l'apport de sang à la tumeur (angiogénèse) ;
- elles induisent la mort de la cellule cancéreuse par apoptose ;
- elles inhibent une enzyme spéciale qui s'appelle l'aromatase, qui transforme normalement les androgènes en estrogènes au niveau de la glande mammaire ;
- elles inhibent d'autres enzymes qui sont impliquées dans la genèse des cellules cancéreuses ;
- elles inhibent la prolifération des cellules tumorales des cancers du foie, du sein, des mélanomes et des cellules leucémiques ;
- elles inhibent la dédifférenciation des cellules des mélanomes, des carcinomes embryonnaires et des cellules leucémiques.

Au total, dans les cultures de cellules cancéreuses, les phytohormones empêchent leur développement. Ces différentes actions varient selon les doses utilisées.

Chez l'animal, elles ont une action préventive sur certains cancers : cancers du côlon, cancers chimio-induits, cancers du foie, cancers des glandes mammaires, cancer de la prostate. La consommation de soja empêche l'accroissement des tumeurs de la prostate, du sein et du côlon. Chez l'homme, les études épidémiologiques montrent que la consommation de soja est associée à un risque plus faible de cancer pulmonaire, de leucémie et de cancer de la prostate.

Un complément très utile

Au total, les isoflavones de soja présentent de nombreux bénéfices pour la santé et le bien-être des femmes au moment de la ménopause. Prises sous forme de complément alimentaire, elles sont très utiles pour toutes celles qui ne peuvent pas ou ne souhaitent pas bénéficier du THM.

Pour optimiser l'efficacité de ces produits, il est important d'avoir une bonne flore intestinale, ce qui nécessite une bonne diététique.

Les premiers effets se font sentir à partir de 50 mg d'isoflavones de soja par jour. Pour une action plus complète, notamment au niveau osseux et cardio-vasculaire, on peut augmenter sans risque les doses et consommer jusqu'à 70 mg par jour.

Un aliment plus que complet

Le soja apporte plus que les seules isoflavones. Il est riche en protéines. Ces protéines contiennent tous les acides aminés essentiels à l'être humain, au même titre que la viande, le poisson, les œufs, les produits lactés. Parmi les végétaux, seul le quinoa lui est comparable. Il peut donc remplacer la viande. De plus, le soja contient peu de lipides et ces lipides sont intéressants car riches en acides gras insaturés Oméga 3. Ces acides gras ont un effet protecteur vis-à-vis des maladies cardio-vasculaires. Le soja apporte aussi des phospholipides qui servent à fabriquer des messagers chimiques utilisés par le cerveau pour la mémoire.

Expérimentalement, les phytoestrogènes empêchent les petits cancers de se développer

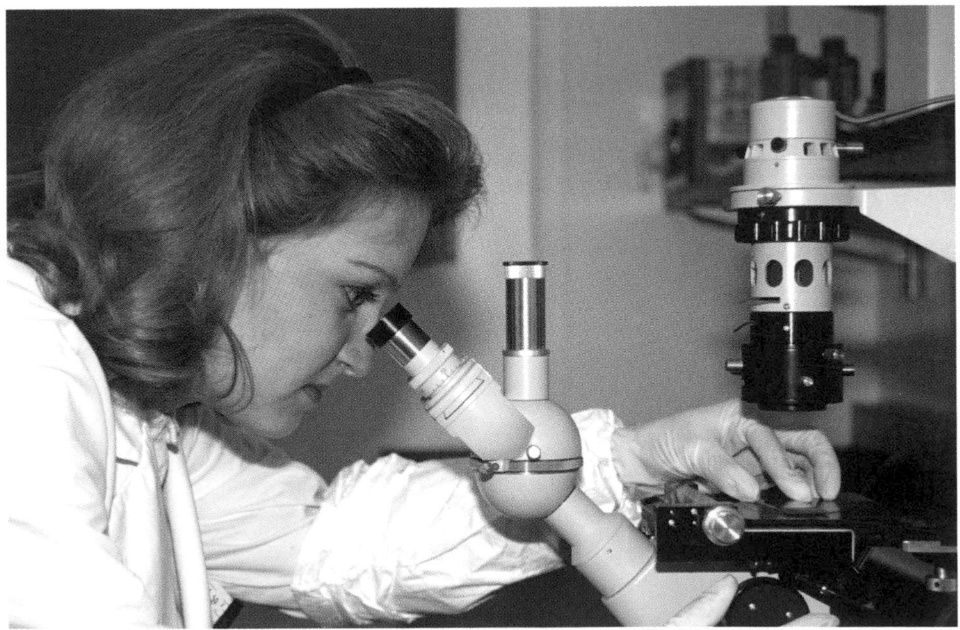

Les phytoprogestérones les plus connues

Plusieurs plantes semblent avoir une action qui ressemble à celle de la progestérone. On dit qu'elles sont *progesterone-like*. C'est le cas, par exemple, du gattilier. Mais celle dont on parle le plus est l'igname sauvage ou *Wild Yam*.

Le *Yam* : réputation surfaite

Le *Yam* sauvage, ou igname sauvage, vient du Mexique. Son nom botanique est *Dioscorea villosa*. La famille des dioscoréides comprend au moins 300 plantes. Seules quelques-unes sont utilisées, soit pour l'alimentation, soit pour leurs vertus médicinales. Le *Yam* sauvage était déjà préconisé par les Aztèques pour le traitement des rhumatismes et en application locale pour diminuer les douleurs. En Amérique Centrale, on l'a employé contre les troubles menstruels et ovariens, et pour faciliter l'accouchement.

Au XXe siècle, on en a extrait une molécule très intéressante : la diosgénine. Par un procédé chimique, cette diosgénine peut être transformée en progestérone. C'est grâce à elle que l'on a pu fabriquer de façon industrielle la progestérone et vers 1960 le premier contraceptif oral féminin. Un peu plus tard, on a découvert un autre procédé chimique pour transformer la progestérone en cortisone.

Malheureusement, la diosgénine du *Yam* ne permet pas d'augmenter la progestérone ou la DHEA dans le sang lorsqu'il est ingéré. Aujourd'hui, les études contrôlées ne montrent pas l'intérêt du *Yam* à la ménopause à l'exception d'un effet antioxydant. L'usage de ce produit exige même une grande prudence car certains fabricants peu scrupuleux rajoutent parfois de la progestérone aux comprimés de *Yam*.

Il existe également dans le commerce des crèmes à base de *Yam*, proposées pour rétablir l'équilibre hormonal. À ce jour, aucune étude menée chez la femme n'a pu mettre en évidence une telle action. Les études montrent en fait, que le *Yam* a une faible action *estrogen-like*. Il est traditionnellement utilisé pour les spasmes, l'aérophagie, les coliques, les nausées de la grossesse et les douleurs inflammatoires.

Le gattilier en préménopause

Si le terme progestérone naturelle est abusif pour le *Yam*, en revanche pour d'autres plantes, l'action *progesterone-like* est bien réelle. C'est le cas du gattilier ou *Vitex agnus castus*.
Le gattilier est utilisé depuis Hippocrate (450 avant J.-C.) pour réguler les troubles des règles, favoriser la délivrance après l'accouchement, stimuler la lactation.
Son action est particulièrement intéressante dans la préménopause car, comme la progestérone, il diminue les douleurs mammaires. Il réduit les œdèmes. Il favorise la régularité des cycles. Il a une action favorable sur les maux de tête, la constipation et les troubles de l'humeur de cette période.
Dans le sang, il agit effectivement sur le taux de certaines hormones et a des actions *progesterone-like*.
Il atténue le syndrome prémenstruel et est particulièrement indiqué en préménopause.

Utilisation : il faut le prendre pendant 3 mois, soit en gélules, soit en teinture mère. Dans ce dernier cas : 40 gouttes chaque jour.

Le gattilier : emblème des Vestales de la Rome Antique

Pline l'Ancien recommande le gattilier aux hommes attaqués par des désirs sexuels violents. Les moines l'utiliseront dans leur nourriture car son goût poivré pimente l'ordinaire tout en atténuant la libido ! C'est pourquoi, on l'appelle également le poivre du moine. Il est devenu un symbole de chasteté.

Les phytoprogestérones sur lesquelles vous pouvez compter

Le gattilier n'est pas la seule plante à se comporter comme un progestatif. Revue de détail des plantes bienfaisantes.

Le magnésium : minéral indispensable

Le magnésium est indispensable au traitement des irrégularités du cycle et aux troubles des règles car sa carence aggrave les symptômes. Le magnésium a des propriétés sédatives. Il intervient dans la contraction musculaire, la régularisation du rythme cardiaque, la transmission de l'influx nerveux, le stockage et l'utilisation de l'énergie.

Des chercheurs ont observé un taux de magnésium sanguin plus faible chez les femmes qui souffraient du syndrome prémenstruel. Une autre étude a montré que la prise quotidienne d'un supplément de magnésium (360 mg) pouvait améliorer l'humeur à cette période critique du cycle.

L'achillée millefeuille *(Achillea millefolium)*

Achille a donné son nom à cette plante car il l'utilisait pour soigner ses soldats blessés. On la trouve dans tout l'hémisphère Nord.
Au plan gynécologique, l'achillée millefeuille régule le cycle menstruel, diminue les saignements et soulage les douleurs au moment des règles.

Utilisation : on utilise les sommités fleuries de juin à octobre.
Pour arrêter les saignements, faire une décoction avec 3 sommités fleuries dans une tasse d'eau, bouillies pendant 3 minutes puis filtrer. Pour les irrégularités menstruelles et les douleurs des règles, on peut utiliser une teinture mère. On prendra 20 à 50 gouttes 2 à 3 fois par jour.

Les Chinois utilisent les tiges d'achillée séchées lorsqu'ils tirent le *yi king*, ouvrage de divination.

L'Alchémille commune *(Alchemilla vulgaris)*

Originaire d'Europe, on la récolte en été.
Elle s'appelle alchémille car elle intéressait beaucoup les alchimistes. Elle aussi était utilisée pour ses propriétés anti-hémorragiques dans les blessures de guerre.
En gynécologie, elle régularise les règles et en atténue les douleurs. Elle est intéressante dans les cas de fibrome et d'endométriose.

Utilisation : on utilise la teinture mère pour les irrégularités menstruelles et les douleurs de règles. On prendra 20 à 50 gouttes 2 à 3 fois par jour.

La salsepareille *(Smilax aspera)*

On utilise la racine de cette plante qui pousse dans les régions tempérées d'Asie et d'Australie.
Son usage est reconnu dans les affections cutanées comme l'eczéma et le psoriasis. Mais elle est également intéressante au plan gynécologique car, comme les plantes précédentes, elle stimule la production de progestérone. Elle est donc indiquée dans le syndrome prémenstruel et les troubles de la préménopause.

Utilisation : on utilise la teinture mère à la dose de 20 à 50 gouttes 2 à 3 fois par jour.

Les autres plantes de la préménopause

La verveine officinale, le grémil, la grande consoude, la mélisse, la marjolaine, le romarin, le serpolet, le thym, la buglosse, la bourrache.

De haut en bas : bourrache, thym, mélisse

L'aromathérapie, l'essence de la plante

Les huiles essentielles extraites des plantes par distillation ont également une activité très intéressante qui complète celle de la phytothérapie.

La quintessence des plantes

Les huiles essentielles sont obtenues par distillation des plantes. C'est « l'eau de vie » ou la quintessence de la plante. Ce sont à la fois des huiles (solubles dans les graisses ou lipophiles) et des essences (solubles dans l'eau et l'alcool ou hydrophiles). Cette double solubilité leur permet de circuler absolument partout dans le corps et d'avoir une très grande efficacité. Mais leur maniement est délicat et ne devrait se faire que sur le conseil d'un spécialiste phytothérapeute ou d'un pharmacien spécialisé.

Les huiles essentielles sont très actives et ne doivent pas être laissées à la portée des enfants. Certaines sont irritantes pour la peau. Il faut donc les utiliser avec précaution. Les quantités à absorber sont infimes : il ne faut pas dépasser 7 gouttes par jour en automédication.

On écrit H.E. après le nom de la plante pour indiquer qu'il s'agit d'huile essentielle.

Basilic H.E. *(Ocimum basilicum)*

Elle est particulièrement efficace dans le syndrome prémenstruel de la préménopause. On l'utilise sur de courtes périodes : prendre 2 gouttes trois fois par jour pendant deux à trois jours au moment des douleurs de règles. On peut également l'utiliser en massage incorporé à une huile de massage : masser le ventre 2 ou 3 fois par jour.

Cyprès H.E. *(Cupressus sempervirens)*

Elle est très intéressante pour les douleurs de règles. Elle améliore également l'humeur avant et pendant les règles.
Elle stimule la circulation veineuse et combat la fatigue nerveuse. Elle est à éviter en cas de cancer hormono-dépendant ou de mastose. On l'utilise sur de courtes périodes : prendre 2 gouttes trois fois par jour pendant deux à trois jours au moment des douleurs de règles.

Estragon H.E.
(Artemisia dracunculus)

Elle a la même indication que les deux précédentes. On l'utilise de la même façon. On peut également employer ces trois huiles essentielles en même temps dès le début du syndrome prémenstruel : en prenant une goutte de chaque, quatre fois par jour les deux premiers jours des règles.

Camomille H.E.
(Ormenis multiple)

Elle a une action relaxante, favorise le sommeil, améliore la libido.

Fenouil H.E.
(Foeniculum vulgare)

Elle contient des phytohormones qui ont une action stimulante sur la peau, sur les reins. Elle favorise la diurèse, l'élimination de l'acide urique.

Sauge sclarée H.E.
(Salvia sclarea)

La sauge diminue la tension nerveuse, la fatigue. Elle stimule la circulation veineuse.

Parmi les huiles essentielles que vous pouvez également essayer figurent celles d'anis vert, de cumin et de carvi.

Huiles essentielles : attention aux enfants

Si un enfant absorbe accidentellement une huile essentielle, il faut appeler rapidement le Centre anti-poisons le plus proche. Certaines huiles essentielles peuvent, en effet, provoquer des convulsions si elles sont ingérées en trop grandes quantités par un enfant.

Les médecines alternatives

Que peuvent apporter en bien-être les alternatives thérapeutiques représentées par l'homéopathie, la médecine chinoise traditionnelle, l'ostéopathie.

Tout ce qui peut contribuer à améliorer le confort et l'état de bien-être est intéressant. Pour chacune de ces alternatives, il sera intéressant de prendre conseil auprès d'une personne spécialisée, médecin, pharmacien ou ostéopathe.

L'homéopathie, des doses infinitésimales

L'homéopathie utilise les plantes, mais aussi les produits provenant des deux autres règnes de la nature : animal et minéral. Le mode de préparation des médicaments est spécifique. Il y a à la fois dilution de la matière première et dynamisation du produit obtenu. Le plus souvent, les remèdes sont imprégnés sur des petites boules de sucre ou granules. Cela en facilite l'absorption. Il faut laisser les granules fondre sous la langue. Les dosages sont très nombreux. Si on veut l'utiliser soi-même, il est prudent d'employer les dosages de 5 CH à 9 CH et de prendre trois granules 1 à 2 fois par jour.

Les principaux remèdes homéopathiques

Lachesis mutus lorsque la ménopause s'accompagne d'un changement de caractère, d'une intolérance à tout vêtement serré, de bouffées de chaleur, de migraines, d'ecchymoses spontanées.
Sulfur lorsqu'il y a en même temps des troubles vasculaires (bouffées de chaleur, hémorroïdes), des troubles cutanés (acné rosacée, urticaire), des troubles articulaires qui sont aggravés par la chaleur, améliorés par le frais.
Sepia officinalis chez les femmes qui deviennent tristes, irascibles, intolérantes à la contradiction et qui présentent une lourdeur du petit bassin, des bouffées de chaleurs internes, des troubles circulatoires.
Graphites si la ménopause s'accompagne de frilosité, de prise de poids, avec des troubles digestifs, des bouffées de chaleur au visage, contrastant avec une pâleur de la peau.
Thuya occidentalis lorsqu'il y a un fibrome, des verrues, un kyste ovarien, avec des douleurs pelviennes plutôt à gauche.

De nombreux autres remèdes sont intéressants. Nous ne pouvons tous les mentionner. En voici quelques autres : *Caulophyllum, Viburnum Opulus, Sabina, Chamomilla, Veratrum Album,* etc. Il sera certainement utile de consulter un homéopathe en cas de doute ou d'inefficacité des produits mentionnés ci-dessus. En effet, ce sont les remèdes les plus fréquemment utilisés mais il en existe bien d'autres.

La médecine traditionnelle chinoise

La médecine traditionnelle chinoise est un ensemble de pratiques de santé dont le but est de prévenir et traiter les maladies, rétablir la santé et prolonger la vie. Elle a de multiples facettes : acupuncture (la plus connue en Occident), plantes chinoises, massages. Mais aussi l'art de se mettre en mouvement avec le *Tai Ji Quan*, gymnastique chinoise de plus en plus connue, et le *Qi Gong*, travail du souffle, ce souffle ou *QI* (ceci se prononce : « tchi ») qui anime la vie de tout ce qui est dans l'univers.

L'ostéopathie

Nulle violence dans le geste de l'ostéopathe. Il est attentif aux souffles qui maintiennent la vie. Il saura accompagner le mouvement naturel de vos muscles et de vos articulations. Il en dénouera les tensions et rendra plus fluides vos mouvements. L'ostéopathie vous aidera à renouer amitié avec votre corps.

Partie V

PROGRAMME NATUREL POUR LA MÉNOPAUSE

Juste une mise au point

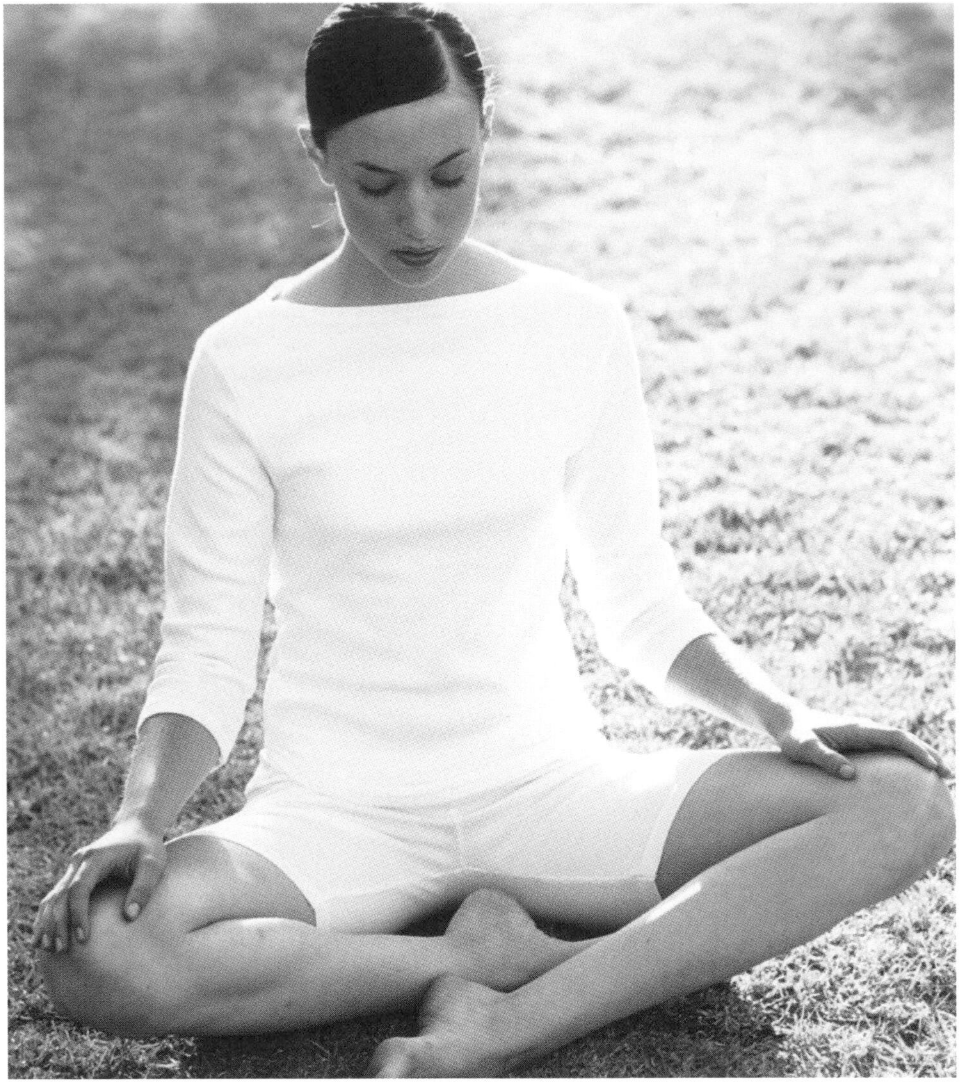

Cinquante ans, c'est le moment de faire le point avec soi-même.

Après de nombreuses années à s'occuper des autres : du compagnon, des parents, des enfants, prenons un peu soin de nous !

Et commençons par faire un check-up afin de mieux nous connaître. Tout d'abord, prendre le temps de s'observer et faire le point avec soi-même.

Le poids

Être ni trop grosse, ni trop maigre. Il est difficile de lutter contre la maigreur car elle est le plus souvent constitutionnelle. La surcharge pondérale est à combattre car elle favorise plusieurs maladies. Cependant, l'objectif doit être raisonnable. Il ne s'agit pas de perdre trop de kilos. Garder quelques rondeurs est aussi un art de vivre. Ne vous soumettez pas à la pensée unique qui s'étale sur les magazines féminins. Pour vous aider, n'hésitez pas à faire appel à des spécialistes de la nutrition. Médecins ou diététiciens vous apporteront leurs connaissances.

Les capacités du cœur

Elles se mesurent par un test simple. Il s'agit de prendre son pouls au repos. Puis de faire un exercice physique qui stimule le cœur : par exemple, 30 flexions rapides. Ensuite on reprend le pouls et on le prend à nouveau après deux minutes de repos.

Le test est favorable si on récupère le pouls au repos après deux minutes et si le pouls à l'effort ne dépasse pas 220 pulsations par minute moins l'âge.

Par exemple, pour 50 ans, il ne faut pas dépasser 170 pulsations par minute à l'effort. Si on le dépasse, cela nécessite un contrôle chez le médecin. La reprise d'une activité physique devra en tenir compte.

On choisira au départ des activités douces.

Les seins

À chacune de vérifier une fois par mois, comment sont ses seins. Personne n'est mieux placé que vous pour observer s'il y a des changements et consulter son médecin en cas de doute.

Les articulations

Y a-t-il des douleurs, des gonflements articulaires, des douleurs dans le dos dont on ne s'est jamais préoccupé ?

Rester zen

Face aux états de stress qui sont de plus en plus importants dans notre société, la prise de nutriments et de plantes anti-stress est très intéressante. Mais il est surtout indispensable de bien analyser ce qui se passe et d'essayer d'acquérir un nouvel art de vivre.

C'est là qu'interviennent toutes les techniques favorisant le repos :

- le repos de l'esprit, c'est la relaxation ;
- le repos du corps et de l'esprit, c'est le sommeil.

La relaxation permet à chacun de devenir plus responsable de sa santé et de sa vie. Elle permet aussi de redécouvrir son potentiel, sa créativité. Elle est indispensable à tous. À chacune de la pratiquer régulièrement. Les techniques sont variées. Elles ont toutes un point commun : c'est la reprise de contact avec le corps et ses différentes fonctions, notamment avec la respiration. Et cela réduit automatiquement le stress. Ces techniques peuvent être utilisées au cours de la journée et aussi le soir pour favoriser le sommeil.

Une visite chez le médecin

À l'approche de la cinquantaine, faites le point avec votre médecin généraliste : bilan général et mise en place d'une surveillance gynécologique.

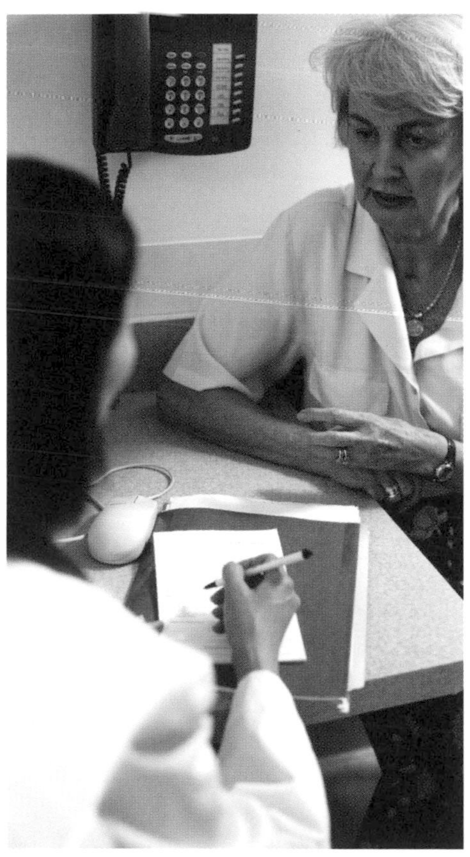

• **Le cœur :** quelques tests simples et l'auscultation permettront de vérifier s'il y a un risque de maladie cardiaque. Dans ce cas, le médecin conseillera certainement une visite chez le cardiologue. Il fera également pratiquer des examens de sang afin de surveiller le cholestérol total, le cholestérol HDL (« le bon »), les triglycérides ainsi que la glycémie.

• **Les vaisseaux :** l'examen pratiqué par le médecin permet de vérifier si toutes les artères sont bien souples et performantes. Ceci par la prise des pouls jusqu'au bout des pieds et par l'auscultation le long des trajets des artères. Il regardera également l'état des veines. Une insuffisance veineuse peut donner des douleurs dans les jambes, ou des varices.

• **Les os :** une ostéodensitométrie permettra de savoir si les os sont bien solides ou s'ils se fragilisent. Le médecin, en fonction de ces résultats, dira si un traitement est nécessaire.

• **L'examen gynécologique :** le cancer du sein, cancer le plus fréquent chez la femme, apparaît le plus souvent entre 50 et 70 ans. Il est donc important de faire des examens radiologiques du sein (mammographies) régulièrement dans cette tranche d'âge, en général tous les deux à trois ans. Lorsque le risque personnel est plus élevé que celui de l'ensemble des femmes, par exemple s'il y a déjà eu des cancers du sein dans la famille proche, il est impératif de mettre en place un suivi précoce.

Le cancer du col de l'utérus se dépiste en pratiquant un frottis au cours d'un examen gynécologique. Le frottis permet de dépister les anomalies bénignes et de les traiter avant qu'elles n'évoluent. Si des frottis ont été pratiqués régulièrement sans qu'aucune anomalie n'ait jamais été détectée, le risque de cancer du col de l'utérus devient faible. Dans ce cas, le frottis peut être fait tous les trois ans. Si vous n'avez jamais eu de frottis avant la périménopause, il est important d'en faire pratiquer un rapidement.

Choisir de traiter ou non sa ménopause

Une fois le bilan de santé terminé, se pose la question de traiter ou non, puis du choix du traitement. Ces décisions doivent être concertées.

En fonction de l'intensité des troubles, de la gêne ressentie et des facteurs de risques, le médecin se doit d'expliquer clairement et en toute objectivité les différentes possibilités qui s'offrent à sa patiente, avec pour chacune les avantages, inconvénients et risques éventuels. Car un traitement bien compris est aussi mieux suivi. Ainsi chaque femme doit pouvoir choisir en connaissance de cause. Le médecin doit s'assurer que le traitement prescrit est bien celui qui convient le mieux, celui que la personne prendra le plus facilement. Il se doit de rester à l'écoute des attentes mais aussi des craintes de sa patiente. À lui de l'informer et, quel qu'il soit, de respecter son choix.

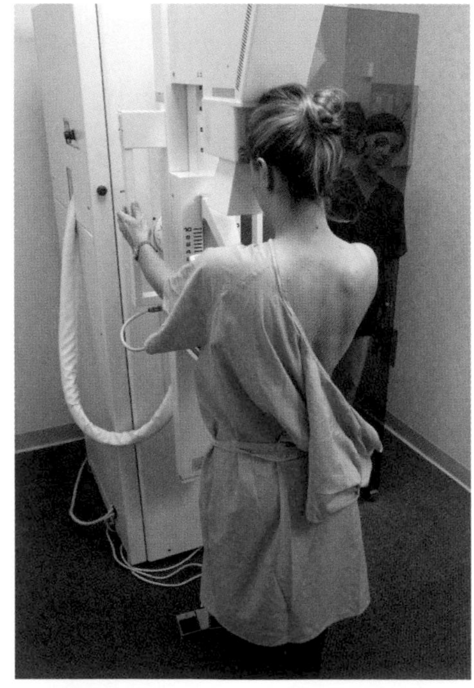

Bouger, bouger, bouger !

Pour combattre les risques d'ostéoporose et de maladies cardio-vasculaires, il faut continuer ou se remettre à bouger. Mais, bien sûr, pas n'importe comment : l'activité physique sera adaptée aux possibilités de chacune.

L'activité sportive, un gage de bonne santé

La pratique du sport réduit les risques de maladies cardiovasculaires. L'exercice régulier fait perdre du poids, diminue la masse grasse, fait baisser la tension artérielle. Il diminue les risques de diabète gras. Il fait régresser les taux de mauvais cholestérol. Les femmes consacrant 4 heures par semaine à une activité physique ont une réduction de 37 % du risque de cancer du sein. Le sport enrichit aussi la vie sociale.

Il ne faut pas malmener votre corps et vous retrouver pleine de douleurs, de crampes, de courbatures après avoir repris de façon inconsidérée le sport de vos 18 ans. Allez-y progressivement.

Les activités à démarrer tout de suite

- la marche et la natation
- la gymnastique douce, le stretching, le yoga ou la Tai Ji Quan (gymnastique chinoise)
- la gymnastique aquatique : son avantage vient du fait qu'elle soulage les articulations et peut se pratiquer sans souffrir même en cas de surcharge pondérale
- le vélo : on peut toujours le commencer en terrain plat
- le tir à l'arc
- la danse bretonne et la danse de salon
- le kayak de mer

Des efforts plus soutenus

Après un peu d'entraînement dans les activités ci-avant, on pourra aller plus loin :

- la course à pied : de très bonnes chaussures de jogging sont indispensables
- les sports de raquette : tennis, badminton. Déconseillés pour les personnes ayant des soucis cardiovasculaires ou de l'hypertension artérielle
- le ski de fond
- le golf : déconseillé pour certains problèmes de dos ou d'arthrose
- la voile et l'aviron

Réservé aux sportives

Et notamment à celles qui n'ont jamais lâché leur sport favori :

- l'équitation
- le foot, le basket, le volley
- la planche à voile
- la plongée
- le ski alpin

Comment reprendre une activité sportive à 50 ans ?

Il faut tout d'abord faire un test d'effort chez un cardiologue. Si ce test est satisfaisant, on peut reprendre un entraînement progressif.

Tout d'abord, déterminer la fréquence cardiaque maximale (FCM) à ne pas dépasser au cours de l'effort. Théoriquement : 220 pulsations moins l'âge. En fait, ceci correspond à un sportif entraîné. Pour un débutant, ce sera 60 % du résultat de cette formule et progressivement, il pourra atteindre 80 % de la formule.

Donc une personne de 50 ans en bonne santé très entraînée peut courir à une vitesse lui permettant d'atteindre 170 pulsations par minute. Pour une débutante, le cœur ne doit pas dépasser 100 par minute. Ce qui correspond à une vitesse de course lors du ré-entraînement d'environ 8 km à l'heure. Ceci pour les premières semaines. Puis progressivement, on peut augmenter la vitesse de course mais sans dépasser 70 % de la FCM, soit 120 pulsations par minute.

N'oublions pas que les muscles et les articulations un peu rouillés nécessitent un échauffement, par le yoga et le stretching par exemple.

Et pourquoi pas le semi-marathon ?

Un peu de folie dans ce monde trop bien policé. Et si folie était sagesse !

Un challenge formidable

Ce que vous n'avez jamais pris le temps de faire, c'est maintenant que vous devez le faire. La vie, grâce aux années passées, aux expériences accumulées, vous a montré ce qui était bon pour vous. Et ce qui est bon pour vous est bon pour ceux que vous aimez. Votre forme, votre bonne humeur rayonne autour de vous et donne de la joie à tous. Donc : faites ce qui est bon pour vous. Et par exemple : préparer le semi-marathon !

Voilà un challenge formidable ! L'entraînement sera régulier et apportera, jour après jour, de merveilleuses récompenses : une forme physique de plus en plus optimale, une bonne humeur de tous les instants, une patience à toute épreuve et la joie. Réussirez-vous à battre Fenya Crown, 88 ans, qui a couru le marathon de Rome le 25 mars 2001 en 7 heures, 29 mn et 3 s ? Mais commençons seulement par le semi-marathon !

Un entraînement progressif

Une qualité est nécessaire dès le départ : la persévérance. Grâce à elle, vous irez loin. Si vous trouvez un ou une amie prêt à vous accompagner, c'est encore mieux.
Chaque cycle d'entraînement se fait sur 4 semaines ou sur 4 fois 9 jours si le temps manque. Il faut trois entraînements par cycle de 7 à 9 jours, soit un entraînement tous les 2 à 3 jours.

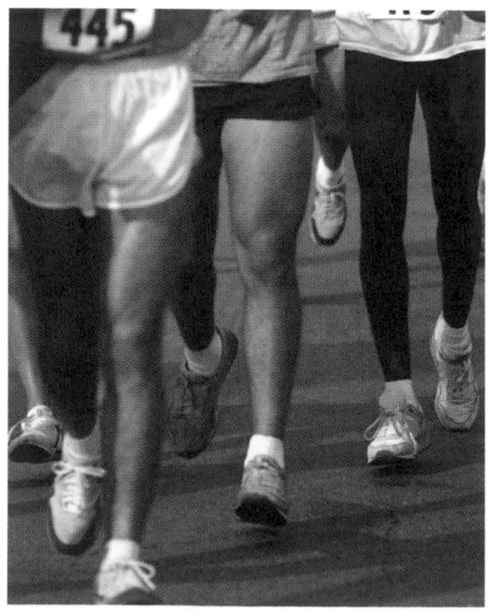

1ère semaine	
Entraînement n° 1 :	30 minutes (mn) alternant course et marche, finissant par une course de 10 mn ;
Entraînement n° 2 :	45 mn alternant course et marche, finissant par une course de 15 mn ;
Entraînement n° 3 :	1 h 30 mn de course, marche et vélo.

2ème semaine	
Entraînement n° 1 :	45 mn alternant course et marche, finissant par une course de 15 mn ;
Entraînement n° 2 :	60 mn alternant course et marche, finissant par une course de 20 mn ;
EEntraînement n° 3 :	durée 2 heures ; après 30 mn de marche, alternance de course et de marche.

3ème semaine	
Entraînement n° 1 :	45 mn alternant course et marche, finissant par une course de 15 mn ;
Entraînement n° 2 :	60 mn alternant course et marche, finissant par une course de 20 mn ;
Entraînement n° 3 :	2 heures ; après 30 mn de marche, alternance de course, marche et vélo.

4ème semaine : programme allégé de récupération	
Entraînement n° 1 :	vélo ou marche pendant 1 heure ;
Entraînement n° 2 :	30 mn en alternant 45 s de course et 15 s de marche ;
Entraînement n° 3 :	vélo ou marche pendant 1 heure à 1 h 15.

On reprendra ensuite un nouveau cycle de quatre semaines, en augmentant progressivement les durées de courses.

Avant de vous lancer dans ce challenge, faites un bon bilan médical pour vérifier que tout fonctionne bien et qu'il n'y a qu'un peu de rouille ! Et pendant la course, vérifiez votre rythme cardiaque pour adapter la vitesse de votre course.

Bien vivre, c'est bien manger

Une nourriture saine et variée réjouit les yeux, le cœur et le corps.

Pour chaque journée, respecter l'équilibre suivant

• **15 % de protéines.** L'idéal est d'avoir pour moitié des protéines d'origine animale (viandes blanches de préférence, poissons, œufs, laitages) et pour moitié des protéines d'origine végétale (céréales surtout complètes, légumineuses comme le soja). Pour les végétariens, les protéines végétales doivent provenir de deux sources différentes. L'une des sources doit correspondre à une céréale et l'autre à une légumineuse. Par exemple, l'association de riz et de lentilles est bonne car elle apporte tous les acides aminés essentiels. Deux sources végétales apportent chacune tous ces acides aminés : c'est le soja et le quinoa.

• **30 à 35 % de lipides (graisses).** La qualité des graisses que nous mangeons influence avec certitude la qualité de nos artères, de nos hormones, de notre humeur. On distingue les bonnes graisses des mauvaises par les acides gras qu'elles renferment. Les bons sont les acides gras insaturés et les moins bons, voire mauvais, les acides gras saturés. Ces derniers se trouvent dans le beurre, les laitages, le fromage, la charcuterie et certaines viandes comme l'agneau. À consommer avec modération car ils augmentent les risques de maladies cardiaques et probablement de certains cancers. Les acides gras insaturés se trouvent dans les huiles végétales. Certaines sont plus intéressantes que d'autres car elles contiennent des acides gras essentiels. Les huiles les plus intéressantes sont l'huile d'olive et l'huile de colza. Cette dernière renferme, en proportion idéale, les deux acides gras essentiels que sont l'acide linoléique et l'acide alpha-linolénique. L'huile d'olive, elle, contient de l'acide oléique qui protège les graisses de l'oxydation. Les oléagineux secs (noix de toutes sortes) sont de bonnes sources de graisses de qualité.

• **50 à 55 % de glucides.** Mais attention, là aussi il y a les bons et les mauvais. Les aliments à index glycémique élevé font monter très vite le taux de sucre dans le sang (sucre, sodas, riz blanc, farine blanche, chips, pommes de terre frites). Ils se cachent aussi dans les pâtisseries, les laitages, le pop-corn, les corn flakes, la plupart des céréales du petit déjeuner, le riz instantané, le pain des fast-foods, etc. Fuyez le plus possible ces sucres rapides et retrouvez l'habitude des sucres à index glycémique faible. Ces derniers sont distribués très lentement au corps. Ils maintiennent la glycémie constante et sont de véritables brûleurs de graisses. Ce sont les meilleurs carburants du cerveau et des muscles. Ils leur permettent de fonctionner dans le calme et la durée. Quelques aliments à index glycémique bas : pain complet, pain de seigle complet, pâtes au blé complet, riz complet, presque tous les légumes et les fruits frais, le soja, les lentilles, le yaourt nature sans sucre.

Faire trois vrais repas :

- Petit déjeuner : 25 % des calories de la journée (riche en protéines)
- Déjeuner : 40 % (riche en protéines)
- Dîner : 35 % (riche en glucides lents)

Ces constituants pour être bien utilisés doivent être accompagnés de vitamines. Pour cela, chaque jour, mangez : 3 fruits frais, une crudité et une part de salade.

Bien manger, c'est bien choisir

Sachez choisir les aliments qui contiennent des composants protecteurs pour la santé.

- **Graisses insaturées Oméga 3 :** poissons gras, huiles de cameline et de colza, laitue, soja, noix de toutes sortes.
- **Graisses mono-insaturées :** huile d'olive, olive, amande, foie gras, confit d'oie, avocat.
- **Sucres lents :** pain complet au levain, pain aux céréales, céréales complètes, légumineuses, féculents.
- **Aliments riches en arginine, ornithine, polyamines :** oléagineux, crucifères, légumineuses, légumineuses germées, soja et dérivés, thé vert.
- **Aliments riches en acides aminés soufrés :** fruits de mer, poissons, œufs, asperge, poireau, crucifères, oignon, ail.
- **Sulfates :** eaux Hépar, Contrexéville, Vittel, Orée du Bois.
- **Potassium :** fruits secs, oléagineux, fruits (banane), légumineuses, soja, légumes, céréales complètes.
- **Calcium :** eaux Hépar, Talians, Contrexéville, Badoit, Vittel, lait de soja enrichi en calcium, gruyère, emmenthal, parmesan, yaourts, crucifères, betterave, sardines entières, amandes, noix.
- **Magnésium :** la plupart des eaux riches en calcium, soja, oléagineux, céréales complètes, légumineuses, légumes verts, poissons, bigorneaux.
- **Zinc :** coquillages, crustacés, poissons, viandes, foie, œufs, gingembre.

Bien manger, c'est éviter les aliments accélérateurs du vieillissement

- Les graisses saturées : charcuterie, porc, beurre, huile d'arachide, fritures.
- Les graisses trans : les huiles et les margarines hydrogénées, « fritures fast-food ».
- Les sucres rapides en excès : confiseries, confitures, boissons sucrées, pain blanc.
- Les excès de sodium (sel), de fer ou de cuivre.
- Les métaux lourds et les nitrates.
- Les graisses, les sucres et le sel cachés.

Malgré le peu de temps que laissent le travail, la maison, les enfants... reprenons le chemin de la cuisine. Il vaut mieux manger des produits frais, cuisinés par nos soins, que les produits tout préparés, riches en sucre, en graisse et en sel, en produits édulcorants et en colorants.

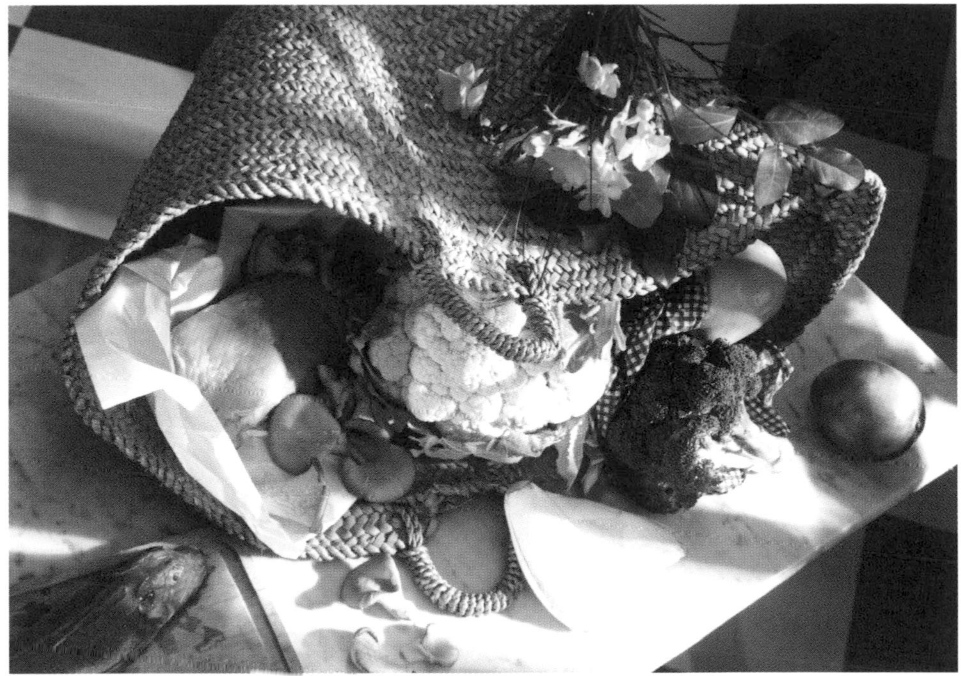

Manger avec plaisir

L'idéal, c'est de se retrouver avec des amis, dans un joli cadre. Prendre le temps de manger tranquillement. Mettre de côté les soucis de la journée. Manger assise.

- **Sélénium :** noix du Brésil, poissons, fruits de mer, viandes, foie, céréales, poivron rouge, cèpe, ail (en fonction de la richesse du sol).
- **Silicium :** céréales complètes, eaux minérales.
- **Vitamines B1, B3, B6, B9, B12, C, E :** les levures comme la levure maltée, les céréales complètes, les légumineuses.
- **Bêta-carotène :** les légumes et fruits « rouges », carottes, myrtilles.
- **Lycopène :** sauce tomate, tomate cuite, papaye, pamplemousse rose, pastèque.
- **Ferments vivants (bifidus, lactobacillus...) :** yaourts, choucroute.

Au moment de la ménopause, c'est choisir tout particulièrement parmi ces aliments ceux qui sont riches en phytoestrogènes. Parmi ceux-ci, le soja est un aliment essentiel.

Bien se protéger, c'est prendre des suppléments de vitamines et minéraux !

« Les suppléments de vitamines et minéraux ne sont pas utiles si l'on bénéficie d'une alimentation variée et équilibrée. » Cette assertion est aujourd'hui remise en cause par bon nombre d'experts.

Moins de calories, c'est moins de vitamines et de minéraux

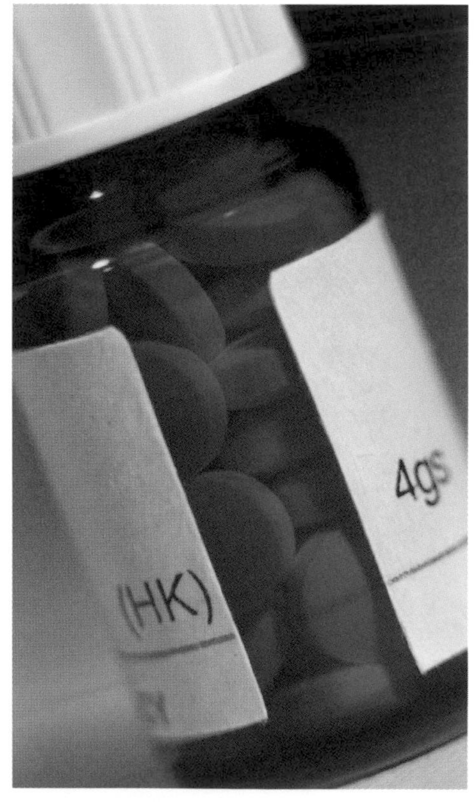

La vie moderne oblige les femmes à courir dans tous les sens, du bureau à la maison, en passant par le studio du petit dernier qui vient juste de s'installer, les parents qui ont besoin d'un coup de main et la meilleure amie qui a un coup de blues affreux. Comment, dans ces conditions, faire ses courses au magasin bio du quartier d'à côté, penser à mettre les pois chiches à tremper et faire une cuisine pleine de saveur, de vitamines, de minéraux et de santé ? De plus, la vie a bien changé. Nous sommes de plus en plus stressés mais nos dépenses en énergie physique ont beaucoup diminué.

De ce fait, nos besoins caloriques ont également baissé. Or pour avoir dans notre alimentation les bonnes quantités de vitamines, de minéraux et d'oligo-éléments, il faudrait sans doute augmenter parallèlement notre quantité de nourriture et le nombre de calories ingérées chaque jour. On aurait alors un risque de prise de poids. Ce que personne ne souhaite.

Les compléments alimentaires viennent alors à notre secours. Ils sont disponibles chez le pharmacien et, de plus en plus, en parapharmacie et dans les magasins diététiques. Mais attention : tout n'est pas bon à prendre et le mieux est l'ennemi du bien. Il faut savoir en toutes choses garder mesure.

Le déficit en magnésium est fréquent

La vie moderne, génératrice de stress, rend le magnésium encore plus nécessaire.

Où le trouver ? Dans ces aliments si bons, si doux mais si caloriques : le chocolat, les fruits secs, la banane. Mais on le trouve aussi dans les céréales complètes, les fruits de mer, les poissons gras, les légumes, le pain complet.

Les besoins de l'adulte sont de 300 à 700 mg par jour en fonction de la personne et de son mode de vie. Plus ce mode de vie est stressant, plus les besoins sont importants.

En France, près de 50 % de la population est en carence de magnésium. Cette carence donne de multiples petits signes qui vont des fourmillements des extrémités à la déprime. Il n'y a pas de risque de surcharge en magnésium. Si on prend trop de magnésium sous forme de complément, il sera éliminé de façon naturelle par le corps, provoquant parfois des diarrhées.

Manque de vitamines ? Voici ce que vous risquez

Situation	Conséquences biochimiques	Conséquences métaboliques	Femmes ménopausées à risque
Déficit en antioxydants (vitamines C, E, sélénium, zinc)	• Protection réduite contre les radicaux libres	• Baisse de l'immunité • Risque d'infarctus et d'accident vasculaire cérébral (AVC) • Risque de cataractes et de dégénérescence maculaire liée à l'âge • Susceptibilité aux infections	• Fumeuses actives et passives • Citadines (villes polluées) • Asthmatiques • Amateurs de soleil • Petites consommatrices de fruits et légumes
Déficit en vitamines B1, B2, B3, B5, B6, C, magnésium	• Baisse des neuro-transmetteurs de la mémoire et de la vigilance	• Risque de troubles cognitifs	• Consommatrices d'aliments sucrés • Personnes âgées
Déficit en vitamines B6, B9, B12	• Augmentation de l'homocystéine (produit toxique de dégradation des protéines)	• Risque d'infarctus et d'AVC • Risque d'Alzheimer et de Parkinson • Risque de cancer côlo-rectal • Risque de dépression	• Toutes les femmes
Déficit en vitamine D	• Diminution du remodelage osseux • Protection réduite contre l'initiation de cancers • Risque d'ostéoporose • Risque de cancers du sein, du côlon, de la peau		• Citadines, l'hiver

Bien se protéger, c'est faire le plein d'antioxydants !

Les antioxydants jouent un rôle essentiel dans la lutte contre le vieillissement et la prévention de certaines maladies. Ils œuvrent en synergie dans l'organisme.

Caroténoïdes : bêta-carotène (provitamine A), lycopène

Des taux élevés de bêta-carotène dans le sang sont associés à un risque moindre de développer certains cancers. Les caroténoïdes diminuent également le risque de cataracte et de dégénérescence maculaire de la rétine.

Où les trouver : dans les carottes, les choux, les condiments rouges (piments rouges, paprika), les fruits jaunes (abricot, mangue, melon, pastèque). Le lycopène est présent en bonne quantité dans les tomates, les brocolis, les épinards. Bêta-carotène et lycopène sont incorporés dans certains compléments alimentaires.

La vitamine C

Les besoins en vitamine C sont l'objet de controverse : selon certains, 10 à 100 mg par jour suffisent ; d'autres avancent des doses 4 à 10 fois plus élevées. Les fumeurs, actifs ou passifs, les femmes qui prennent la pilule, les personnes atteintes d'asthme, de diabète, de maladies chroniques ont besoin d'au moins 500 mg par jour.

Où la trouver : dans les fruits frais : kiwi, acérola, cynorrhodon, agrumes. Les suppléments de vitamine C peuvent être pris par tous sauf les personnes atteintes d'hémochromatose, les insuffisants rénaux.

La vitamine E

Antioxydant très puissant, elle protège les cellules des agressions des radicaux libres.

Où la trouver : dans l'huile de germe de blé, les amandes, les noisettes. Les besoins sont difficiles à apprécier. Les carences sont fréquentes et les besoins augmentés dans les régimes amaigrissants trop sévères et dans certaines maladies.

Si des compléments sont nécessaires, les choisir avec de la vitamine E naturelle. Il n'y a pas de risque de surconsommation de vitamine E, mais prudence chez les personnes qui doivent subir une intervention chirurgicale, les hémophiles, les personnes ayant une maladie qui touche la vision appelée *retinitis pigmentosa*.

Le sélénium

Puissant antioxydant, il ralentit le vieillissement cellulaire. Le sélénium est également un détoxifiant. En se liant aux métaux lourds, il entraîne leur élimination urinaire. Enfin, il a une action sur la fluidité sanguine.
Où le trouver : surtout dans les poissons, fruits de mer, œufs, viande. Certains végétaux (céréales en particulier) peuvent en contenir selon la richesse des sols. En France, les apports moyens ne représentent que 60 à 70 % des doses recommandées. Le sélénium est incorporé à de nombreux compléments alimentaires.

Sélénium et cancers

Les déficits en sélénium peuvent favoriser l'apparition de certains cancers (prostate, sein, côlon et foie). Aux États-Unis, une étude menée en double aveugle contre placebo sur 1 312 personnes a montré que dans le groupe qui prenait le supplément de sélénium (200 µg/j), la mortalité totale par cancer avait été divisée par deux.

Le zinc

Il intervient dans la régulation des gènes, de l'insuline, dans l'immunité et dans la vision. Enfin, le zinc joue aussi un rôle dans la protection antioxydante de l'organisme.
Où le trouver : surtout dans les viandes, les poissons et les fruits de mer. 80 % de la population en France est carencée en zinc. Le zinc est associé à des multivitamines que l'on trouve en pharmacie.

Des os plus solides

Pour prévenir l'ostéoporose, il faut d'abord du calcium. L'idéal est d'en apporter à votre corps entre 1,2 à 1,5 grammes chaque jour. Mais cela ne suffit pas.

Le calcium est le principal constituant de l'os et 99 % du calcium de l'organisme est concentré dans le squelette. Il est capital d'apporter à l'organisme des quantités suffisantes de ce minéral, mais cela ne suffit pas pour garantir des os solides. En effet, l'absorption, la rétention et la fixation du calcium dépendent fortement de nombreux paramètres : activité physique, équilibre acide-base mais aussi présence de vitamine D.

Où trouver du calcium ?

Bien sûr, dans le lait et ses dérivés. Mais celles qui ne veulent pas des laitages trouveront suffisamment de calcium dans les légumes et les fruits secs et les eaux minérales très riches en calcium. On peut aussi en prendre sous forme de comprimés, d'ampoules ou de poudre.

Il faudra souvent l'associer à la vitamine D3. Demandez conseil à votre médecin car certaines maladies interdisent de prendre du calcium : les hypercalcémies et les insuffisances rénales sévères.

Les produits laitiers avec parcimonie

Pour les femmes qui prennent du poids facilement, le fromage n'est pas très indiqué car il est souvent très riche en matières grasses. Cependant, les fromages de chèvre et de brebis contiennent moins de graisses que les fromages au lait de vache. À noter que plusieurs grandes études, dont une sur 80 000 femmes, n'ont pas trouvé que la consommation de produits laitiers prévient les fractures d'ostéoporose.

La vitamine D : indispensable à la solidité des os

Notre organisme se procure surtout cette vitamine par exposition au soleil mais c'est très difficile en hiver en France, même en exposant visage et bras au soleil, du fait de la faiblesse de l'intensité des rayons solaires. Il s'ensuit une baisse du taux de vitamine D dans le sang qui engendre des déficits réels, lourds de conséquence en particulier pour les personnes de 50 ans et plus. La vitamine D est aussi apportée en petite quantité par l'alimentation (poissons gras, jaune d'œuf, foie, laitages). Des suppléments de vitamine D3 seront souvent nécessaires en hiver et en automne.

L'équilibre acide-base à surveiller

Quand le corps est trop acide, du fait de la consommation excessive de protéines animales et de céréales, il rétablit son équilibre en puisant dans le calcium des os. L'un des éléments les plus importants de cette régulation, c'est le potassium, que l'on trouve dans les fruits et légumes ou sous forme de compléments. Des études ont montré que ces compléments permettent de renforcer l'os en freinant la fuite de calcium osseux.

L'exercice physique, bien sûr

Les populations des pays en voie de développement consomment peu de calcium mais ne connaissent pas l'ostéoporose probablement parce qu'ils sont plus actifs que nous. Tous les sports sont bons pour les os, à l'exception peut-être de la natation car elle ne permet pas d'exercer une pression suffisante sur l'os.

De plus, pour vaincre l'ostéoporose, des traitements efficaces existent aujourd'hui.

Les aliments riches en calcium (mg/100 g)

Yaourt nature	140–170
Fromage à pâte dure : emmental	1 000
Fromage de chèvre	140
Sardines fraîches	290
Amandes	250
Soja en grains (pois mungo)	255
Persil frais	200
Crevettes	200
Cresson	160
Noix et noisettes	175
Figues sèches	160
Olives vertes	100
Épinards cuits	256
Endives	100
Brocoli cuit	100
Jaune d'œuf	140
Haricot blanc cuit	60
Haricot rouge cuit	112

Les boissons riches en calcium (mg/l)

Lait de vache	1 200
Contrexéville	545
Hépar	545

Traiter les bouffées de chaleur avec le soja

Les bouffées de chaleur sont le signe d'une carence en estrogènes. Les extraits de soja peuvent aider à les traiter.

Soja : nature ou en extraits

On peut l'utiliser comme aliment ou bien en complément de l'alimentation, sous forme de gélules qui contiennent un extrait standardisé en isoflavones de soja.

Certaines études montrent que la consommation de 35 à 80 mg d'isoflavones de soja par jour permet de réduire la fréquence et l'intensité des bouffées de chaleur. On peut donc commencer par 35 mg d'isoflavones par jour. Il faut attendre au moins 20 jours pour juger de l'efficacité. Toutefois, il est possible d'augmenter les doses sans aucun problème (multiplier par 2 ou par 4) et les répartir dans la journée. Par exemple, pour éviter les sueurs nocturnes, on pourra prendre 2 gélules le soir avant de se coucher.

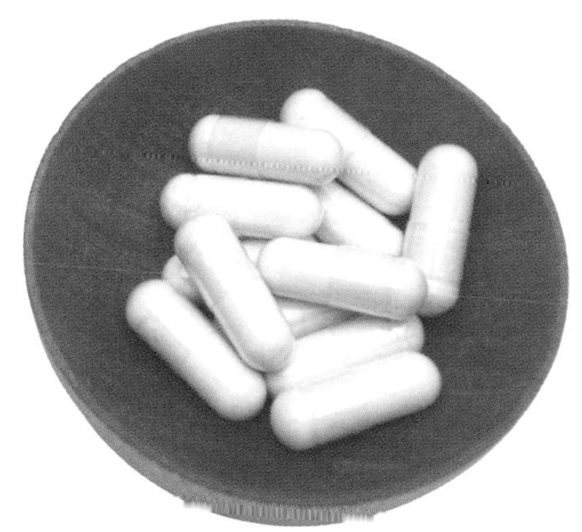

Choisir un complément alimentaire riche en phytoestrogènes

Les doses à apporter en phytohormones doivent être supérieures à 35 mg d'isoflavones par jour. Actuellement, en Europe, l'alimentation en apporte seulement 5 mg. Il peut donc être intéressant pour les Européennes de prendre des compléments alimentaires à base d'extraits de soja.

La plupart contiennent des extraits de soja, auxquels sont parfois adjoints d'autres produits : extrait d'igname sauvage, magnésium, antioxydants…

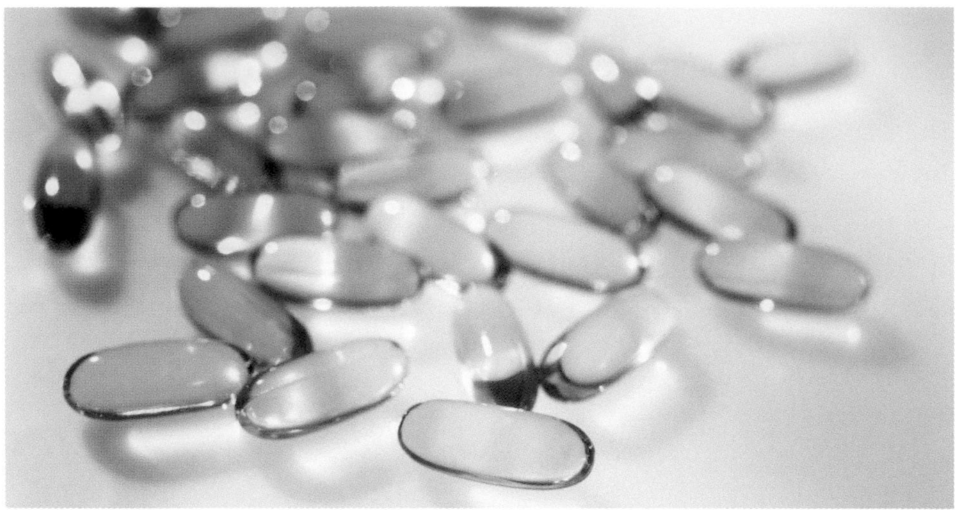

Où va la recherche ?

Les biochimistes tentent de comprendre quelles sont les molécules actives dans le soja. Ils en ont extrait la génistéine, la daidzéine et la glycitéine. Puis, ils ont synthétisé, à partir de la daidzéine, une nouvelle molécule : l'ipriflavone. Celle-ci s'avère particulièrement intéressante dans le traitement de l'ostéoporose. Plusieurs études ont démontré son efficacité si bien qu'elle est aujourd'hui proposée en Italie et au Japon, ainsi qu'en Hongrie. Malheureusement, on ne dispose pas d'un recul suffisant pour affirmer que cette molécule ne présente aucun effet secondaire. La recherche se poursuit.

Le plus important est de savoir quelle est la quantité d'isoflavones disponibles dans chaque gélule. En effet, le soja et ses extraits contiennent des quantités très variables d'isoflavones selon le type de soja, le lieu où il a été semé et le moment où il a été ramassé. La dose idéale d'isoflavones à prendre chaque jour est de 35 à 90 mg par jour. En prendre plus serait hasardeux.

Pour choisir un complément, la pharmacie paraît l'espace le mieux adapté. Orientez-vous vers les produits qui ont fait l'objet d'études cliniques sérieuses, publiées dans des journaux médicaux. Le mieux est de prendre l'avis de son médecin ou de son pharmacien. D'autant plus qu'il n'est pas conseillé à une femme atteinte d'un cancer hormono-dépendant de consommer des extraits de soja.

Phytoestrogènes en salade

Les phytoestrogènes sont présents dans plus de 600 plantes. Ces plantes ne sont pas toutes comestibles. Seules une vingtaine sont intéressantes pour nous.

Les sources alimentaires de phytoestrogènes sont donc principalement :

- **Pour les isoflavones :** les fèves de soja, les pois chiches, les lentilles, les oignons, les pommes, les haricots verts, les raisins, l'huile d'olive, le vin rouge, les agrumes, le thé vert et le thé noir. Les plus riches en isoflavones sont les fèves de soja.
- **Pour les lignanes :** les graines de céréales complètes, les graines oléagineuses (le lin, l'olive, le tournesol), les flageolets, les lentilles, les cerises, les pommes, les poires, le pamplemousse, l'ail, le thé vert et le thé noir. Les plus riches en lignanes sont les graines de lin.
- **Pour les coumestans :** les pousses de soja et l'alfalfa que l'on utilise dans certaines recettes de cuisine.

Petit menu d'un soir

Salade de pissenlits aux olives suivi d'un velouté de pois chiches et fenouil.

Ce petit menu apporte 450 kcal par personne, avec un excellent équilibre entre macronutriments et micronutriments. Aliments riches en phytohormones : fenouil, pois chiches, soja, ail.

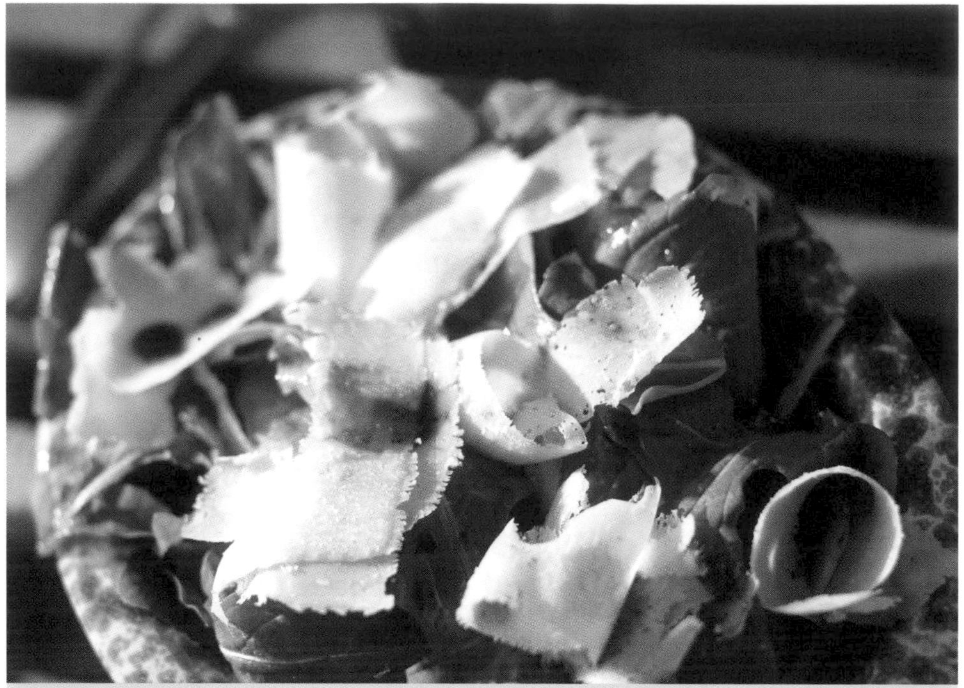

Salade de pissenlits aux olives

200 à 250 g de pissenlits
2 tranches de pain rassis
24 olives noires
40 g de parmesan
1 gousse d'ail
1 cuillérée à soupe de vinaigre balsamique
3 cuillérées à soupe d'huile d'olive
sel, poivre

Nettoyer, laver, essorer et essuyer les pissenlits. Ôter la croûte du pain, la détailler en croûtons. Détailler le Parmesan en copeaux. Assaisonnement : écraser la gousse d'ail dans le sel et le vinaigre avant d'ajouter deux cuillères à soupe d'huile. Au moment de servir, mettre les croûtons à dorer à la poêle dans la cuillerée d'huile d'olive. Mélanger les pissenlits et l'assaisonnement, ajouter les olives noires, les croûtons chauds ; mélanger et parsemer de copeaux de parmesan avant de servir.

Velouté de fenouil et pois chiches

500 g de bulbes de fenouil
100 g de pois chiches
2 gousses d'ail
300 ml de lait de soja
sel, poivre
verdure de fenouil émincé

La veille, mettre les pois chiches à tremper. Les faire cuire selon la recette de base. Pendant ce temps, laver les fenouils, ôter les parties dures, abîmées et filandreuses, réserver la verdure. Couper les fenouils, en lanières, les mettre à cuire avec l'ail, le sel et le poivre dans 3/4 de litre d'eau, amener à ébullition, laisser cuire 20 minutes. Vérifier la cuisson. Rassembler les deux préparations, passer au presse-purée de manière à obtenir une purée très onctueuse. Remettre dans la casserole avec le lait de soja, saupoudrer de la verdure réservée.

Extrait de : *La Nouvelle Cuisine familiale : 150 menus, 300 recettes pour l'hiver* de Brigitte Fichaux (Éditions GabriAndre, Liévin, 1998).

Traiter les bouffées de chaleur avec d'autres plantes

Plusieurs plantes peuvent compléter les effets du soja sur les bouffées de chaleur.

L'actée à grappes noires *(Cimicifuga racemosa, Actea racemosa)*

Originaire d'Amérique du Nord, l'actée à grappes était utilisée par les Indiens pour soigner les troubles des règles. Elle a été redécouverte récemment et étudiée par un service de recherche allemand dans les années 1990. On utilise sa racine séchée. On la prépare en décoction ou on utilise la teinture mère préparée en pharmacie. L'actée à grappes noires agit sur les récepteurs de la sérotonine.
Il semblerait qu'elle n'ait pas d'action œstrogénique.

Ses indications sont essentiellement gynécologiques et rhumatismales : elle soulage les règles douloureuses. Elle améliore les troubles liés à un excès relatif de progestérone et ceux qui sont liés à la ménopause, comme la fatigue, la déprime et les bouffées de chaleur. Elle est également sédative.
Décoction : une tasse deux fois par jour.
Teinture mère : 50 gouttes 3 fois par jour.

L'avoine

La sauge

L'avoine
(Avena sativa)

Originaire de l'Europe du Nord, elle est cultivée partout. Elle est utilisée depuis longtemps pour le système nerveux. Elle corrige la dépression et améliore la libido. Elle est également fortifiante.

On l'utilise dans l'alimentation sous forme de flocons d'avoine. On peut la prendre en gélules, en infusion, en teinture mère ou en extrait fluide.

La sauge officinale
(Salvia officinalis)

La sauge a longtemps été considérée comme une panacée. Ce qui explique son nom latin : salvia signifie sauver.

Elle a de nombreuses actions : antiseptique, tonique digestif, stimulant hormonal. La sauge régularise le cycle menstruel. Elle a une action *estrogène-like*. De plus elle régule la transpiration. Ce qui en fait un très bon remède contre les bouffées de chaleur. On utilise les feuilles fraîches ou séchées. On la prend en gélules, infusion ou en teinture mère.

Elle est contre-indiquée pendant la grossesse et en cas de cancers hormono-dépendants.

Le houblon
(Humulus lupulus)

Originaire d'Europe et d'Asie, il est surtout utilisé pour le brassage de la bière. Mais il a également des vertus médicinales.
C'est un tonique du système digestif. Il est également sédatif. Et a une action *estrogène-like*. Il réduit la nervosité.
On utilise les fleurs femelles (ou strobiles) séchées, en infusion, en gélules ou en teinture mère. Il est préférable de l'éviter en cas de dépression.

Bien d'autres plantes ont des actions estrogenes-like.
Ce sont : la réglisse, le saule blanc, le mouron rouge, le lin, le souci, le jus de pamplemousse, l'angélique chinoise, la luzerne (alfalfa).

Le houblon

Retrouvez des jambes légères

À la ménopause, deux Françaises sur trois se plaignent de leurs jambes. Les médecins évoquent le manque d'exercice, la consommation de tabac, le travail stationnaire, l'excès de poids. Voici comment réagir.

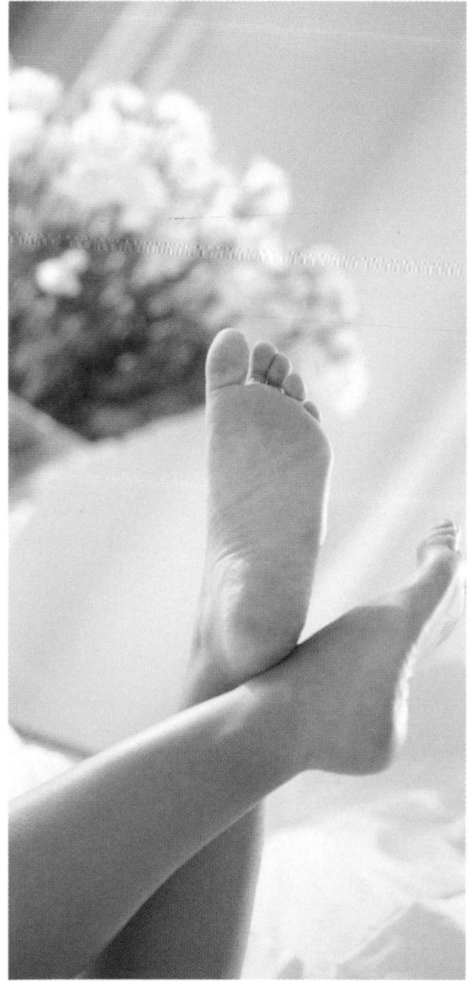

Les veines des membres inférieurs doivent assurer le retour du sang vers le cœur en se jouant de la pesanteur. Pour y parvenir, la jambe toute entière est mise à contribution : en se contractant, les muscles chassent le sang vers le haut, aidés par la plasticité de la paroi vasculaire. Mais tous ces efforts seraient inutiles si les valvules, échelonnées le long de la paroi, n'empêchaient le sang de refluer vers les pieds. Les fourmillements, les picotements, les crampes nocturnes, la sensation de jambes lourdes sont le signe que l'un de ces trois acteurs est défaillant. Le sang stagne dans les veines ; celles-ci s'élargissent et deviennent variqueuses.

Mais il n'y a pas de fatalité. À celles qui sont menacées ou déjà atteintes, les médecins conseillent la marche, le vélo, la nage qui réduisent la pression veineuse. Votre travail vous impose la station debout ou assise ? Fléchissez fréquemment genoux et chevilles, levez-vous, marchez. En fin de journée, surélevez vos jambes d'environ 30 centimètres par rapport au cœur.

Faites circuler le sang

Votre alimentation doit vous apporter dans l'idéal 3 fruits et 3 à 6 portions de légumes par jour. Ceux-ci renferment des flavonoïdes qui combattent l'inflammation, fluidifient le sang, stimulent la contraction veineuse, renforcent les parois vasculaires, et les protègent des agressions de l'oxygène. À rechercher aussi dans le vin (pas plus d'un verre par jour), le thé, les tisanes, le jus de raisin et même le chocolat ! Plus radical ? Tournez-vous vers les plantes. Elles sont d'extraordinaires usines à synthétiser les flavonoïdes, saponosides et autres antioxydants dont vos jambes ont besoin (lire encadré). Enfin, choisissez pour l'assaisonnement de vos légumes des huiles riches en acides gras de la famille Oméga 3 (colza, noix, soja). Elles rendront vos globules rouges plus fluides. Un dernier coup de pouce à cet indispensable retour veineux.

Les plantes amies de vos vaisseaux...

La phytothérapie soulage efficacement les troubles de la circulation sanguine : jambes lourdes, varices, hémorroïdes. Vous les trouverez en pharmacie sous forme de gélules ou d'extraits fluides prêts à l'emploi :

L'hamamélis : puissant vasoconstricteur et cicatrisant. On utilise l'écorce et les feuilles.

Le ginkgo biloba (feuille) : il agit sur la micro circulation et la circulation périphérique. Il protège le cerveau contre les accidents vasculaires cérébraux.

Le marronnier d'Inde (écorce) : il diminue la perméabilité capillaire. Il est anti-œdémateux.

La vigne rouge (feuille et fruit) : c'est un tonique veineux. Il diminue la perméabilité capillaire.

Le fragon (souche radicante) : tonique veineux et également diurétique. Il améliore aussi la résistance des capillaires.

Le mélilot : il fluidifie le sang et diminue les mécanismes inflammatoires.

... et de la vessie

La muqueuse de la vessie est très sensible à la diminution des hormones. Il peut y avoir des douleurs en urinant, avec des besoins fréquents et peu efficaces, qui ne sont pas dus à une infection mais à une inflammation. Dans ce cas, quelques plantes sont bien utiles :

Busserole : antiseptique et astringente ;

Genévrier : diurétique, antiseptique et antalgique ;

Propolis (résine) : anti-inflammatoire naturel ;

Romarin : antiseptique.

Renouez naturellement avec la bonne humeur

À la ménopause, les femmes sont souvent victimes de troubles du sommeil. Des perturbations qui viennent augmenter le stress et l'anxiété qui accompagnent cette période. Des solutions existent.

Le traitement habituel du stress, de l'insomnie, de l'anxiété passe habituellement par la prescription de médicaments appelés benzodiazépines. Le traitement de la dépression par l'administration de médicaments antidépresseurs. Tous ces médicaments ont des effets secondaires potentiels. Ils peuvent aussi entraîner une dépendance. Avant de les prendre, demandez à votre médecin ou votre pharmacien son avis sur les plantes et les compléments alimentaires dont nous vous proposons une liste ci-dessous. Il vous orientera peut-être vers l'un d'entre eux.

Le traitement naturel des troubles de l'humeur et du sommeil

Substance	Indications principales	Posologie
Aubépine	stress, anxiété	gélules : 1 à 2 g par jour en trois prises
Ballote	stress, anxiété	gélules : 1 à 2 g par jour en trois prises
Passiflore	insomnies	gélules : 1 à 2 g par jour en trois prises
Valériane	insomnies, désintoxication tabagique	gélules : 1 à 2 g par jour en trois prises
Millepertuis	dépression légère à modérée	gélules : 600mg à 1g par jour en trois prises
Ginseng	insomnies liées à un épuisement nerveux	gélules : 1 à 2 g par jour en trois prises
Magnésium	stress chronique (avec syndrome de côlon irritable), anxiété du syndrome prémenstruel	500 mg par jour
Acide folique (vitamine B9)	irritabilité	500 à 5 000 mg par jour (toujours associé à la vitamine B12)
Nicotinamide (niacine vitamine B3)	insomnies avec anxiété ou irritabilité, fluctuation de l'humeur dépression bipolaire légère	500 à 1 500 mg le soir
Cobalamine (vitamine B12)	insomnies avec rupture du rythme veille-sommeil ou mouvements incontrôlés	1 000 mg par jour (1 ampoule dans de l'eau à la fin du dîner)
Huiles de poisson (EPA, DHA)	agressivité, stress chronique	gélules : 3 par jour en trois prises

Remarque importante : ce tableau s'appuie sur des données issues de la recherche. Les produits, les dosages, les associations éventuelles, doivent être adaptés à votre cas, d'autant qu'il existe des contre-indications et des interactions possibles avec les médicaments. Il est impératif de consulter votre médecin ou de prendre l'avis du pharmacien avant de consommer les produits ci-dessus. Tous ces produits sont disponibles en pharmacie.

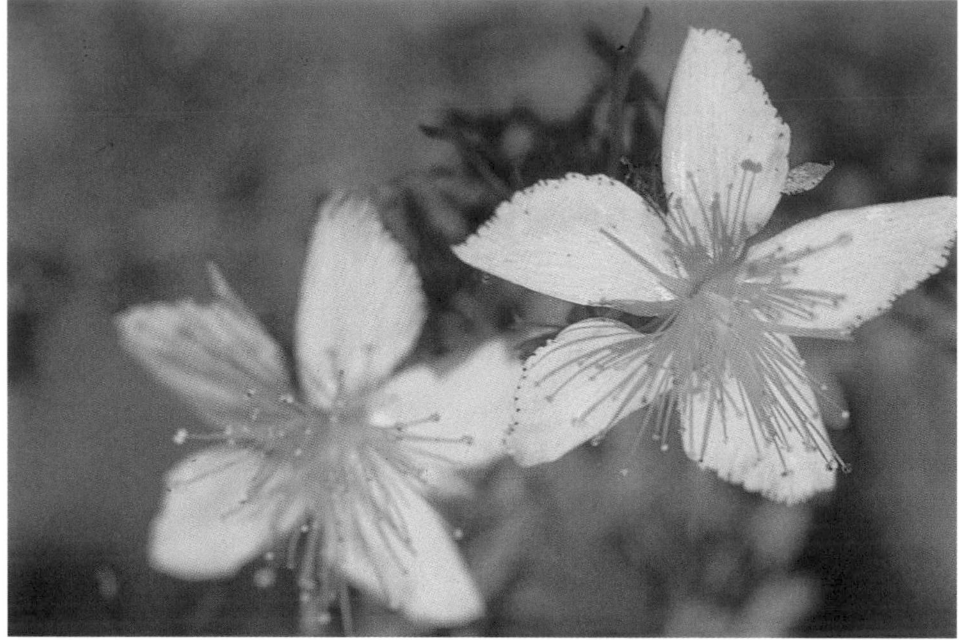

Le houblon

Le millepertuis : une alternative naturelle et sûre aux antidépresseurs

Le 3 août 1996, le prestigieux British Medical Journal publie l'étude d'un groupe de chercheurs sur un traitement de la dépression.

Ces chercheurs ont synthétisé les résultats de 23 études au cours desquelles une plante a été donnée à des patients, alors que d'autres recevaient un placebo.

Leur conclusion : cette plante est significativement plus efficace qu'un placebo sur les symptômes des dépressions légères à modérées. Le millepertuis vient de faire une entrée fracassante dans le monde médical. Depuis 1996, le millepertuis a été testé dans bien d'autres essais cliniques. Non seulement le millepertuis améliore les états dépressifs légers à modérés, mais il se révèle aussi efficace que les traitements conventionnels, avec des effets secondaires moindres.

Toutefois, **le millepertuis ne traite pas la dépression sévère.** Seul un médecin est à même de juger de la sévérité du syndrome dépressif et de l'intérêt éventuel du millepertuis.

Le millepertuis peut donner quelques effets indésirables notamment de type digestif. Il est contre-indiqué pendant la grossesse et l'allaitement. Attention aussi à ses interactions avec certains médicaments (contraceptifs oraux, anti-vitaminiques K, théophylline, antirétroviraux et certains immunosuppresseurs).

Jusqu'à l'autorisation récente de mise sur le marché (AMM) des gélules d'extrait sec d'Arkopharma, le millepertuis sous forme de poudre était interdit en France. Elles offrent aujourd'hui à une partie des 1,2 million de patients et aux médecins qui les soignent une alternative thérapeutique naturelle, confirmée et sûre.

Le lithium : l'oligo-élément anti-déprime

Le lithium a un rôle essentiel dans le traitement des symptômes de nervosité avec troubles du sommeil, irritabilité, anxiété grâce à son action neurosédative. Il soulage également les maux de tête de la femme ménopausée. Le lithium à dose élevée est utilisé en psychiatrie pour le traitement des états maniaco-dépressifs.

CONCLUSION

Programme santé pour toutes

Cette période de déséquilibre hormonal est vraiment désagréable. On ne peut se fier à son calendrier. Les règles viennent ou trop vite, ou trop tard. Parfois fort peu abondantes, parfois presque hémorragiques. Les bouffées de chaleur commencent à se faire ressentir. Un peu d'anxiété assombrit le quotidien. Et si l'on n'y prend pas garde, la nervosité et l'insomnie s'installent. Les difficultés finissent par envahir tout l'écran. Il est grand temps de découvrir un nouvel art de vivre, de mettre en pratique toutes ces nouvelles connaissances pour goûter la tendresse de la vie.

Retrouvez l'art de bien manger

Invitez à votre table le soleil avec fruits et légumes de toutes les couleurs. Enrichissez votre table de recettes riches en fibres : les céréales complètes seront au rendez-vous, en parfaite association avec les légumineuses. La viande se fera plus discrète ainsi que le beurre et la crème fraîche. Le poisson vous apportera régulièrement ses acides gras. D'excellentes huiles d'olive et de colza parfumeront les crudités. Le soja, pris sous toutes ses formes, régulera un peu le mouvement capricieux des hormones.

Réapprenez à bien bouger

Nos jours se suivent et se ressemblent : course après le temps, entre le bureau, la maison, les tâches ménagères. L'épuisement nous gagne et, le soir venu, nous nous affalons devant une télévision qui nous hypnotise mais ne nous repose pas. Il est temps de changer tout cela. Commençons par soustraire à la télévision une ou deux soirées de la semaine. Retrouvons-nous avec notre compagnon ou notre meilleure amie dans une activité de détente : gymnastique aquatique, petite balade au bord du canal ou dans la forêt proche. Cette première détente nous donnera envie d'aller plus loin et de commencer (ou recommencer) une activité sportive qui apportera souplesse aux articulations, force aux muscles, apaisement de l'esprit.

Apaisez votre stress

De nombreuses techniques existent et vous aideront : le yoga et ses techniques de respiration, la sophrologie, le *Qi Gong*, la méthode Vittoz, le training autogène. Plantes, compléments de vitamines, minéraux et oligo-éléments vous aideront.
Et si tout cela ne suffit pas, il n'est jamais trop tard pour commencer un travail avec un psychologue pour comprendre pourquoi tout est ressenti comme si stressant.

Apprivoisez vos hormones

Quelques plantes vous aideront à régulariser les cycles et à diminuer les bouffées de chaleur : l'onagre, la sauge, l'actée à grappes et le houblon. Sans oublier les compléments alimentaires d'isoflavones de soja comme Phyto Soya® qui diminue la fréquence et l'intensité des bouffées de chaleur. Pensez également au ginseng ; il normalise le sommeil, fait céder les palpitations et améliore la libido.

Si vous n'y arrivez pas toute seule, consultez votre médecin.

MÉNOPAUSE : Les réponses à vos questions

Les bouffées de chaleur sont-elles fréquentes et combien de temps durent-elles ?

Pour les femmes ayant un mode de vie occidental, elles gênent environ 70 % d'entre elles à la ménopause. Chez les femmes asiatiques, elles ne concernent que 30 % des femmes ménopausées. En moyenne, elles durent 3 ans, puis s'estompent petit à petit, pour disparaître en 5 à 8 ans au total. Mais certaines femmes peuvent être gênées pendant plus d'une dizaine d'années.

Les bouffées de chaleur apparaissent-elles à un moment particulier de la journée ?

Pour beaucoup de femmes les premières bouffées de chaleur apparaissent plutôt la nuit. Puis dans la journée. Parfois, c'est l'inverse. Mais pour toutes, certains facteurs les provoquent : le stress, l'énervement, la fatigue, la prise d'alcool, de café, d'épices ou de tabac.

Peut-on prévenir des cancers en consommant du soja ?

Des études indiquent que les personnes qui consomment beaucoup d'aliments contenant des phytoestrogènes, dont le soja, ont moins de risque de développer un cancer du sein, un cancer de l'endomètre ou un cancer du côlon. Toutefois d'autres recherches n'ont pas permis de conclure dans le même sens. Le rôle préventif du soja pour les cancers est donc pour l'instant hypothétique.
Ce qui est sûr, c'est que le mode de vie des femmes asiatiques réduit leur risque de développer un cancer du sein ou de l'endomètre. L'hypothèse selon laquelle cette réduction est liée à la consommation de phytoestrogènes est probable. Mais il y a certainement d'autres éléments qui entrent en jeu.

Les phytoestrogènes donnent-ils le cancer ?

Les phytoestrogènes apportés par l'alimentation n'augmentent pas le risque de développer un cancer. En revanche, des doses élevées de phytoestrogènes prises sous forme de compléments alimentaires n'ont pas fait la preuve de leur innocuité. Par prudence, il n'est pas conseillé à une femme atteinte d'un cancer hormono-dépendant de consommer des phytoestrogènes.

Peut-on prévenir des maladies cardiovasculaires avec des phytoestrogènes ?

L'ingestion quotidienne de protéines de soja, à la place des protéines animales, permet de réduire le cholestérol total et le mauvais cholestérol (LDL). Le soja diminue également le taux de triglycérides. Les isoflavones données seules n'ont cependant pas une action aussi efficace.
Aux États-Unis, on admet que la consommation journalière de 25 grammes de protéines de soja, associée à un régime pauvre en graisses réduit le risque de maladie coronarienne.

Faut-il consommer des phytoestrogènes toute la vie et plus particulièrement lorsqu'on a un risque de cancer du sein ?

La consommation de soja, aliment le plus riche en phytoestrogènes, peut être conseillée à tous et à toutes. Et donc particulièrement aux femmes à risque de cancer du sein. Mais on ne peut pas élargir ce conseil à la consommation de compléments alimentaires riches en phytoestrogènes pour l'instant. Les études scientifiques ne sont pas assez nombreuses pour en prouver l'intérêt et l'innocuité.

Peut-on remplacer le lait de vache par du lait de soja ?

Le lait de soja apporte 35 calories (kcal) pour 100 g ; le lait de vache 1/2 écrémé en apporte 48. Si vous avez une intolérance aux protéines de lait de vache, le lait de soja est tout indiqué. De même, si vous souhaitez faire baisser un taux de cholestérol trop élevé. Mais choisissez un lait de soja enrichi en calcium, car sans cet ajout il en contient très peu (21 mg pour 100 g, contre 118 mg pour 100 g de lait de vache).

LEXIQUE

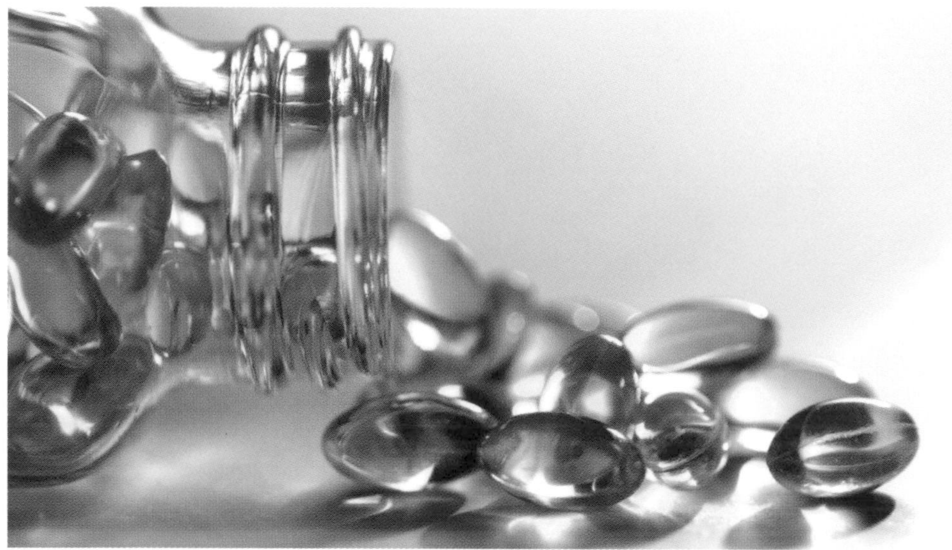

Acides gras
Élément principal des graisses.

Acide gras essentiel
Acide gras que l'organisme est incapable de synthétiser et qui nous est indispensable.

Agrégation plaquettaire
Phénomène d'accolement des plaquettes pour arrêter un saignement par exemple. L'hyperagrégation plaquettaire augmente le risque de caillot.

Anémies
Diminution de la quantité d'hémoglobine dans le sang. Cette diminution est presque toujours proportionnelle à la diminution des globules rouges dans le sang.

Angine de poitrine (Syn. Angor)
Douleur généralement dans le thorax, souvent constrictive, liée à un infarctus.

Antioxydant
Substance qui protège contre les radicaux libres, substances fabriquées dans l'organisme lors des réactions d'oxydations.

Athérome
Dépôt de graisse et de cholestérol oxydé dans une artère, avec épaississement de la paroi et formation de tissu fibreux.

Athérosclérose
Durcissement et épaississement des artères par suite de l'accumulation de graisses oxydées, comme les particules de cholestérol LDL. L'amas de particules provoque la formation d'une plaque d'athérome qui diminue l'ouverture de l'artère et freine le passage du sang.

Candida albicans
Champignon microscopique responsable de mycoses (muguet ou infections vaginales).

Corps jaune
Glande temporaire développée au niveau des follicules ovariens après la libération de l'ovule lors de l'ovulation.

Corticosurrénale
Région périphérique de la glande surrénale, qui est elle-même située au dessus des reins.

Décoction
Mode de préparation des plantes consistant à faire bouillir dans de l'eau les plantes séchées ou fraîches, pendant 10 à 20 mn.

Endomètre
Muqueuse tapissant la paroi interne de l'utérus.

Fibrome utérin
Tumeur bénigne développée aux dépens du tissu musculaire de l'utérus.

Follicule ovarien
Petite formation anatomique située dans les ovaires, en forme de petit sac, contenant un ovocyte.

Glucide
Ou hydrates de carbone, ou sucres : une des trois sources d'énergie provenant de l'alimentation, avec les lipides et les protéines.

Glycémie
Taux de sucre dans le sang.

Infusion
Mode de préparation des plantes consistant à faire bouillir de l'eau, puis à mettre les plantes dans cette eau hors du feu.

Lipide
Ou graisses. Une des trois sources d'énergie provenant de l'alimentation, avec les glucides et les protéines.

Ménopause
Période de la vie des femmes où les règles s'arrêtent définitivement.

Métabolisme
Ensemble des processus de transformation de matière et d'énergie dans les cellules ou l'organisme aboutissant à la synthèse ou à la dégradation de substances biologiques.

Neurotransmetteurs
Messagers chimiques que fabriquent les neurones pour communiquer.

Oligo-éléments
Minéraux présents à l'état de traces dans l'organisme.

Ostéoblastes
Cellule osseuse présente dans le tissu cartilagineux ou dans le cartilage en voie d'ossification.

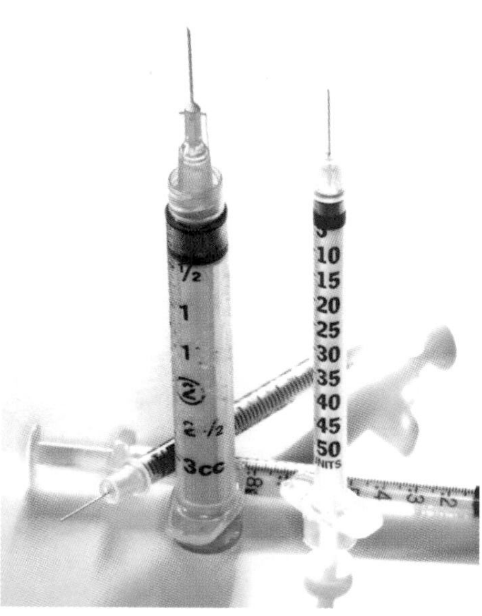

Ostéoclastes
Cellules géantes situées le long des travées osseuses et dont le rôle est de favoriser la résorption osseuse.

Ostéoporose
Maladie caractérisée par une fragilité osseuse, liée à une diminution de la densité de l'os, et favorisant la survenue de fractures.

Ovocyte
Cellule située dans les ovaires et aboutissant, par maturation, à l'ovule.

Ovulation
Libération, au niveau d'un ovaire, d'un ovule devenu apte à s'unir avec un spermatozoïde, si celui-ci est présent.

Ovule
Cellule femelle qui peut être fécondée et donner naissance à un œuf.

Phytoestrogène
Hormone végétale ayant une action similaire aux estrogènes.

Plaquettes du sang
Éléments du sang, ne comprenant pas de noyau, jouant un rôle important dans la coagulation.

Protéine
Une des trois sources d'énergie provenant de l'alimentation, avec les lipides et les glucides.

Radical libre
Molécule produite au cours d'une réaction d'oxydation et ayant un électron libre. Cette molécule va chercher dans son environnement une molécule équilibrée pour lui « voler » un électron.

SERM
Selective Estrogen Receptor Modulator : médicament ayant la particularité de se fixer sur les cellules ayant des récepteurs aux estrogènes. Une fois fixé, ce médicament a une action différente de celle des estrogènes selon le type de récepteurs.

Spermatogénèse
Ensemble des processus qui aboutissent à la formation des spermatozoïdes.

Stéroïdes
Groupe de susbstances hormonales ayant une structure commune dérivée des stérols.

Stress oxydatif
Agression au sein des cellules liée aux phénomènes d'oxydation.

Teinture mère
Solution obtenue par macération des plantes dans de l'alcool.

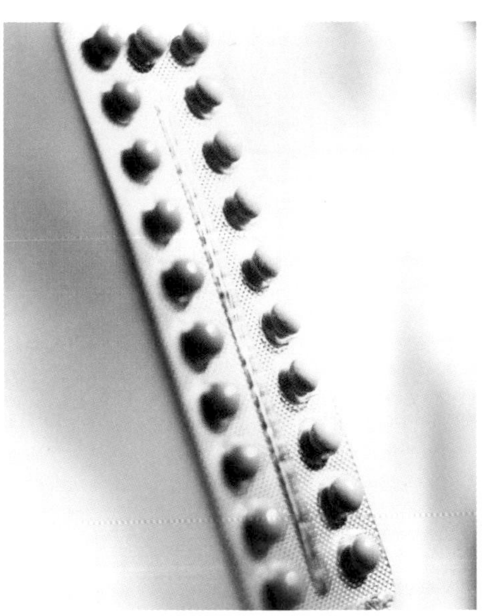

THM (Traitement Hormonal de la Ménopause)
Traitement consistant à prendre des hormones pour remplacer les hormones qui ne sont plus produites par l'organisme ou qui le sont de façon insuffisante.

Triglycérides
Graisses circulant dans le sang. Leur augmentation dépend de l'alimentation, tout particulièrement de la prise en excès de sucre et d'alcool.

Vitamine
Substance indispensable à la vie que l'organisme ne sait pas synthétiser directement.

INTERNET UTILE :
www.espritphyto.com
Boutique en ligne de phytothérapie

BIBLIOGRAPHIE

AFSSA : *Sécurité et bénéfices des phytoestrogènes apportés par l'alimentation.* Avis du 9 mars 2005.

ALBERTAZZI P. : *The effect of dietary soy supplementation on hot flushes.* Obstetrics and Gynecology, 1998, 91 : 6-10.

ATKINSON C : *The effects of phytoestrogen isoflavones on bone density in women : A double-blind, randomized, placebo-controlled trial,*Am J Clin Nutr, 2004 ; 79 : 326-33.

BEZANGER-BEAUQUESNE L. : *Plantes médicinales des régions tempérées.* Maloine, Paris, 1990.

CHEN C. : *Hormone replacement therapy in relation to breast cancer.* JAMA, 2002, 287 : 734-741.

DAVID H.-U. : *Vasomotor symptom relief by soy isoflavone extract tablets in postmenopausal women.* The Journal of the North American Menopause Society, 2000, 7 (4) : 236-242.

DRAPIER-FAURE E. : *Effects of a standardized soy extract on hot flushes : a multicenter double blind, randomized, placebo-controlled study.* Menopause 2002, 9(5) : 329-334.

FAZZIOLI E. : *Les Jardins secrets de l'Empereur.* La Maison Rustique, Paris, 1990.

FICHAUX B. : *La Nouvelle Cuisine familiale 150 menus, 300 recettes pour l'hiver.* GabriAndre, Saint-Jean-de-Valériscle, 1998.

FOURNIER A, CLAVEL-CHAPELON F : *Breast cancer risk in relation to different types of hormone replacement therapy in the E3N-EPIC cohort.* Int J Cancer (2005).

GREENWOOD S. : *The role of isoflavones in menopausal health : consensus opinion of the north american menopause society.* The Journal of the North American Menopause Society, 2000, 7 (4), 215-229.

HOSTETTMANN K. : *Tout savoir sur le pouvoir des plantes sources de médicaments.* Favre, Lausanne, 1997.

JOYEUX H. : *Femmes, si vous saviez... (83 questions-réponses) Hormones-Ménopause-Ostéoporose.* François-Xavier de Guibert, Paris, 2001.

LAMBERT-LAGACÉ L. : *Ménopause, nutrition et santé.* Les Éditions de l'Homme, Montréal, 2000.

LOPES P., TREMOLLIERES F. : *Guide pratique de la ménopause.* MIMI Éditions, Masson, Paris, 2001.

OSMERS R, FRIEDE M, LISKE E et al. *Efficacy and safety of isopropanolic black cohosh extract for climacteric symptoms.* Obstet Gynecol 2005;105:1074-8

PADRINI F. ET LUCHERONI M.-T. : *Les Huiles essentielles pour retrouver la vitalité, le bien-être, la beauté.* De Vecchi, Paris, 1997.

SCAMBIA G. : *Clinical effects of a standardized soy extract in postmenopausal women: a pilot study.* The Journal of the North American Menopause Society, 2000, vol. 7, n° 2 : 105-111.

SCARABIN PY et al, *les premiers résultats d'ESTHER,* Lancet 2003 ; 362 : 428-432.

SILBERNAGL S ET DESPOPOULOS A : *Atlas de poche de physiologie.* Médecine-Sciences, Flammarion, Paris, 1992.

SOUCCAR T. et CURTAY J.-P. : *Le Programme de longue vie.* Seuil, Paris, 1996.

TAYLOR M. : *Alternatives to conventional hormone replacement therapy.* Comp Ther, 1997, 23(8) : 514-532.

VINCENT A : *Soy isoflavones : are they useful in menopause ?* Mayo Clin Proc, 2000, 75 : 1174-1184.

WAKAIK K : *Dietary Intake and sources of isoflavones among Japanese.* Nutrition and Cancer, 1999, 33 (2) : 139-145.

WOMEN'S HEALTH INITIATIVE: Effects of conjugated equine estrogen in postmenopausal women with hysterectomy, JAMA, avril 2004 ; 291 : 1701-1712.

Les titres disponibles chez Alpen Éditions :

- *300 remèdes naturels*
- *Alcool, vin et santé*
- *Arrêter de fumer*
- *Arthrose rhumatismes arthrite*
- *Asthme : vers un nouveau souffle*
- *Bien se nourrir pour vivre mieux*
- *Candida Albicans*
- *Ces aliments qui guérissent*
- *C'est la thyroïde docteur ?*
- *Chasser la déprime avec les plantes*
- *Comment mieux dormir*
- *Combattre les allergies*
- *Contrôlez votre acidité : L'équilibre acido-basique*
- *Cystite, prostate : les solutions*
- *Dites non au cholestérol*
- *Docteur, c'est la prostate ?*
- *Docteur, j'ai un psoriasis*
- *En finir avec le ronflement*
- *En forme grâce aux épices*
- *Énergie et médecine chinoise*
- *Équilibrer ses émotions avec les fleurs de Bach*
- *Être heureux avec le millepertuis*
- *Fatigue chronique, fibromyalgie*
- *Fini les jambes lourdes*
- *Fini malaises et vertiges*
- *Garder la forme après 40 ans*
- *Gardez une peau saine*
- *Je nourris mon enfant*
- *L'alimentation des ados*
- *La chirurgie esthétique*
- *La cuisine Sain-plement*
- *La diététique du diabète*
- *La nouvelle ménopause*
- *La numérologie pratique*
- *La nutrigénétique*
- *Le bien être par la relaxation*
- *Le dico des bobos*
- *Le Feng Shui pratique*
- *Le guide de phytothérapie*
- *Le guide pratique des vitamines*
- *Le mal de dos, c'est fini*
- *Le nouveau régime flexitarien*
- *Le pouvoir des oméga-3*
- *Le précis des oligoéléments*
- *Le précis de l'homéopathie*
- *Le régime anti-cholestérol*
- *Le régime potassium*
- *Le régime protéiné*
- *Le régime sans sel*
- *Les 130 plantes médicinales*
- *Les aliments qui guérissent : fruits, légumes, épices*
- *Les bienfaits de la mer*
- *Les bons aliments pour maigrir*
- *Les compléments alimentaires*
- *Les couleurs*
- *Les enfants hyperactifs*
- *Les étirements faciles*
- *Les massages*
- *Les médicaments de demain*
- *Les méthodes douces qui soignent*
- *Les migraines c'est fini*
- *Les miracles du soja*
- *Les plantes qui soignent*
- *Les remèdes de la ruche*
- *Les secrets de santé des antioxydants*
- *Les secrets de santé du thé*
- *Les secrets du ginseng*
- *Les secrets d'une belle peau*
- *Les soins par les huiles essentielles*
- *Les vertus du soja*
- *Les vertus santé du cacao*
- *Les vitamines*
- *L'hypertension artérielle*
- *L'hygiène bucco-dentaire*
- *L'oignon fait des merveilles*
- *L'ostéoporose*
- *Ma santé dans mon assiette*
- *Maigrir après 40 ans*
- *Maigrir à l'aide des compléments alimentaires*
- *Maigrir avec la diététique chinoise*
- *Maigrir avec la méthode chrono-asiatique*
- *Maigrir avec le régime paléo*
- *Maigrir sans faire de régime*
- *Maigrir selon vos hormones*
- *Maladie cœliaque : mieux assimiler le gluten*
- *Montignac : les index glycémiques*
- *Montignac : Maigrir avec la cuisine méditerrannéenne*
- *Montignac : Recettes minceur midi et soir*
- *Mémoire totale*
- *Plus jamais fatigué !*
- *Plus mal au ventre*
- *Prévenir Alzheimer*
- *Prévenir et guérir l'infarctus*
- *Programme anti-âge*
- *Programme Detox*
- *Programme jeunesse*
- *Rester jeune après 60 ans*
- *Revivre après une séparation*
- *Rhumatismes : votre ordonnance naturelle*
- *Secrets de jouvence*
- *Secrets d'Olive et diète méditerranéenne*
- *Soigner et préserver ses cheveux*
- *Stress contrôle*
- *Une grossesse heureuse*
- *Vaincre enfin la cellulite*
- *Victoire sur l'arthrose*
- *Vinaigre, bicarbonate, citron*
- *Votre santé par les huiles essentielles*

TEACHING ENGLISH ONE TO ONE

Priscilla Osborne

Teaching English One to One

Published by: **Pavilion Publishing and Media Ltd**
Rayford House
School Road,
Hove, BN3 5HX

Tel: +44 (0)1273 434 943
Fax: +44 (0)1273 227 308
Email: info@pavpub.com
Website: www.pavpub.com

First published 2005, this reprint 2013

A catalogue record for this book is available from the British Library.

ISBNs:
Print: 978-1-898789-12-3
PDFebook: 978-1-908993-24-3
Epub: 978-1-909810-26-6
Kindle .mobi: 978-1-909810-27-3

Cover design by Martin Shawcross
Editor Helen Jennings
Cartoons by Steve Midgely
Printing by CMP Digital Print Solutions

Contents

Dedication

To my parents with love

Thanks

I'd like to thank Helen Mattacott for giving me the opportunity to write this book in the first place.

A big thank you to all my colleagues at Regent London, not only for giving me ideas and suggestions for different aspects of this book, but also for their tolerance. I am particularly grateful to Bette Bowling for her ideas about teaching teenagers, to Brendan Maye and Danny Norrington-Davies for information about homestay teaching and to Michael Bundy and Gemma Smith. The various forms used throughout the text are based on those used at Regent London, for which also many thanks.

I greatly appreciated the time, help and enthusiasm of all the homestay teachers working for Regent who talked to me in the preparation of this book. Thank you also to Stephen Cutler of London Life English, Inspiral Learning, for his contribution to my understanding of homestay teaching.

Betka Zamoyska and Genny Claret gave me very useful tips for teaching teenagers. Thank you.

And finally I am completely indebted to James Schofield and Janette Schofield for their help, useful comments, patience and tact.

Introduction

One-to-one teaching often affords the teacher a satisfaction that can be difficult to achieve when teaching a group: the student obviously learns from you, but you can also gain a great deal from your interactions with him or her. Given the right kind of student, the time you spend in the classroom can be extremely enjoyable and you may have the privilege of teaching exceptional human beings. There is also the satisfaction of helping your student to progress very quickly, since this individual approach allows you to target the student's exact linguistic requirements and to focus upon these in a manner that is not possible in the group classroom.

The ideal one-to-one language learner would be courteous, open minded, creative, dynamic, an original thinker, and so on. But of course, there is no such thing as the perfect language learner, and the 'nightmare' student can be even more of a nightmare in a one-to-one scenario! In short, one-to-one teaching can encompass the best and the worst aspects of teaching. With the right teaching techniques and approach, though, we can minimise the difficulties and turn the experience into a positive and enjoyable challenge. We may even find that the 'nightmare' student turns out to be charming to teach, once we get to know the individual and understand what teaching methods he or she will respond to.

This book contains many tried and tested suggestions for managing your students and your teaching time, on both a personal and a pedagogical level, so that even when the circumstances are less than ideal you can make the one-to-one teaching experience a rewarding and productive one.

Chapter 1

Getting Started

In this chapter we will discuss:

- the main difference between teaching one-to-one in the past and nowadays;
- the differences between one-to-one and group tuition;
- how to be successful at teaching one-to-one (including creating a good first impression).

Until a few years ago, teaching one-to-one could be a nightmare for the teacher. Many students who sign up for one-to-one classes have very specific needs, which in the past were often impossible for the teacher to fulfil, or required a great deal of time and effort. This used to be one of the most difficult aspects of one-to-one teaching. Since the 1990s, the Internet has revolutionised teachers' lives with material from the web, designed for both language students and the wider public, readily available for classroom use. But the Internet has been even more of a godsend for one-to-one teachers, particularly teachers dealing with executive students. (See **Definition of Terms**.) Today, all the teacher needs to do is enter the key words into a search engine and there, by magic, is a mass of information.

Now that one of the principal barriers – lack of materials – has been removed, the teacher is free to concentrate on the heart of one-to-one teaching, namely building the relationship between teacher and student.

Definition of Terms

Executive student: In this book 'executive student' refers to a business English student who already has job experience.

Differences in teaching groups and one-to-one

The main difference between group and one-to-one teaching is that in the latter you can devote 100% of your attention to every aspect of a single student's requirements; all elements of the course depend upon this individual. More specific ways in which one-to-one instruction differs from teaching groups are discussed in this section.

The teacher/student relationship

Two students in a class is a group, albeit a tiny one, and most group classes are far bigger than that. But even in a group of two, the student only gets 50% of the teacher's attention. Although learning a language one-to-one can be extremely tiring, students usually bask in the teacher's undivided attention. Individuals who like constant attention may not function well in a group, but often find one-to-one lessons very satisfying. Students who are difficult in a group situation can be charming when they no longer have to share the teacher. This means that the teacher has a good start when teaching one-to-one in that students normally have a positive attitude to the classes (unless they are being forced to take the lessons or have had negative experiences in the past).

Being in a tête-a-tête situation allows you to build a close relationship with your student; this relationship is often less 'artificial' than that of the group classroom, as

GROUP	ONE TO ONE
This can be either a prescribed course, or a course based on a negotiated syllabus that takes all the students' needs into account.	One-to-one students expect a tailor-made programme. They may have very specialised needs. The student is the syllabus. Once the programme is written, you can change it at any time to suit requirements of the student.

you will sometimes need to step out of the role of teacher (e.g. by acting as confidant(e), sounding board, or 'sparring partner' in discussions). (See page 10), *Roles of the teacher.*)

Course content

Basing a course around your students' individual needs and circumstances can be difficult when teaching a group, but is the whole purpose of a one-to-one course. It can be done, for example, by:

- using the student's interests and experiences as the focus of lessons;
- using any documentation that the student has brought with him or her (e.g. company reports);
- practising business skills within the context of the student's job.

These individual requirements dictate the course content *(course programme)*, and once the programme is written you can change it at any time to suit new or evolving requirements on the part of the student. You are also free to alter the course programme to respond to the student's mood on a particular day or during a particular lesson.

Materials

It is unlikely that any course will be able to cover the specific needs of each individual in a group. Although a teacher may need to find material for groups with highly targeted needs (for in-company courses, for example), group classes often don't require the teacher to use specialised materials. In a one-to-one situation you may be more dependent on authentic materials in order to meet the student's specific wants and needs, for example:

- a teenager who wants to study the lyrics of her favourite bands;

- an executive student wishing to work with his company's annual report;
- a supermarket buyer who wants to improve her vocabulary for discussing frozen fish;
- a university student who is planning to become a surfboard designer.

You can write or adapt materials with the student's specific needs in mind.

The student as resource

In a one-to-one class, the experience and knowledge which students bring to the classroom can more easily be exploited for both input and output activities, meaning less work for the teacher. You can also learn a great deal from the student; the business knowledge that you accumulate in teaching executive students, for example, can help you in your teaching of other business English students.

Feedback and specific areas of difficulty

It is easier to give personalised feedback after output activities in a one-to-one lesson, and one-to-one classes can address specific areas of linguistic difficulty much more effectively.

Speed of progress

Progress in a one-to-one class is often more rapid than can be achieved in the group classroom, so this method of learning often represents a better investment of time and money.

Less intimidating for new teachers

Less experienced teachers can feel intimidated teaching groups; the one-to-one environment is more intimate, with none of the complexities of group teaching. Similarly, it is reassuring for students who are shy or need 'hand-holding'.

Variety

Because students have specific needs and interests, one-to-one teaching means varied teaching.

Addresses the student's specific needs

In this sense, all one-to-one students are ESP *(English for Specific Purposes)* students, although the term ESP is normally used for describing courses which address a specific usage of language – e.g. Legal English; English for the banking sector; English for hairdressing; academic English.

Autonomy

Students learning in a group have limited control over classroom activities, but you can give the one-to-one student a great deal of control over his or her own learning process.

Flexibility

The teacher in a group situation can be flexible, but is unlikely to be in a position to change a lesson plan completely if an activity does not suit one or two members of the group. The teacher in a one-to-one class, on the other hand, can be completely flexible; if a prepared activity doesn't suit the student for some reason, the teacher can modify or junk that activity and move on to something different.

One-to-one lessons also offer flexibility of location in that they can take place anywhere: at a school, in a coffee shop, in the student's office, at the student's home, at the teacher's home. Some classes take place without student and teacher ever meeting face-to-face: by telephone, by email, or over the Internet.

Ability

Students' ability levels and prior learning experiences may vary within a group, and this can present a problem for the teacher. In a one-to-one class, though, it is easy to tailor all activities to the abilities/learning experiences of your one student.

Timings and pace

In a group class, more able students can become frustrated if they feel that the weaker students in the group are slowing down the progress of the course, whereas less able students will feel demotivated if the pace of the lessons is too fast for them to keep up. In a one-to-one class you can work to the individual's pace and allow him or her to control the timings of activities (although you will need to discuss this with the student and make it explicit).

Interesting discussions

Discussion classes can be very stimulating if you have a student with interesting views. You can also participate if the discussion needs to be interactive.

External activities

It is easier to arrange external activities such as sightseeing or shopping in a one-to-one situation, as you do not have to take anybody else's wishes into consideration (although note that for Health and Safety reasons, organisations such as language schools need to know if you and your student are going to be out of the building).

Learning styles

Individuals within a group may have very diverse learning styles, and the teacher has the task of providing a teaching style which will fit the overall group. In a one-to-one scenario, you only have to tailor your approach to fit one individual's learning style.

The teacher as participant

In a group scenario, you can act as observer or monitor while the students work in pairs or small groups. This allows you to focus on how the students are *using* the language rather than what they are saying. One drawback of teaching one-to-one, however, is that you are the only person with whom the student can interact – so you need to focus on the *content* of the conversation, as well as the language used, in order to maintain a meaningful discussion or role-play (see **Definition of Terms**) – thus having no opportunity to monitor the proceedings as a dispassionate observer. It can be very tricky to play a role (particularly if the role-play is complex, e.g. a negotiation) and concentrate on the student's linguistic performance at the same time.

Teaching techniques

You cannot use some teaching techniques, such as pair/group and peer correction, in a one-to-one situation.

Psychological factors

If you have a personality clash with a member of a group, it shouldn't have a dramatic effect. It may be difficult for you to teach a one-to-one class, however, if there is a personality clash between you and the student.

Cost/value for money

Taking individual lessons is a comparatively costly way of learning a language, but this does not mean that students taking such lessons are necessarily well-off.

Executive students normally have the course paid for them by their employers, and some students may be independently wealthy, but others may have saved for a long time for the experience of one-to-one tuition. Having decided to make such a large financial investment in the course, students sometimes have very high expectations and can be demanding. On the other hand, because the student gets 100% of the teacher's time and attention, one-to-one tuition is a very cost-effective way of learning a language if the teacher gets it right.

Expectations

If the student feels that the course has not been sufficiently tailored to his or her needs (which may be highly specialised), this can be a source of frustration. When the student has a specific need, the teacher normally wants to meet that need as far as possible. This can mean research and preparation of materials specially designed for the individual student: in short, a lot of extra work. There can be a great deal of pressure on teachers delivering one-to-one courses, but it is important that you don't promise anything that the course cannot provide. It may be necessary

Definitions of Terms

Role-play Drama-like classroom activity in which students assume the roles of different participants in a given situation and act out what might typically happen in that situation (*Longman Dictionary of Language Teaching and Applied Linguistics,* p.460*)*.

Enactment The student enacts the situations that they actually meet in their jobs (e.g. a meeting in which they have previously participated, or a negotiation in which they will be involved in the future).

For the purposes of this book I am using the term 'role-play' very loosely to mean any output activity (role-play or enactment whereby the student needs to practise a skill through acting out a given scenario ('learning by doing')).

to lower the student's expectations from the outset if they are too high.

Intensity

Students learning in a group have the opportunity to 'switch off' occasionally if they feel tired. The individual in a one-to-one lesson, on the other hand, needs to concentrate all the time. One-to-one classes can therefore be extremely tiring, especially on intensive courses, so are less suitable for beginners and low-level students.

From the teacher's point of view, too, the intensity of one-to-one teaching can be draining; whereas in group teaching there are usually opportunities to 'escape' from the classroom (mentally or even physically!) for a few moments, one-to-one tuition presents no such opportunities. Linguistic quirks on the student's part, which tire or irritate the average listener, can exhaust the one-to-one teacher.

Personality and learning style of the student

The personality of the student is all-important in one-to-one teaching. In an ideal world, our students would all be extrovert, imaginative, flexible – and talkative! In reality, we could find ourselves with a taciturn, demanding or less than creative individual, or with that which many one-to-one teachers dread most – the boring student. In fact, one of the problems with individual classes is that there is no pressure on the student to be interesting, whereas students in group classes can feel the obligation to be creative and engaging because they are scared of boring the others!

Social aspects

The atmosphere in the group classroom is sociable, and students can interact outside of lessons if they wish. The one-to-one student, on the other hand, can feel isolated with no classmates to exchange ideas with, to learn from or to socialise with after lessons. Very extrovert students who enjoy working with others can find one-to-one lessons confining. In a one-to-one environment some teachers, too, miss the sociability of the group and the interaction between group members.

The absence of fellow students to interact with also has pedagogic implications; whilst students in a group can bounce ideas off each other, learn from each other and provide mutual motivation and support, the one-to-one student has only the teacher for motivation and to share ideas with. One-to-one learning also has drawbacks for students who want to practise group activities such as socialising and business meetings.

Combination courses – part group, part one-to-one – are an ideal way of getting the best of both worlds and are a less expensive solution.

Movement within the classroom

Group teaching can be tiring because the teacher usually needs to move round the classroom. Teaching one-to-one can be tiring for exactly the opposite reason; both teacher and student are very static – particularly if the classroom is small, as one-to-one classrooms generally are.

Exposure to other cultures

In a multi-national group, students benefit from exposure to other cultures and different accents. The one-to-one student misses out on this exposure.

How to be successful at teaching one-to-one

Good 'people skills' are essential for all teaching, but because one-to-one instruction so depends on understanding the psychology of the student and working out the best way to respond to him or her, the teacher's interpersonal skills become paramount. **Establishing a good rapport with the student is the key to successful one-to-one teaching.** Apart from helping the lessons go more smoothly from a pedagogical point of view, a good relationship means that you can talk to the student openly about any problems they experience in class. But you will also need to be discreet, as when the student wants to talk about company secrets or his or her marital problems! Normally both parties work hard at building a relationship, but in this case the onus is very much on the teacher to

create the rapport.

We could include the following in a definition of 'people skills':

- patience;
- empathy;
- discretion;
- ability to communicate (and awareness of your abilities in this area);
- social skills;
- ability to motivate;
- sensitivity to cultural issues;
- sensitivity to the student's state of mind;
- ability to evaluate the student's mood and energy levels;
- awareness of non-verbal clues of communication such as facial expressions, body language, gesture and tone of voice;
- good listening skills;
- an interest in other people.

It's easy to understand that students normally prefer cheerful, easy-going, unflappable teachers, although this is not always easy for less confident teachers to achieve.

Given the choice, most students would probably prefer an enthusiastic, motivating, *inexperienced* teacher, who has a genuine interest in them, to the experienced teacher who plans the perfect lesson for the student's needs but who lacks the motivation to genuinely engage with him or her. Students will forgive mistakes in technique – even inefficiencies – if they like and believe in you.

Roles of the teacher

When teaching groups you take on other roles from time to time, but fundamentally you remain the teacher. With a one-to-one student you may find yourself taking on any or all of these roles:

- **Teacher:** instructing the student; helping the student learn.
- **Interlocutor:** the person with whom the student communicates his or her ideas.
- **Therapist:** sympathetic listener to the student's concerns and occasional 'de-stresser'.
- **Mother/father figure:** with younger students the teacher represents a temporary parent substitute.
- **Friend and confidant(e):** someone with whom the student shares his or her intimacies.

First impressions

A warm, cheerful welcome is crucial; even if your world is collapsing around you, you need to make sure you create a good impression.

Remember: the student is more terrified of not liking you than you are of him or her. After all, he or she is paying a lot of money to spend time with you. So you need to do whatever you can to make the first couple of lessons enjoyable and relaxing. After that, the hard work of creating a rapport (genuine or not) has been done, and the relationship should develop more easily.

Clothing plays a part in creating the initial impression. If you have an executive student, dress smartly for the first couple of lessons; once they know that you are a professional, well-organised teacher, then you can become more casual. Teenagers

> One student occupied a very senior position in a European company which had an alliance with a company in the USA. He took one week out of his busy schedule to do an English course.
>
> At the beginning of the week he talked about a colleague who had decided to give up his job and go to Australia.
>
> By mid-week the student had his head in his hands (after long telephone calls from the office), saying he too wanted to pack it all in and go to Australia. The course programme was abandoned while he talked about his job, colleagues and American boss who needed no sleep, had no interests outside work and terrorised everyone.
>
> By the middle of the week the teacher had moved beyond playing the sympathetic listener to suggesting that the student downsize his commitments, re-evaluate his life and get a less well-paid but also less stressful job.
>
> By Friday, however, the student decided that going to Australia wasn't really viable: although his wife had a well-paid job, his children expected a certain life-style....

and younger children, on the other hand, could be put off by a teacher in a formal outfit – so the basic rule is to dress according to the student.

Conclusion

The relationship between the student and teacher is at the heart of one-to-one teaching, and it is your responsibility to make it work. The teacher needs to focus as much on the interpersonal side of the relationship as the pedagogical aspects.

2

Chapter 2

Pre-course Preparation

Often, you will not get an opportunity to meet your one-to-one student before the course actually begins; however there is still a lot you can do to prepare and to obtain some background information on your student. In this chapter we will discuss what we can do to prepare both teacher and student for the course before it starts.

Before the start of a one-to-one course, ideally we would know the following about our student:

- the exact level of English needed;
- past learning background;
- comments on the student's performance by current or previous teacher(s);
- Current activity (e.g. in work, studying);
- why the student wants to take the course;
- student's objectives for the course;
- current use of English;
- predicted use of English in the future;
- likes and dislikes in language learning;
- interests and hobbies.

For an executive student we would also have details of his or her company, job, need for and use of English in the workplace.

What we can do before the course starts

1 Meet the student if possible.
2 Contact the agent or training manager.
3 Conduct a telephone interview.
4 Test language skills.
5 Fax or post needs analysis form(s) to the student.
6 Fax or post pre-course questionnaire(s) to the student.
7 Do some background research (e.g. visit the website of the company that the student works for).
8 Establish email contact with the student.
9 Ask the student to prepare a short piece of writing.
10 Direct the student to the website of the organisation providing his or her one-to-one lessons.
11 Ask the student to bring appropriate resource material along to the first lesson.
12 Talk to the student's current or previous teachers.

1 Meet the student if possible.

The best course of action is to meet the student face-to-face before the start of the classes and carry out language tests, an in-depth interview and a needs analysis. However, this depends on you being reasonably close to the student geographically. Contacting the student directly by phone or email is the next best way, but you may be dependent on an intermediary to put you in touch with him or her.

2 Contact the agent or training manager.

Language schools often do not have direct access to a student, but rely on agents and training managers to provide information about him or her. Sometimes it can be difficult to find out much about the student from these intermediaries, and any information they give you about ability levels may be unreliable. It is far more useful, therefore, to obtain the student's contact details and get in touch directly.

3 Conduct a telephone interview.

If we cannot meet the student face-to-face before the course, the telephone interview is often the next best thing. The Director of Studies, if there is one, can contact the student to find out when would be a suitable time for him or her to be called for a telephone interview. These interviews, either by the Director of Studies or by the teacher, are very useful for evaluating the approximate level of the student and his or her speaking and listening skills. But you do need to be cautious in your assessment:

- It is always more difficult to speak in a foreign language on the telephone than face-to-face.
- A phone call is 'abrupt', giving the student little time to warm up. (Pre-arranging

Telephone Interviews

Personal details
(name, nationality, etc.)

....

Key questions:
You can develop questions along the following lines:

- Language learning history
- Current activity
- Current language use
- Hobbies and interests

Alternatively you can develop themes such as:

- The student's most recent holiday
- A typical day in their working life; what they like and dislike about their jobs
- A recent film or book that they have seen or read

Teacher's comments
Approximate level:
Speaking ....
Listening ....
Pronunciation ....
Confidence: ....
Overall impression: ....
....

a time for the call can help with this.)

- Some students dislike talking on the phone even in their own language.

Consequently, when you talk to a student on the phone, it's wise to bear in mind that his or her English may be better than it seems. You can prepare a specific form to structure your telephone interviews; an example is shown on the previous page (**Telephone Interviews**).

4 Test language skills.

Some organisations have grammar, vocabulary and listening tests on their websites, which the student can complete before the start of the course. Alternatively, you can fax or email any existing in-house tests. However, you need to consider:

- Is the test reliable and valid in the first place?
- Has the student used external sources of help to complete the test? (Asking the student not to consult friends and family, or use reference books, can fall on deaf ears!)

Even when an internationally recognised standard is used, does the information mean anything to you? When you find out that 'Mr Claret is at x level on the TOEFL scale/GMAT scale', are you familiar enough with the TOEFL/GMAT scale to get a feel for the student's ability level? 'Ms Giocanti is a level 3.5 on the company scale' will be meaningless to the teacher without access to the data regarding the company's assessment scales. And even if you are au fait with these different scales, they don't necessarily represent the student's level of spoken English.

5 Fax or post needs analysis form(s) to the student.

It can be difficult for a student to complete a needs analysis form alone, without the guidance of a teacher; good needs analysis depends on the skill of the teacher and the questions that they ask to elicit information from the student, and upon the student having a clear idea of what he or she wants to do during the course. For this reason, it is best for you to complete the needs analysis form face-to-face with the student.

6 Fax or post pre-course questionnaire(s) to the student.

As one would expect, pre-course questionnaires are based around the themes of the student's learning history, learning preferences, current activity, expectations and objectives for the course. The questionnaire overleaf, designed for students in jobs, elicits a basic amount of information and asks the student to self-assess his or her level of English.

Pre-course questionnaire

Please complete this questionnaire and fax it back to us so that we can plan your course.

Name:	Course date:
Company:	Job title:

How often do you speak English at work?

☐ Never	☐ Sometimes	☐ Often	☐ Every day

What is your basic level of English?

☐ Basic	☐ Good	☐ Very good	☐ Advanced

How important are these skills for you?:

☐ Speaking	☐ Listening	☐ Reading	☐ Writing

How important are these business skills for you? (5=essential, 1=not important)

[...] Meetings	[...] Negotiations	[...] Presentations
[...] Telephoning	[...] Socialising	[...] Business reading
[...] Business writing		

Please give details of any other business skills or topics you want to include in your course – for example, job-related vocabulary:

....

....

Important! Please bring along any company literature that we could use in class. Please bring examples of any emails, letters, reports or presentations you have written in English.

Thank you!

However, these pre-course questionnaires should be administered with caution. For example, one response from an executive student (i.e. someone we would have expected to have specific aims for his or her language course) to the question *Why do you want to take a language course?* was *To improve my English.* In fact, such a short questionnaire administered in isolation can do more harm than good. For example, one student, in a senior position in a European Ministry of Finance, said she had a good level of English with no special needs; she also assigned the same level of importance to all the business skills. However, it turned out that she was an advanced speaker with extremely specific requirements for financial English, and with a need to practise her writing skills. (In fact, her financial English needs were so specific that the only way she could have got the information she wanted would have been to set up meetings at the financial institutions she was interested in!) In this case the pre-course questionnaire was counter-productive, whilst a telephone call, or a detailed needs analysis form sent to the student before the course, would probably have picked up on her special requirements. It would also have allowed the Director of Studies to make it clear to her what the school could and could not do for her. In conclusion, therefore, care must be taken not to rely too heavily upon a pre-course questionnaire; whilst it can be a useful means of eliciting student requirements, it may not provide all the information the teacher needs.

7 Do some background research.

- **Executive students**
  Checking the website of your student's workplace works creates a good impression and can often provide a wealth of material for use in the classroom. You can also look in newspapers (or on their websites) for articles about the company.
- **Information on the student's home country and interests**
  If you are not familiar with the student's home country, you can do some research.
- **Information on the student's interests**
  You can prepare some materials based on the student's interests for the first couple of classes.

8 Establish email contact with the student.

Being able to correspond with your student before the start of the course is very handy. It allows you to establish a relationship with the student and can give you an indication of his or her writing skills. It can also be a tool for finding out, in an informal way, the student's interests and his or her language learning likes and dislikes, needs and wants (although it should not replace the formal needs analysis that you do with the student).

9 Ask students to prepare a short piece of writing.

This can give you an idea of the student's general writing skills and grammatical accuracy, use of vocabulary, and understanding of style and register – although it won't, of course, tell you anything about his or her speaking or listening skills.

10 Direct the student to the website of the organisation providing his or her one-to-one lessons.

This will allow students to obtain information and to see what they are letting themselves in for! It should also give them some indication of whether their expectations are likely to be met.

11 Ask the student to bring appropriate resource material along to the first lesson.

In the case of students who are in jobs and want to learn English for work purposes, always ask them if there is any written material they can bring in. This could include:

- faxes, emails or reports that the student has written;
- presentations that the student has prepared, or is preparing for the future;
- company literature of any kind (e.g. annual reports; brochures; manuals).

This material can be a terrific resource.

Students who are going to do their one-to-one study overseas often forget to pack any literature or useful documents, so it is worth reminding them several times to bring any appropriate material they may have!

12 Talk to the student's current or previous teachers.

Contacting the student's current or previous teacher, if you can, always provides a great deal of useful information.

Preparing materials in advance

Resist doing too much advance preparation of materials until the needs analysis has been completed; you may spend a lot of time preparing materials only to discover that the student's needs are not as you anticipated. For example, you receive information that your student works for a company which deals with hospital facilities management, so you prepare some activities based on material from the Internet. However, when the student actually arrives and you do the needs analysis, you discover that she is not interested in talking about facilities management, but just wants to improve her general English.

Preparing the classroom

If you work in a school, you will probably have no control over the classroom environment; space is often at a premium and one-to-one teaching rooms are often cramped and pokey. However, in a one-to-one situation you do of course have greater mobility and may be able to use various other parts of the school building. If you are a homestay teacher, you have many more options for creating an optimal learning environment. Such an environment would ideally include:

- sufficient space;
- plenty of light – ideally a window (with blinds if the room is sunny);
- a large desk for dictionaries, papers, reference books etc;
- a blackboard or whiteboard (useful, but not essential as the teacher can use paper instead);
- a clock;
- maps of the local area.

Useful equipment

Ideally, the teacher will have access to:

- a TV and video recorder;
- a radio;
- a cassette recorder (for recording the student during speaking exercises, as well as for playing audio cassettes);
- an OHP, if the student wants to practise a presentation;
- telephones, if your student wants to practise telephoning;
- a computer, for doing lessons on the Internet, or so that the student can do written homework or send emails home;
- a plug socket for the student's laptop, if he/she has one.

These days, executive students doing language courses overseas normally remain in constant touch with their office, answering emails and making and receiving phone calls. Many homestay executive students turn their bedrooms into mini-offices. The homestay teacher can make sure that students with laptops have access to a telephone line.

Seating arrangements

This will depend on the layout of the room and on the student's attitude towards space (which is often influenced by his or her cultural background). It is worth bearing in mind that some students do not like the teacher sitting too close or prefer the teacher to sit opposite, rather than next to them.

Conclusion

Sometimes you have little or no information about the student you will be teaching until you first meet him or her. Does that matter? Usually not, but in a one-to-one situation knowing something about the student in advance can be helpful in terms of the teacher's psychological comfort. An experienced teacher may feel confident about walking into a classroom knowing next to nothing about the student, but inexperienced teachers will often feel more secure if they know what to expect and have been able to do some forward planning. Even experienced teachers need to know about very specific needs before the beginning of the course – although, thanks to the Internet and the much wider range of published materials available today, we can normally satisfy even unusual requirements at relatively short notice.

Chapter 3

Needs Analysis

One-to-one courses are, by definition, tailor-made courses. For many students taking private lessons, this is the whole *raison d'être* of paying the extra money. Private lessons have their disadvantages, but these can be counterbalanced by the fact that students can do exactly what they want – give or take a few limitations. It's a wonderful opportunity for a student, but the teacher has to get the needs analysis right and transform it into a programme that reflects those needs. This is not always easy, and getting it wrong can potentially lead to the student being dissatisfied with part – or all – of the course. Performing a needs analysis can be challenging, and inexperienced teachers who have only learned how to teach groups on their initial training courses, relying on fixed syllabuses and course books, may feel intimidated by the prospect.

In this chapter we will discuss:

- what needs analysis is, and why it is important;
- factors affecting the needs analysis process;
- things that the teacher needs to ascertain during the needs analyses process;
- various types of needs analysis form and their advantages and drawbacks;
- needs reviews;
- some relevant case studies.

Factors which affect the needs analysis process

Age

The student's age and experience of taking language courses will affect his or her ability to express specific needs. A fifteen-year-old student is likely to look completely blank when you ask her what she would like to do during her lessons; she will probably expect to use her school textbook. However, you may get the same reaction from older age groups too. Many adult students have very little idea of what they want, apart from improving their English in general (although their ideas usually clarify quite quickly once the course has begun).

Pier-Luigi

- Worked for an Italian spectacle frame manufacturer.
- Elementary level.
- The course covered all basic language skills, together with vocabulary for reading and talking about different types of spectacle design and manufacture.

Level

The lower the student's ability level, the more likely it is that the course will encompass core linguistic elements which the student needs in order to function in English. However, even at an elementary level, the student may have very specific additional needs which the teacher can meet (see **Pier-Luigi**).

Cultural background

Individuals who come from cultures where students are not given much autonomy in the classroom may have difficulty with the whole concept of needs analysis; they often expect the teacher to decide the course content, and may interpret being asked for their preferences as an abdication of responsibility on the part of the teacher.

Needs, lacks and wants

Needs: the things that the student *needs* to do (e.g. prepare for an exam; improve writing skills; practise English in a meetings context).
Lacks: areas where the student needs to *improve* (e.g. poor pronunciation; lack of vocabulary; lack of accuracy).
Wants: the student may *need* to practise telephone calls, and additionally his or her grammatical accuracy may be *deficient.* However, he or she may be completely uninterested in either formal grammar sessions or telephone role-plays, preferring to

improve his/her overall speaking skills by talking as much as possible. So, more important than either *needs* or *lacks* are the student's *wants*.

If you have a student who wants to talk a lot but is uninterested in grammatical accuracy, and you feel that this lack of accuracy is interfering with his or her communication skills, you will have to resort to a) your powers of persuasion, b) your ability to teach grammar in disguise, and c) any other tactic you can think of whereby you improve the student's grammatical accuracy without their being overtly aware of it.

Don't – however much you are tempted – make the mistake of forcing an activity on a student because, in your perception, it is 'good for them' or because 'they need it'. Perhaps your student does need it – but if they do not want it, then you run the risk of antagonising him or her and wasting time in class, because he or she will be less receptive. If you truly believe that your student would benefit from a particular exercise or activity, then 'sell' it to them. If you are persuasive, they will accept it. If they are not convinced, then give up!

What we need to know about our students

The student's learning background

e.g. recent language courses; exposure to communicative methods; exams taken.

Reasons for taking the course

e.g. compulsory or optional; intrinsic or extrinsic motives.

Language skills

Grammar: is learning grammar a priority for the student? From the teacher's point of view, does the student need to increase his or her grammar knowledge? Or, before learning new grammatical structures, does he or she need to utilise existing knowledge more effectively?

Phonological elements: does the student have problems with areas such as syllable stress, sentence stress, rhythm, intonation, linking, articulation?

Vocabulary: activating passive vocabulary; phrasal verbs; vocabulary specific to the student's job.

Listening skills: listening for gist; listening for detail; listening strategies.

Speaking skills: fluency versus accuracy; ability to speak concisely.

Reading: reading for general understanding ('gist'); reading for detail; reading strategies; reading newspaper headlines.

Writing: use of linking words; grammatical accuracy.

The situations in which the language will be used

How **will the language be used?**
General: e.g. listening to the lyrics of pop songs; travelling abroad; taking exams; writing emails to friends.
Business: e.g. telephoning; presenting information; meetings; negotiations; writing reports; interviews.

What **will the content areas be?**
General: e.g. film; music; relationships.
Business: e.g. banking; insurance; human resource management.

With whom **will the students use the language?**
Native speakers or non-native speakers?

Where **the language be used?**
In the office? Abroad? In the classroom?

How often **will the language be used?**
Frequently? Seldom? Every day?

As discussed in Chapter 2, the information gleaned from a needs analysis form which the student has completed alone, before the start of the course, can be of dubious help. By far the best way to obtain this information is through a face-to-face needs analysis. The amount of time needed to perform this can vary a lot, according to:

- how clearly the student is able to explain what he or she wants from the course;
- how clearly the teacher understands what the student wants from the course (clarifying his or her needs can take time);
- how much time the teacher needs to find out the student's job context.

It is always a good idea to establish the student's context before performing the needs analysis itself. For example, with an executive student you may have to look at the wider context of the appropriate industry in order to develop a clear understanding of his or her job. As soon as you feel confident that you understand the student's work environment, then you can start the needs analysis.

The most important point regarding the needs analysis is that is should not be hurried. It is best to get it right as far as possible, from the beginning of the course, rather than having to sort out problems mid-way through – particularly since some students are too shy to say that they are not getting what they want.

If the teacher does not get it right first time, this may be his or her own 'fault', the student's 'fault' or nobody's fault. The important point is to check regularly with the student that he or she is happy with the programme and with the way the lessons are going (do not expect the student to take the initiative in providing this information). Then, be completely relaxed about making changes to the programme when necessary; it is not a sign of failure, but an indication of a professional teacher responding to changed circumstances (and is a very common occurrence).

One-to-one needs analysis forms

There is no such thing as a perfect needs analysis form; you could potentially go on redesigning your form forever. Some teachers prefer working with blank pieces of paper, finding these less constricting than forms; they feel confident enough to find out the student's needs without the aid of a form. However, blank pieces of paper do not go down well in administration-conscious language training organisations – nor are they good enough for the British Council inspectors. Even if you develop enough skill and confidence to work without a form while you are with the student, you still need to complete any official documents required for the student's administrative file and for the school's records, if the student has come to you via a school.

The advantage of using a form is that it gives a structure to the needs analysis process, and helps the student prioritise. As has already been mentioned, though, allowing the student to fill it in without guidance can be dangerous. Students may tick all of the options available rather than prioritising, or may misunderstand what is required of them. (For example, when asked to specify what topics she would be interested in during her course, a student wrote *I like to sea* (sic*) a musical. I saw 'Les Miserables' five years ago in London. I want to see again.)* In fact, it is not even necessary for the student to see the needs analysis form – the teacher can complete it, asking the student relevant questions in order to elicit his or her requirements.

You will find some sample needs analysis forms in this chapter, together with references to published materials and Internet sites where you can find more formats. Again, remember that you can take any of these basic formats and then tailor it to a design you like to work with.

Needs analysis forms – various formats

Most organisations have their own, self-designed needs analysis forms. You can also find examples in published materials such as:

- Emmerson, P., *Business Builder Modules* (Macmillan, 1999);
- Donna, S., *Teach Business English* (CUP, 2000) (pp 10-11);
- Brieger, N., *The Teaching Business English Handbook* (York Associates, 1997) (pp 91-93).

You will find details of these materials in **Recommended Resources** at the end of the book. Macmillan's website www.onestopenglish.com has a comprehensive needs analysis form in its *Teaching Business English and ESP* section which, although designed for use in a group class, can be used in a one-to-one situation.

It's easier to find needs analysis forms for business English students than for general English students, since needs analysis is seen as the lynchpin for one-to-one business English courses. However, this should also be true for students of general English; the difference is that executive students normally have a clearer idea of what they want to do on their course, whereas the response from general English students often tends to be *Everything is useful* or *I want to use my school course book.*

On the next few pages you will find sample needs analysis forms for both general and business English. Business English needs analysis forms can have the same basic format as those used for general English, but with an added section covering business skills.

The needs analysis form should set out to elicit the following:

- what the student *needs* to learn;
- what the student *wants* to learn;
- the student's *priorities* for the course;
- what kinds of *activities* the student enjoys, and doesn't enjoy, in the classroom.

Ex. 1 (General English)

Part 1: Personal information

Name: ....

Nationality: ....

Job/status: ....

Age: .... Sex: .... Level: ....

Part 2: Learning history

How long have you been learning English? ....

What are your reasons for learning English?

....

....

How do you think that being able to speak English will help you in the future?

....

....

Do you enjoy learning languages, and how many do you speak?

....

....

Part 3: Learning styles

What do you like doing during lessons? What sort of activities do you not like doing?

....

....

Part 4: Needs analysis

1. You have 40 points to 'spend' for your language skills. How would you allocate these 40 points? (NB: 2 is the minimum number of points you can 'spend' per skill).

Speaking	[.....]	Reading	[.....]	Writing	[.....]	Listening	[.....]
Grammar	[.....]	Vocabulary	[.....]	Pronunciation	[.....]		

2. How useful do you think the activities below will be to you?

	Very useful	*Useful*	*Not very useful*	*Not necessary*
Speaking	☐	☐	☐	☐
Listening	☐	☐	☐	☐
Reading	☐	☐	☐	☐
Writing	☐	☐	☐	☐
Pronunciation	☐	☐	☐	☐
Grammar	☐	☐	☐	☐
Vocabulary	☐	☐	☐	☐
Homework	☐	☐	☐	☐
Testing	☐	☐	☐	☐
Recycling/reviewing	☐	☐	☐	☐
Error correction	☐	☐	☐	☐
Projects	☐	☐	☐	☐
Presentations	☐	☐	☐	☐
Role-plays	☐	☐	☐	☐
Games	☐	☐	☐	☐
TV and video	☐	☐	☐	☐
Newspapers and magazines	☐	☐	☐	☐
Business English	☐	☐	☐	☐
Study skills	☐	☐	☐	☐

Specialised topics (e.g. law, music lyrics) *Please specify* ....

....

Other *Please specify* ....

Part 5: Personal aspirations

Please write down a little about yourself, why you want to study English and what you hope to do in the future. Use a separate piece of paper if necessary.

....

....

....

Ex. 2 (General English)

Homestay

Pre-course needs analysis

Name: ....

Course Type: ....

Level**: ....

Date of Course: ....

(***As already discussed, it is risky to ask the student to assess himself/herself, but may be necessary if there is no other way of finding out the information*).

This questionnaire will help us to design an individual course for your needs. Think about the language skills you are good at and the ones you are weak at, and about what you want to do in English in the future. Then complete the questionnaire.

LANGUAGE SKILLS:

Which skills do you want to improve the most?

	1 = Not at all important				5 = Very important
Speaking	1	2	3	4	5
Listening	1	2	3	4	5
Reading	1	2	3	4	5
Writing	1	2	3	4	5
Grammar	1	2	3	4	5
Pronunciation	1	2	3	4	5
Vocabulary	1	2	3	4	5

English for travel and 'survival' (e.g. shopping, making appointments)

1 2 3 4 5

English for social situations (e.g. meeting people, going to restaurants with friends)

1 2 3 4 5

TOPICS:

Which topics are you interested in? Write them here.

....

....

Ex.3 (Business English – for students in work)

As we saw earlier, some teachers have difficulty working with any kind of form and prefer to use blank pieces of paper, following a structure such as the one below.

(A blank piece of paper)

Student's name

Learning background
Where and how have you learned English in the past?

Your company
What are your company's main activities?

Your job

- What do you do in your job?
- What do you do in English?
- What difficulties, if any, do you have when you carry out these activities in English?
- Do you want to improve your performance in any of these activities during your course? Which one(s)?

Requirements for the course
Do you have clear ideas of what you want to do during your course? If so, what?

Language skills
Which of the following language skills are you interested in covering during your course? (*Teacher can write these on the whiteboard or have a form available*).

☐ Speaking ☐ Listening ☐ Grammar
☐ Pronunciation ☐ Vocabulary ☐ Reading ☐ Writing

Summary

1. Teacher writes down the student's areas of interest and asks him or her to confirm them.
2. The teacher then asks the student to number his or her areas of interest in order of priority.
3. Finally the teacher confirms the priorities with the student, and tells the student when he or she will receive a copy of the course programme.
4. If the teacher feels confident doing so, he or she can sketch out a broad outline of the course programme in class for the student.

Ex. 4 (Business English)

Name: ....

Date: ....

Teacher: ....

Language Area

	I want to improve	Priorities for this course
SPEAKING		
Meeting visitors	....	....
Giving presentations	....	....
Telephoning	....	....
Formal meetings	....	....
Informal meetings	....	....
Negotiating	....	....
Social discussion	....	....
Travel (hotels, restaurants, airports)	....	....
Other	....	....
LISTENING		
Telephoning	....	....
Formal meetings	....	....
Informal meetings	....	....
Presentations	....	....
Training sessions	....	....
TV/radio/video	....	....
Social discussion	....	....
Other	....	....
READING		
Faxes/memos/letters	....	....
Business reports	....	....
Newspapers/magazines	....	....
Trade press/company newsletters	....	....
Legal contracts	....	....
Technical manuals	....	....
Other	....	....

continued...

...Continued.

Language Area

	I want to improve	Priorities for this course
WRITING		
Faxes / email / memos	....	....
Business letters	....	....
Reports	....	....
Presentations	....	....
Legal contracts	....	....
Other	....	....
GRAMMAR	....	....
PRONUNCIATION	....	....

TOPICS OF INTEREST FOR DISCUSSION

e.g. marketing, finance, job-specific, company-specific, numbers, etc.

Please list the topics:

....

....

....

VOCABULARY BUILDING

e.g. general English, general business, marketing, finance, numbers, etc.

Please list the topics:

....

....

....

Is there anything else we should know when planning your course?

....

....

....

Analysing business skills needs

BUSINESS SKILLS	To be covered during this course
Deal with visitors	
Entertain	
Attend meetings	
Chair a meeting	
Other	

Compared to the box above, the one below is more helpful in terms of eliciting useful information – differentiating, for example, between wants, needs and priorities. However, all the box-filling can become quite confusing – hence the advantage of the 'blank piece of paper' approach to needs analysis.

BUSINESS SKILLS	I do this now	I will do this in the future	I want to improve this	Priorities for this course
Deal with visitors				
Entertain				
Attend meetings				
Chair a meeting				
Other				

However detailed the description of the business skills upon which the student wishes to focus, you will always have to ask more questions to get to the heart of what a student really wants. If the teacher doing the needs analysis is not the student's sole teacher, then the other teacshers involved will probably have to ask more questions relating specifically to the activities to be covered in their lessons.

The following is a typical conversation between teachers:

DREW:	*Ellen, can you cover meetings with Axel? He's preparing for a big meeting next month and he wants to focus on that.*
ELLEN:	*Sure. Did you find out anything about the meeting? Or what he thinks his problems are in meetings?*
DREW:	*I just know that it's in Switzerland and he's going to be the chairman – but I didn't go into any more details because I think it's better if you find out what it's all about when you have your lesson with him. He said that he can't find the words to express himself – the usual things. You'll find out quickly enough if that's the real problem when you do a role-play.*
ELLEN:	*OK, leave it to me.*

The difficulties of one-to-one needs analysis

As we have already seen, doing a needs analysis is not always a straightforward procedure. This can be simply because the student doesn't really know what he or she wants to do, but it can be more complicated than that, as the following scenarios show.

1. The student:
   - has a *clear* idea of his or her needs;
   - *is able* to verbalise them.
2. The student:
   - has a *clear* idea of his or her needs;
   - *is unable* to verbalise them.
3. The student:
   - has some idea about his or her needs but is *uncertain*;
   - is *able* to verbalise this uncertainty.
4. The student:
   - has some idea about his or her needs but is *uncertain*;
   - is *unable* to verbalise this uncertainty.
5. The student
   - is *uncertain* about his or her needs but *not confused* about the needs analysis process.
6. The student:
   - is *uncertain* about his or her needs and *is confused* about the needs analysis process.

It is important to define terms; do not assume that you and your student have the same understanding of terms such as *negotiations*, *meetings* and *social English*. For example, a student could understand *social English* to mean talking about subjects such as sport, holidays and art, while the teacher has in mind social situations such as inviting someone to a restaurant or dealing with complaints.

Possible pitfalls

Tailor-made courses are ideal in many ways, but there are several things you need to watch out for during the needs analysis process, particularly with executive students:

1. Students may have unrealistic expectations (e.g. that you can help them talk about derivatives in English).
2. You have to be careful not to promise to deliver something you can't (see above).
3. You may be involved in a lot of extra work to meet the student's expectations – so you need to be realistic and let the student know if he or she is asking for something which is not feasible.

The needs analysis process is the ideal time for identifying these possible pitfalls and addressing them.

Needs reviews

It is important to remember that the needs analysis is just the beginning of the general, ongoing process of ensuring the course matches the student's requirements – it does not begin and end on day one. You need to be constantly re-evaluating whether the course content matches what the student actually wants from the course. Students often do change their minds once their course has started, so always be ready to throw part (or all!) of the course programme out of the window and start again.

Formal needs reviews

It is best to write the course programme for manageable blocks of time (e.g. all mornings of one week; five ninety-minute lessons over a five-week period) and then do a needs review to ascertain what to do over the remaining time period. Long courses will require regular needs reviews.

Informal needs reviews

You can carry these out on an ongoing basis by simply checking at the end of each activity, each lesson, each day – or whenever is appropriate – that the student is happy with the course content. You can ask, for example:

Did you find that interesting? Did you enjoy it? Was it useful? Would you like to do more of this activity, or is that enough for this course? (For example, *Do you want to listen to more songs in the next lesson, or would you like to do something different?*)

Overall objectives of a language course

After the needs analysis has been performed, you will use it to supply the student with a course programme which should clearly show the objectives for the course. This course programme shows the objectives at a 'micro' level (i.e. the finer details) and usually ignores the 'macro' level (i.e. the bigger picture). It is worth spending time at the beginning of the course explaining what these macro-level objectives are. The more the student understands about what you are trying to achieve for him or her during the course, the better it will be for classroom dynamics.

Macro-level objectives

To GIVE the student:

1. confidence;
2. strategies for dealing with difficult situations;
3. a better understanding of his or her strengths and weaknesses.

To HELP the student:

1. to use what he or she already knows more effectively;
2. to improve his or her overall communicative ability.

To CHECK:

the student's learning strategies, and to show him or her how to learn more efficiently and independently if necessary.

To SHOW the student how to:

1. learn English without a teacher;
2. learn 'on the job' (for executive students).

Case Studies

On the following pages you will find the results of the needs analyses filled out by the teacher for four general English students and two business English students. In the next chapter, *Writing Course Programmes,* you will find copies of their course programmes.

Needs analysis - General English

Part 1: Personal information

Name: Jenny
Nationality: Taiwanese
Job/status: Secretary at transportation company
Age: 25 Sex: Female Level: Pre-advanced

Part 2: Learning history

How long have you been learning English? School. Studied one-to-one for one year, once a week for 90 minutes. Did grammar, conversation, listening - everything.
What are your reasons for learning English? English is an international language. Is thinking about doing CAE (Cambridge Advanced English exam).
How do you think that being able to speak English will help you in the future?
If she has good English, has a chance to work for a foreign company.
Do you enjoy learning languages, and how many do you speak?
Yes. Can also speak a little Japanese.

Part 3: Learning styles

What do you like doing during lessons? What sort of activities do you *not* like doing?
She enjoys listening, speaking and grammar. Does not like reading as cannot concentrate in the class - prefers reading at home.

Part 4: Needs analysis

1. You have 40 points to 'spend' for your language skills. How would you allocate these 40 points? (NB: 2 is the minimum number of points you can 'spend' per skill).
Speaking [10] Reading [3] Writing [3] Listening [4]
Grammar [6] Vocabulary [12] Pronunciation [2]

Continued ...

...Continued.

2. How useful do you think the activities below will be to you?

	Very useful	*Useful*	*Not very useful*	*Not necessary*	
Speaking	☑	☐	☐	☐	
Listening	☑	☐	☐	☐	
Reading	☐	☑	☐	☐	
Writing	☐	☑	☐	☐	
Pronunciation	☐	☐	☑	☐	
Grammar *	☑	☐	☐	☐	* Wants to do
Vocabulary	☑	☐	☐	☐	it diagnotically
Homework	☐	☐	☐	☑	
Testing	☐	☑	☐	☐	
Recycling/reviewing	☑	☐	☐	☐	
Error correction	☑	☐	☐	☐	
Projects	☐	☐	☑	☐	
Presentations	☐	☑	☐	☐	
Role-plays	☐	☑	☐	☐	
Games	☐	☐	☐	☑	
TV and video	☐	☐	☑	☐	
Newspapers and magazines	☐	☑	☐	☐	
Business English	☑	☐	☐	☐	
Study skills	☐	☑	☐	☐	

Specialised topics (e.g. law, music lyrics) *Please specify* Law, History

Other *Please specify* ....

Part 5: Personal aspirations

Please write down a little about yourself, why you want to study English and what you hope to do in the future. Use a separate piece of paper if necessary. I've studied English for several years, two hours a week, as English is one of my favourite subjects at school. However, I didn't work very hard at that time. If I had known how important English is, I would have studied it much harder when I was younger. In the future I hope I can get a job in a foreign country (English speaking).

Teacher's comment: She says lack of confidence is her biggest problem. She wants to improve everything. Writing not so important though. At the moment she reads newspapers from time to time and classic novels (graded readers – e.g. *Emma).* She likes going out with her friends and into the countryside. She doesn't do any sports or cultural activities. She doesn't like reading in Chinese – prefers comic books. Will do everything to improve her English. Would like to experiment with role-plays (telephoning, interviewing, socialising – possibly presenting information). Is willing to read a graded reader for homework for discussion in class.

Needs analysis - General English

Part 1: Personal information

Name: Pinar
Nationality: Turkish
Job/status: Trainee Lawyer
Age: 22 Sex: Female Level: Upper-intermediate

Part 2: Learning history

How long have you been learning English? A very long time – since high school when she was 14. She also had private lessons for 6 months with an American teacher. Studied 'English Grammar in Use'.

What are your reasons for learning English? She wants to do an MA in EU law in the UK and then join an international company in Turkey.

How do you think that being able to speak English will help you in the future? It will be useful for her studies and job.

Do you enjoy learning languages, and how many do you speak? She speaks German as well as English. She enjoys learning languages. But the one-to-one classes were the best. 'You can't run away. You have to be there and learn something.'

Part 3: Learning styles

What do you like doing during lessons? What sort of activities do you not like doing? She likes reading and discussing what she's read. Doesn't like pair work, group-work, role-plays.

Part 4: Needs analysis

1. You have 40 points to 'spend' for your language skills. How would you allocate these 40 points? (NB: 2 is the minimum number of points you can 'spend' per skill.)

Speaking [8] Reading [8] Writing [5] Listening [8]
Grammar [3] Vocabulary [5] Pronunciation [3]

continued ...

...Continued.

2. How useful do you think the activities below will be to you?

	Very useful	*Useful*	*Not very useful*	*Not necessary*
Speaking	☑	☐	☐	☐
Listening	☑	☐	☐	☐
Reading	☑	☐	☐	☐
Writing	☑	☐	☐	☐
Pronunciation	☑	☐	☐	☐
Grammar	☐	☑	☐	☐
Vocabulary	☑	☐	☐	☐
Homework	☑	☐	☐	☐
Tcsting	☑	☐	☐	☐
Recycling/reviewing	☐	☑	☐	☐
Error correction	☑	☐	☐	☐
Projects	☐	☑	☐	☐
Presentations	☐	☑	☐	☐
Role-plays	☐	☐	☐	☑
Games	☐	☐	☐	☑
TV and video	☐	☐	☑	☐
Newspapers and magazines	☐	☑	☐	☐
Business English	☐	☐	☑	☐
Study skills	☐	☑	☐	☐

Specialised topics (e.g. law, music lyrics) *Please specify* European Union Law

Other *Please specify* ....

Part 5: Personal aspirations

Please write down a little about yourself, why you want to study English and what you hope to do in the future. Use a separate piece of paper if necessary.

I am a 22 year-old trainer (sic) lawyer from Turkey. I want to learn English to make a master degree in UK. I need English for my job too. I want to be a contract lawyer in an international company so I have to speak English very well.

Teacher's comment: Wants to watch TV in her own time. Confident. Cheerful. Needs work on her pronunciation. Wants to do European Union law, but her first priority is general English. Discrepancy between the points she 'spent' on pronunciation and how useful she thinks it will be.

Needs analysis – General English

Part 1: Personal information

Name: Atsuko
Nationality: Japanese
Job/status: Graduated last month; licensed to be a Shinto priest
Age: 22 Sex: Female Level: Upper-intermediate

Part 2: Learning history

How long have you been learning English? 9 years at school. Couple of years at language school while at university.

What are your reasons for learning English? Many foreigners near her house in Shibuya, Tokyo. Wants to study another culture. She doesn't need to study English, she wants to do it.

How do you think that being able to speak English will help you in the future? Doesn't need it for her job. Wants it for meeting foreigners in Shibuya.

Do you enjoy learning languages, and how many do you speak? She enjoys studying English, but it was more fun at the language school than at school. She doesn't speak any other languages.

Part 3: Learning styles

What do you like doing during lessons? What sort of activities do you not like doing? She enjoys games. She doesn't like 'imagine and describe' activities.

Part 4: Needs analysis

1. You have 40 points to 'spend' for your language skills. How would you allocate these 40 points? (NB: 2 is the minimum number of points you can 'spend' per skill).

Speaking [10] Reading [4] Writing [4] Listening [8]
Grammar [2] Vocabulary [4] Pronunciation [8]

continued ...

...Continued.

2. How useful do you think the activities below will be to you?

	Very useful	*Useful*	*Not very useful*	*Not necessary*
Speaking	☑	☐	☐	☐
Listening	☑	☐	☐	☐
Reading	☑	☐	☐	☐
Writing	☑	☐	☐	☐
Pronunciation	☑	☐	☐	☐
Grammar	☐	☑	☐	☐
Vocabulary	☑	☐	☐	☐
Homework	☐	☑	☐	☐
Testing	☑	☐	☐	☐
Recycling/reviewing	☑	☐	☐	☐
Error correction	☑	☐	☐	☐
Projects	☑	☐	☐	☐
Presentations	☑	☐	☐	☐
Role-plays	☐	☑	☐	☐
Games	☐	☑	☐	☐
TV and video	☐	☑	☐	☐
Newspapers and magazines	☐	☑	☐	☐
Business English	☐	☑	☐	☐
Study skills	☑	☐	☐	☐

Specialised topics (e.g. law, music lyrics) *Please specify* ....

Other *Please specify* ....

Part 5: Personal aspirations

Please write down a little about yourself, why you want to study English and what you hope to do in the future. Use a separate piece of paper if necessary.

I want to study English. Because English is very international language. And I want to study other country's culture. English is very important for me to study that. I hope to get communicate with people all over the world and understand each other.

Teacher's comment: She appears to want everything. She is confident and accurate.

Needs analysis – General English

Part 1: Personal information

Name: Hye Sun
Nationality: South Korean
Job/status: Housewife
Age: 32 Sex: Female Level: Pre-intermediate

Part 2: Learning history

How long have you been learning English? 6-7 years at school. Grammar at school, not speaking and writing or everyday English.

What are your reasons for learning English? She wants to take IELTS. She's very keen to get a qualification. Her husband needs to learn English as he will be doing a post-graduate course starting in September – possibly in the UK.

How do you think that being able to speak English will help you in the future? She's not sure. She may need English for studying or for a job next year – but she wants a baby – perhaps the year after next.

Do you enjoy learning languages, and how many do you speak? Yes. English.

Part 3: Learning styles

What do you like doing during lessons? What sort of activities do you not like doing? She likes speaking and reading. She doesn't like writing because it's hard work, but she's very keen to learn how to write in English. Grammar is somewhere in between.

Part 4: Needs analysis

1. You have 40 points to 'spend' for your language skills. How would you allocate these 40 points? (NB: 2 is the minimum number of points you can 'spend' per skill).

Speaking [10] Reading [4] Writing [10] Listening [4]
Grammar [2] Vocabulary [4] Pronunciation [6]

continued ...

...Continued.

2. How useful do you think the activities below will be to you?

	Very useful	*Useful*	*Not very useful*	*Not necessary*
Speaking	☑	☐	☐	☐
Listening	☑	☐	☐	☐
Reading	☑	☐	☐	☐
Writing	☑	☐	☐	☐
Pronunciation	☑	☐	☐	☐
Grammar	☑	☐	☐	☐
Vocabulary	☑	☐	☐	☐
Homework	☑	☐	☐	☐
Testing	☑	☐	☐	☐
Recycling/reviewing	☑	☐	☐	☐
Error correction	☑	☐	☐	☐
Projects	☐	☑	☐	☐
Presentations	☐	☑	☐	☐
Role-plays	☑	☐	☐	☐
Games	☐	☑	☐	☐
TV and video	☐	☑	☐	☐
Newspapers and magazines	☑	☐	☐	☐
Business English	☐	☑	☐	☐
Study skills	☑	☐	☐	☐

Specialised topics (e.g. law, music lyrics) *Please specify* ....

Other *Please specify* ....

Part 5: Personal aspirations

Please write down a little about yourself, why you want to study English and what you hope to do in the future. Use a separate piece of paper if necessary.

I hope to got a high score on IELTS. IELTS is a useful qualification. I want study or got a job

Teacher's comment: She had some difficulty understanding me. Is much too low to do IELTS.

Conclusion

1. Performing a good needs analysis:
    a. is a skill which gets better with practice.
    b. depends on asking the right questions.
    c. depends on clarifying, checking and summarising.
    d. requires good listening skills.
2. The student's needs can be constantly re-negotiated – flexibility is the key word.
3. Doing a good needs analysis and writing a good course programme go hand in hand.
4. Teachers tend to over-estimate, rather than under-estimate, what can be achieved.

Once you feel satisfied that you have a good understanding of the student's needs over the course of an initial period (e.g. the first week of a three-week intensive course; the first five lessons of a course of indefinite duration), you can prepare a course programme.

Transforming the results of the needs analysis into a course programme is covered in the next chapter.

4

Chapter 4

Writing Course Programmes

Once you have completed your needs analysis, the next step is to design a course to fulfil the student's needs. The visual representation of that design will be an actual paper document that you give to the student - a course programme. This is a vitally important document which needs to be easily understood by the student (and by anyone else who looks at the programme, such as other teachers, Directors of Studies, agents and training managers), and this chapter tells you how to go about constructing it.

Caption: 'Red line' in German means 'the thread of an argument'.

Reasons for having a course programme

- It structures the course.
- It makes the course objectives-orientated.
- Executive students expect it.
- It prevents aimlessness and vagueness.
- It acts as a tool to show progress.
- It allows management to know what is going on in class.
- It helps teachers to liaise and co-ordinate.
- It can be used as a marketing tool (e.g. the teaching organisation can show examples of previous course programmes to agents or training managers).

Features of a course programme

- It provides an outline of the course content.
- It comes directly from the needs analysis.
- It gives the student a clear idea of what will be covered in the course (but without excessive detail).
- A copy is given to the student.
- It is done on a regular basis (e.g. weekly on an intensive course; once every five to ten lessons on an extensive course).
- It may need modifying before the next needs review, as a result of what takes place in class in the meantime.

In almost all cases the student should be given a copy of the course programme. Even if a textbook is to be the main component of the course, you can still give your student a course programme in which you can indicate how many units you anticipate covering in a certain time period, and mention any supplementary activities you will do with the student. However, there may be occasions when you do not give the student a course programme – such as the following example in which the objectives were decided with the student at the end of each lesson.

(NB: The course programme can be called by other names, such as *scheme of work* or *course outline;* provided everybody understands what it refers to, the name is irrelevant.)

Changes to the course programme

You will often find that you need to adjust the programme in the light of what takes place during lessons. Course programmes should never be 'fixed in stone' because:

- students often change their minds about what the course should cover;
- students think of additional things they would like included in the programme;

- you realise that the course programme is not best adapted to achieving the student's aims and, after consulting the student, you decide to make changes.

If this happens in your class and you are not the course programmer, you need to inform him or her as well as any other teachers involved in the course. If you are the course programmer, you can either hand-write changes on to the original course

Hendrik

Hendrik was a very advanced speaker of English, having spent one year working in the mergers and acquisitions department of a large British accountancy firm. Although he spoke excellent English, he felt a need for language training. His company paid for 20 private lessons to be taken at lunchtimes once a week.

After the first lesson the teacher decided that Hendrik needed to:

- improve his articulation, which was sometimes slurred;
- slow down his delivery;
- do some remedial pronunciation work for certain sounds, in particular /d/ (/dɪd/), /ʌ/ (/kʌp/), /θ/ (/θɪn/), /ð/ (/ðen/);
- focus on eradicating grammatical slips, and improve his use of prepositions, which was well below his overall level.

The teacher and Hendrik decided that the best way to achieve these short-term objectives was to look through a newspaper and choose a couple of headlines for discussion. After this initial assessment, the course content was decided lesson by lesson. At the beginning of the class, the teacher explained the objectives for the lesson and what activities the student would be doing. At the end of the class, the teacher and Hendrik agreed the objectives for the next lesson and any homework Hendrik needed to do.

NB: The course covered:

- Speaking (based on current affairs);
- Pronunciation of specific sounds which are difficult for Dutch speakers;
- Work on stress, rhythm and intonation;
- Role-plays covering conflict management (corresponding to situations Hendrik encountered at work);
- Writing 'for and against' essays;
- Work on words and phrases for linking ideas;
- Remedial grammatical work.

programme given to the student, or print out a new copy including the modifications.

Be careful: there should always be very good reason for changing the programme. You must not make alterations to the content of the course simply because you feel like it. If the changes are at random and for no real purpose, the student will feel confused.

Format of a course programme

Language teaching organisations have their own styles for course programmes; you can also design your own. It does not matter what the design consists of, provided that the information is clear and the potential for misunderstanding minimised; (the teacher should go through the document with the student to make sure that he or she understands everything).

You will find typical 'blank' programmes for both intensive and extensive courses on the following pages. First we will look at programmes for intensive courses, and then for extensive ones.

Programmes for intensive courses

Format 1 – one-week programme

Compare the two programme formats on p.50. It's easier to use Format 1 than the second, more detailed Format 2. The first one also has the advantage of helping the teacher to think in terms of a whole week rather than just a day.

Now compare the two on page 51. You will see that the Format 1 is more flexible than Format 2, but note that you have to explain to the student that all three activities take place in the 0900 – 1040 slot every day – not one activity per day. - Format 3 (p.52) is even clearer. Also tell the student that these activities can be re-negotiated at any time, as it may transpire that the student will want to concentrate on something else, or will request a change of activity, towards the end of the week.

Format 1

Programme for: Joao Alberto **Dates:** 1-5 April **Week:** Week 1 of 4

	09:00-10:40	11:00-12:40	14:10-17:00
Mon	**Needs analysis** Discussion of programme for Week one		
Tues			
Wed			
Thurs	**Needs review** Discussion of programme for following week		
Fri	**Progress check** Discussion of progress made so far		

Format 2

	Monday	Tuesday	Wednesday	Thursday	Friday
08:30-10:30					
COFFEE					
11:00-13:00					
Afternoon	Self-study and visits				

Format 1

Programme for: Joao Alberto **Dates:** 1-5 April **Week:** Week 1 of 4

	09:00-10:40	11:00-12:40
Mon Tues Wed Thurs Fri	**Diary writing** Joao Alberto to keep a daily diary, checked by teacher **Listening** Joao Alberto to listen to various types of material such as excerpts from different films (e.g. *Notting Hill*), CNN News and radio programmes in order to: - improve his listening skills - expand his knowledge of colloquial English - expand his vocabulary for current affairs **Speaking** Joao Alberto to make comments on the films he has seen.	

Format 2

	Monday	Tuesday	Wednesday	Thursday	Friday
08:30-10:30	**Diary writing** Joao Alberto to keep a daily diary. **Listening** Joao Alberto to listen to various types of material such as excerpts from different films (e.g. *Notting Hill*), CNN News and radio programmes **Speaking** Joao Alberto to make comments on the films he has seen.	**Diary writing** Continued. **Listening** Joao Alberto to watch various CNN News items to expand his vocabulary for current affairs. **Speaking** Joao Alberto to comment on the news stories	**Diary writing** Continued. **Listening** Joao Alberto to listen to radio programme *The Money Programme.* More work with films.	**Diary writing** Continued. **Listening** More work with CNN News stories. **Speaking** Joao Alberto to comment on the news stories	**Diary writing** Continued. **Listening** More work with films. **Speaking** Joao Alberto to comment on the films

Format 3

	Monday	Tuesday	Wednesday	Thursday	Friday
08:30-10:30	**Diary writing:** Joao Alberto to keep a daily diary, checked by teacher. **Listening:** Joao Alberto to listen to various types of material such as excerpts from films (e.g. *Notting Hill*), CNN News and radio programmes in order to: - improve his listening skills; - expand his knowledge of colloquial English; - expand his vocabulary for current affairs. **Speaking**: Joao Alberto to make comments on the films he has seen.				

Programme for combination group/one-to-one course

The following is an example course programme for a student combining one-to-one with group classes on an intensive course.

Programme for: **Pascal Dates:** 1-5 April **Week:** Week 1 of 4

	0900-1040	1100-1240	1410-1700
Mon		**Needs analysis:** Discussion of programme for Week 1	
Tues	**Group classes**	**Socialising** Input: Typical useful phrases for different social situations, and practice exercises. Output: Role-plays based on types of social situations that Pascal will encounter in his job.	**Group classes**
Wed		**Speaking practice** - Pascal will talk about various general topics in order to improve his overall fluency. - Activities will include summarising articles from newspapers.	
Thurs		Trainer will give feedback. Error analysis will focus on Pascal's sentence construction and pronunciation	
Fri		**Needs Review:** Discussion of programme for following week. **Progress Check:** Discussion of progress made so far.	

On the following pages you will find a blank and a completed homestay course programme. In this type of course programme the teacher completes the programme by hand and sends it to the Homestay Director of Studies.

Student's Weekly Course Plan and Report

Name: .... **Level:** ....
Course Name: .... **Course Dates:** ....
Week: 1 / 2 / 3 / 4 / 5 (Please circle correct week)
Please complete Section A and B at the start of each week, and Section C at the end of each week.

Section A

Main Course Objectives

....

....

....

Section B

Speaking

....

Listening

....

Reading

....

Writing

....

Grammar

....

Vocabulary

....

Pronunciation

Section C

Comments and Suggestions

....

....

Please sign and give one copy to the student each week

Student: .... Teacher: .... Date: ....

Student's Weekly Course Plan and Report

Name: Polina **Level:** Pre-intermediate
Course Name: English and Fashion **Course Dates:** 11–24 June
Week: 1 / 2 / (3) / 4 / 5 (Please circle correct week)
Please complete Section A and B at the start of each week, and Section C at the end of each week.

Section A

Main Course Objectives
To expand vocabulary in the area of fashion and improve ability to talk and understand about fashion-related topics.

Section B

Speaking To activate passive knowledge of English and improve fluency and confidence when speaking. Topics to include: fashion, clothing, materials, colours and hobbies, day-to-day life in London, family and future studies.
Listening To improve extensive listening skills, e.g. in social conversation and on television. Additional practice in intensive listening to help identify contractions, weak forms and other features of native speaker speech.
Reading To practise skim-reading using magazines such as *Elle* and *Vogue* as a basis for vocabulary expansion and discussion.
Writing This skill will only be used to reinforce new areas of grammar, vocabulary and to practise spelling.
Grammar Areas to include SVO word order, yes/no and Wh-question forms (especially present tense); other areas to be dealt with as need arises.
Vocabulary Areas to include – clothing, fabrics, colours, fashion as well as everyday topics for life in London.
Pronunciation To improve awareness of stress, rhythm and intonation and focus on z/ and v/w.

Section C

Comments and Suggestions Polina has made steady progress this week due to her methodical and hard-working approach to study. She has expanded her fashion vocabulary and has gained confidence in speaking on this topic. Her listening has also improved, particularly in social conversation. We will do more work on pronunciation next week.

Student: Polina Teacher: David Date: 16 June

Course programmes for extensive courses

On the following pages you will find examples of programmes for extensive courses. (However, whether the course is intensive or extensive, the principles remain the same.)

Format 1

Weeks 1-6 **12 hours**	**COURSE PROGRAMME FOR MARIE ROSE**
1630-1830 Mon	**Areas which will be covered:**
1st September	**Essay writing** Marie Rose will write an essay each week which she will email to the teacher in advance for discussion in the class. Teacher will comment on the following areas:
8th September	Overall impression ■ Strength of arguments ■ Coherence ■ Cohesion ■ Logic
15th September	Linguistic comment ■ Grammar ■ Vocabulary ■ Punctuation
22nd September	Teacher will prepare any necessary language work based on the language errors.
29th September	**Vocabulary expansion – idiomatic phrases** Marie Rose will expand her knowledge of idiomatic phrases by reading reviews from cinema and music magazines. + Discussion of the films and music concerned. + Feedback. + Recycling of new vocabulary.
6th October	■ Assessment of Marie Rose's progress so far ■ Needs review for the next six weeks

Format 2

Course programme for Saltuk at 1800-1900 for 6 sessions

Monday 1 September	Wednesday 3 September	Friday 5 September	Monday 8 September	Wednesday 10 September	Friday 12 September

Pronunciation

- Saltuk will practise all the sounds that create difficulties for Turkish speakers, such as /θ/ (/θɪn/), /δ/ (/δen/) and /r/ (/red/).
- Teacher will correct mis-pronunciations throughout the class.

Job interviews

- Saltuk and teacher will prepare typical job interview questions.
- Practice job interviews with the teacher.
- Feedback on Saltuk's performance.

Writing CVs and covering letters

- Saltuk will prepare his CV with the teacher.
- He will also prepare covering letters to accompany his job applications. The letters will be tailored to each application.

Grammar

Grammar will be dealt with diagnostically. If Saltuk needs any remedial work, the teacher will do a short input in class and then give him suitable exercises for homework.

Other language needs may appear during the course. If necessary, the teacher may alter the programme to address these needs.

Avoid this type of format as it allows less flexibility and requires more detail.

Format 3

Monday 1st September	**Job interviews** ■ Saltuk will discuss the kind of jobs he will be applying for. ■ Teacher and Saltuk will discuss the structure of a job interview, potential questions and potential answers. **Writing – letters to accompany job applications** ■ Saltuk will write a letter to accompany his job applications, with help from the teacher. **Pronunciation** ■ Saltuk will spend ten minutes working on his intonation with the teacher.
Monday 8th September	**Job interviews continued** ■ Saltuk and teacher will role-play a job interview. Feedback from teacher. **Diagnostic work based on feedback** ■ If necessary, Saltuk will spend time doing any remedial work (presentation skills, pronunciation, vocabulary, grammar, etc.) which arises from the role-play.
Monday 15 September	(etc…)

Until you become familiar with the process, writing course programmes can be time-consuming. You need to be clear in your mind what the objectives of the course are and how those objectives will be reached. You also need a good understanding of all the components that make up a business skill, and you need to know how to break down language skills into their component parts. Finally, you have to be able to write the programme in a language which is accessible for the student.

You need to consider the following factors:

- **The student's aims**: Are they realistic for the student's level and for the time available? Do you agree with the student's stated needs and objectives?

- **Input sessions v. output sessions:** On an intensive course the students will be more receptive at the beginning of the class – or in the morning if the class is over the whole day. The principle is the same for extensive courses.
- **Input v. output:** There should be a balance between the two.
- **Feedback sessions and error analysis:** You need to include details about feedback sessions and error analysis after discussion work or role-plays or simulations.
- **Grammar and pronunciation:** If you don't intend to include formal sessions on grammar and pronunciation, then you should indicate in the course programme that these areas will be handled diagnostically/remedially.
- **Revision and recycling:** You can include information about recycling and revision activities.
- **Variety of activities:** You need to include a variety of activities.
- **Reviewing needs:** A session for reviewing the student's needs should be included.
- **Student's level/progress assessment:** You need to include a formal time for discussing the student's level, his or her progress and your recommendations for future study.
- **Avoid jargon:** It's important to use 'ordinary' English rather than EFL terminology, so that the student can understand the course programme. (e.g. use *vocabulary* instead of *lexis).*

A good course programme:

- is clearly linked to the student's needs;
- states the objectives of the course and how they will be achieved;
- is detailed but not over-specific;
- is logically set out;
- has balance and variety;
- includes information about:
    - *feedback;*
    - *needs reviewing;*
    - *any diagnostic grammar and pronunciation work;*
    - *recycling activities;*
    - *assessment of the student's level and progress together with recommendations for the future;*
- looks professional.

Teachers who are new to writing course programmes often find it a struggle, usually because they try to make the programme too detailed and lose sight of the overall objectives. If you find it difficult, try reducing the information to the absolute minimum; once you feel you can manage the overall objectives, then you can start adding details.

Micro-level objectives

Giving the objectives for each lesson

The course programme gives the student the course objectives on a 'macro' level. However, it is also a good idea to write the objectives and activities for each lesson on the board before the start. Then the student knows exactly what is going to happen in each class.

In the example below, Svetlana read various graded readers for discussion in class. At the time of this class she was reading *The Remains of the Day*.

Tuesday 20th February (60 minutes)

1. Review feedback sheets from the previous class.
2. Grammar clinic – go over the grammar from previous class (e.g. *could* v. *was able to; even if* v. *even though*).
3. Reading homework – check understanding – discuss the story – look at the vocabulary – highlight interesting bits of grammar – predict what will happen next.

In the next example Sabrina was a very fluent speaker; however, she had never learned to write, so struggled to express herself in writing. In order to improve this, she wrote a diary for every lesson and also practised writing emails (written in class with guidance from the teacher).

Monday 13th July (90 minutes)

1. Check homework (vocabulary exercise – linking words).
2. Check diary.
3. Email writing:
   – Read email*;
   – Write short email in response;
   – Feedback on email.
4. Colloquial English: change dialogue in very formal English into everyday English.
5. Fluency practice: short talk on whether it's better to sell your body than your soul.

* *The email was written by the teacher who played the role of a pen pal. Sabrina's main task was to react to what was said in the email, rather than writing about what she had done, as the latter was covered in the 'diary' section.*

Wording a course programme

Teachers develop their own styles, and one teacher's way of wording a programme may not suit another. But provided everyone who reads the programme knows what is going on from the first glance, the style does not matter too much. Below are some example phrases to help you with the wording of a programme.

Language skills

Speaking

Suzanne to practise her speaking skills by talking about different topics.
Suzanne will choose the topics together with her teacher. Subjects to include:

- Holidays
- Sport
- Shopping
- Feedback and error analysis.

Thomas will speak about various business topics in order to improve his fluency. Subjects will include:

- Leadership
- Working in teams
- Other subjects agreed with Thomas; feedback to concentrate on Thomas's sentence construction

---

Listening

Various types of listening material (e.g. CNN News, *The Money Programme*; Radio 3 News) will be used in order to:

- improve Pinar's listening for general understanding, listening for detail and listening strategies;
- expand her vocabulary.

Felix will practise his listening for detail by doing:

- short dictations;
- intensive listening tasks.

Vocabulary

Madeline's vocabulary will be expanded by:

- doing various exercises from vocabulary books;
- reading short texts.

Madeline will choose topic areas in conjunction with the teacher.

Pronunciation
Teacher will correct mispronunciations throughout the class.

Pascal's pronunciation will be corrected when necessary by all teachers.

Jorge to practise different sounds in English which create difficulties for Spanish speakers, such as /ʌ/ (/kʌp/), /ɜː/ (/bɜːd/) and /ə/ (/əˈg4ʊ/).

Job interviews
Saltuk and teacher will prepare typical job interview questions.

- Practice job interviews with the teacher.
- Feedback on Saltuk's performance.

Writing CVs and covering letters
Saltuk will prepare his CV with the teacher. He will also prepare covering letters to accompany his job applications. The letters will be tailored to each application.

Grammar
Alain and teacher to do a 'grammar clinic' every lesson, based on the feedback sheets.

- Suitable practice exercises for homework if required.
- Teacher guidance as to the best way to approach specific grammatical difficulties.

Diagnostic grammar: to be dealt with if and when necessary.

Grammar will be dealt with diagnostically. If Saltuk needs any remedial work, the teacher will do a short input in class and then give him suitable exercises for homework.

Teacher to cover areas of difficulty for Xiang such as:

- Modal verbs (certainty and uncertainty; obligation; advice and recommendations);
- Conditionals (talking hypothetically);
- Verb constructions (e.g. verb+infinitive; verb+preposition+gerund);
- Any other area of grammatical difficulty that arises during the course.

Writing
Andrea will do structured writing tasks in order to improve her general writing skills. The tasks will include:

- short summaries based on reading texts;
- very short essays (e.g. 'for and against' essays).

The teacher will provide a structure and relevant vocabulary for all of these tasks.

Reading
Ami will choose and read a newspaper or Internet article for every class. She will then summarise the article in the form of a short presentation. The teacher will give feedback.

In order to improve his different reading skills, Gert will read short texts in class such as:

- reading for general understanding;
- reading for detail;
- understanding reference words;
- understanding linking words.

Business skills

Telephoning

Input
Useful telephone phrases

Output
Telephone role-plays based on Laura's own work situation, with feedback from teacher.

Meetings
Alessandro will discuss different case studies in order to improve his English for discussions and meetings. The teacher will give feedback and do any remedial work necessary.

Negotiations

Output
The negotiation practice will be based on Mathias's own negotiations with supermarket suppliers
+ Feedback

Input

The language input will depend on the feedback from the negotiation role-play.

Socialising

Maria to learn useful phrases and expressions for different social situations such as:

- dealing with visitors;
- entertaining.

All new language will be practised either in role-plays or with consolidation exercises.

Writing

- Teacher and Roland to go through the work reports that Roland has brought with him.
- Teacher to suggest ways Roland can improve his report writing skills, and to give Roland practice exercises if necessary.
- Focus will be placed on overall clarity rather than detailed linguistic errors.

- Leila will write different emails based on the telephone calls practised in class, in order to consolidate her email writing skills.
- Feedback from teacher.

Case studies from Chapter 3

On the following pages you will find course programmes for the four students who were interviewed for the needs analysis in Chapter 3.

Course programme: JENNY (extensive course)

Dates: 2 AUG – 3 SEP **Number of hours**: 10

	1800-2000
Week 1	**Vocabulary expansion** The emphasis of the course is to expand Jenny's vocabulary and use of idiomatic phrases. This will be done through: ▪ Reading newspaper articles; ▪ Reading graded readers; ▪ Listening to a variety of materials; ▪ Using exercises from topic-based vocabulary books (e.g. talking about the environment). *(No reading in class – all reading will be done for homework.)* Teacher will recycle the new vocabulary with Jenny each lesson. **Speaking** Some of the speaking activities will be linked with the reading activities, e.g.: ▪ Jenny will discuss the newspaper articles and graded readers she looks at for homework. ▪ Discussion around vocabulary from topic-based vocabulary books. ▪ Other topics decided with Jenny at the end of each class so she can prepare for the next one. **Telephoning, socialising and job interviewing role-plays** ▪ Jenny will do telephoning, socialising and job-interviewing role-plays. If she enjoys them, we will look at each area in more depth in a later lesson. ▪ Feedback and error correction. **Course evaluation (Week 5)** Jenny will discuss with her teacher her progress, strengths and weaknesses, and areas for further study. **Needs review (Week 5)** Jenny will discuss the objectives for the next five lessons.
Week 2	
Week 3	

Course programme: PINAR (intensive course)

Dates: 9-13 June **Week number:** 1 of 2

Teacher	0900-1030 Ellen	1100-1230 Anthony	1400-1530 Cheryl
Mon Tues Wed Thurs Fri	**Needs analysis** Discussion of programme for week 1. **European Union law** ■ Pinar will discuss EU law issues with her teacher. Input will come from EU law websites and translation services. Pinar will decide which aspects of law will be most useful for her. ■ All new words will be recycled. ■ Please note that the main objective of this session is to give Pinar the opportunity to talk about EU law, not simply to expand her knowledge about it. ■ Teacher will give feedback on the speaking activities. **Pronunciation** ■ Pinar will practise sounds which create difficulties for Turkish speakers. ■ Work will be done on stress, rhythm and intonation. **Tutorial & needs review** Pinar will discuss her progress with the teacher. The objectives for the next week will be decided.	**Listening** ■ Pinar will listen to audiocassette materials including radio programmes such as the daily news. ■ Teacher will check Pinar's listening strategies. **Writing** Pinar will decide with her teacher what kind of writing will be most useful for her (e.g. general writing skills, emails, letters, reports, essays). **Input** The input will depend upon the difficulties Pinar has in writing. **Output** ■ Teacher will give Pinar short writing tasks for homework. ■ Feedback from teacher and error correction. **Diagnostic grammar** Grammar will be done diagnostically by all teachers. Any areas of difficulties will be dealt with.	**Reading** Pinar will decide with teacher the kind of reading she would like to do (e.g. graded readers; articles from websites or newspapers). The reading material will be used: ■ to expand her vocabulary; ■ for discussion. **Speaking** Pinar will: ■ discuss different topics of her choice; ■ give short talks (using informal presentation skills); ■ make comments on her reading material. Feedback and error analysis (attention will be paid to Pinar's pronunciation).

Course programme: Atsuko (intensive course)

Dates: 9-13 JUNE **Number of hours:** 15 HOURS

	1400-1515	BREAK	1530-1700
Monday	**British Culture** The emphasis of the course is to improve Atsuko's: ■ speaking; ■ listening; ■ reading; ■ pronunciation; ■ vocabulary; through learning about British culture and comparing it with Japanese culture. **Areas of British culture to be covered** These will be confirmed with Atsuko, but could cover 'dos and don'ts', royalty, food, architecture, historical monuments, music, marriage and family life. **Materials to be used** Atsuko's own impressions, websites, reading texts and videos about life in Britain. **Feedback and error correction** Atsuko will receive feedback and error correction where appropriate. **Writing** Atsuko will be given optional writing homework. Tasks to be decided with Atsuko, but could include a) writing a letter to a friend about her stay in Britain, or b) short essays looking at various aspects of British life.		
Friday	At the end of the week Atsuko will make a short presentation outlining what she feels are the main differences between the two cultures. **Course Review** Teacher and Atsuko will assess her progress. Teacher will make recommendations for future study.		

Course programme: Hye Sun (extensive course)

Date: October-November **Number of hours**: 15 HOURS

1000-1200	1400-1515 BREAK 1530-1700
Week 1	**Needs analysis** Discussion of programme for the next five weeks. **Writing** Hye Sun will be given structured writing tasks in order to improve her overall writing skills. The following types of writing will be covered. ■ *Writing narratives*: use of past tenses; use of sequencing words (e.g. *then, after that)* and time phrases.
Week 2	■ *Writing short reports:* use of linking words (e.g. *although; as a result);* language for cause and effect; making recommendations. All writing activities will be done at home and checked with the teacher in class.
Week 3	**Speaking** Hye Sun will prepare a short talk at home for each lesson. Topics to include: ■ the Korean education system; ■ Korean food. + Feedback
Week 4	The teacher will provide useful vocabulary before the writing and speaking activities. Diagnostic vocabulary and grammatical work will be based on the writing and speaking feedback.
Week 5	**Course evaluation** Teacher and Hye Sun will discuss her progress and areas for further study. **Needs review** Hye Sun will discuss the objectives for the next five lessons.

5

Chapter 5

Teaching Techniques For One-to-One Classes

As we have already pointed out, with one-to-one lessons you can tailor your teaching techniques to the context and interests of your individual student. As we will see in this chapter, at the same time you can give him or her the tools with which to continue the learning process independently after the end of the course.

Using the student as a resource

You can exploit the student's knowledge, experience and interests for use in both input and output activities in the classroom. Your skill here lies in eliciting information from the student, the way you exploit that information and the quality of feedback you give, together with any language summaries and recycling activities you may need to prepare *after* the class. (See **Axel**, below). For example, you can go into a classroom for a sixty-minute class with nothing more than a handful of

Axel

Axel is a commercial project manager for a European electrical giant. The teacher has included 'Job Talk' (see Chapter 7) in the course programme, using the following format:

- Axel explains a specific aspect of his work (e.g. problems with suppliers).
- The teacher listens and takes notes (and records the conversation as a backup).
- The teacher gives Axel feedback (e.g. introducing him to key vocabulary that he lacks for describing the client/supplier relationship; reformulating sentences; working on stress, rhythm and intonation). The recording is used judiciously to highlight point such as difficulties with intonation and over-complicated sentence constructions.
- New vocabulary is recycled in later lessons.

paper, with the basis for the lesson coming entirely from the student. This means less work for you – even zero preparation sometimes – and is very motivating for the student. It is easy to use this approach with older students; with younger age groups, however, you need to find the right contexts to access their experience and knowledge.

Framework materials

These are materials, usually aimed at business English learners, that allow you to use the student's experience and knowledge as the basis for a lesson: they present the structure for a discussion, sometimes with key vocabulary on one page or less. A current example of this type of book is *Framework Materials* (2002) by Paul Emmerson.

Language summaries

Even if the student provides the input for a lesson, it is useful for him or her to have a language summary of what has been covered in class (e.g. when a student explains an aspect of his or her job and you provide the missing vocabulary and structures). You can neatly hand-write a summary as the lesson progresses, which you can give to the student at the end of the class, or if your notes are too untidy, you can type up the language summary after the class. Typing up language summaries can be time-consuming, though, so it is usually only worth doing it for lower-level learners who greatly benefit from having a clear language reference; summaries for these levels also tend to be quite short. You can use these summaries as a basis for creating exercises for the student in later classes.

You can construct the language summaries in two ways: either by creating a list of useful vocabulary and grammatical structures, or by writing a narrative.

Example 1

Anke worked for the German subsidiary of a large international haircare company. Although she was an elementary level student, only a small part of her course was spent using a course book. A large part of the time was devoted to describing hair and hair products. The teacher then prepared language summaries of all the new vocabulary after the lessons. (See Example 1 in the box on the next page.)

Example 2

Peter wanted to practise making presentations to his clients. As part of the preparation for the presentation, Peter explained his company's fee structure. The teacher then prepared a language summary, using whole sentences instead of just a list of words and phrases. (See Example 2 in the box on the next page.)

Example 1: Anke

Vocabulary for describing hair and hair products

Manageability Her hair is easy (difficult) to manage (to control) (Un) manageable **Where products are sold** Salon-only products **Good (bad) for the hair** Too much silicone is bad for the hair Alcohol is bad for your hair A little bit of silicone (the right kind of silicone) (Vitamins) is (are) good for your hair **Duration of the effect** The effect lasts for six to eight washes The colour lasts for up to twenty-one washes **Frequency of use** The shampoo is for daily use (frequent use)	**What a product does** The shampoo conditions (revitalises; reconstructs; strengthens) the hair The product cleans (protects; conditions; coats…gives the hair a 'film'…) **The scalp** The scalp can/can't breathe **The popularity of the product** The product is popular (successful; well-known) The sales of product X are good (reasonable; not very good) **Brushes** A brush with plastic (natural) bristles This brush is good for fine (coarse); straight (curly); long (short) hair

Example 2: Peter

Explaining the fee structure to a client

(1) The Management Fee

This includes the costs of all staff and all our daily running costs.
Our clients (the hospital) usually pay this fee monthly. However, if you prefer, you can pay the fee quarterly, or once every six months, or once a year. It is flexible.
This fee is fixed and does not vary from month to month.

(2) The Percentage of Savings

We ask a percentage of any savings that we make for you – if you save, for example, £30,000 on your cleaning costs, then we would ask for (5%) of this figure…

etc.…

The teacher then exploited this language summary by creating different exercises such as gap-fills, or giving only the key words (e.g. *fee – fixed – vary*) and asking the student to recreate the sentences.

Vocabulary

Students learn a great deal of vocabulary 'incidentally', as most classroom activities throw up new words. It is important for both student and teacher to make a note of the new word or phrase, and the context in which it is used, in order to recycle it later. You also need to encourage the student to write down the sentence in which the word or words occurred (e.g. *The noise was driving me crazy; I tried to persuade him; I don't mind doing it as long as it doesn't take too much time.)*

You can also do specific activities targeted at vocabulary expansion:

- **Reading texts:** e.g. authentic materials such as newspaper articles.
- **Vocabulary books:** the teacher can let the student choose topics of interest from the table of contents.
- **Using listening inputs for vocabulary building:** e.g. watching news or current affairs TV programmes is an excellent way of broadening the student's vocabulary, albeit in a 'news-based' way. However, it is not a good idea to link the two together if the lack of vocabulary will hinder the student's ability to listen.

Recycling vocabulary

Recycling vocabulary is a quick and very important activity that the teacher can use on a regular basis. It is also very handy when you have a spare ten minutes or so to fill. When we think what it means to 'know' a word (what is the connotation of the word? is it formal or informal? what about the spelling, the word partnerships, the grammatical construction of the word, its frequency of use, and so on?), we can see the potential activities that can be used to recycle the new words and phrases.

The main aim is to have recycling activities which the teacher can use spontaneously in class without preparation, or which can be prepared with the minimum amount of work. The following list includes typical recycling activities:

- **Word partnerships (collocations):** practising the words most likely to be associated with the original word; e.g. *set (meet, miss, extend) a deadline; a demanding person (job, activity).*
- **Associated uses:** e.g. *RISK: to take a risk; to put something at risk; to do something at your own risk.*
- **Opposites:** Not all words have a direct opposite: 'opposites' exercises are good for discussion rather than finding an exact opposite.

- **Making sentences:** This is the most difficult way to recycle new vocabulary. Only do it if you think the student has understood the basic meaning and you now want him or her to look at the usage. However, it is a very worthwhile activity if the student can manage it, as you can create sentences based on his or her own life and activities.
- **Grammatical structure:** Check your student can manipulate the underlying grammar of a word e.g. *She is afraid of the dark; she is afraid that she might not pass her exams.*
- **Gap fills:** You can handwrite gap-fill sentences, e.g. *I was just a________ to go out when the telephone rang; I'd like to have a garden as __________ as I could have a gardener.*
- **Synonyms:** You can give the student synonyms of the new words (e.g. *He doesn't want to work this weekend*); the student provides the new word (*He is __________ to work this weekend*).
- **Word-building:** See page 73.
- **Crosswords:** If you have some spare time, you can prepare crosswords for your student by using the crossword function at www.puzzlemaker.com.

Some guidance in generating recycling activities

Example 1

The student has written down the following words over the last two lessons. You have decided it is time to recycle them.

Worn out	*To let go of the reins*
Shabby	*I felt overwhelmed*
Hindsight – with hindsight	*To crumble*
It drives me crazy	

You don't need to prepare anything in advance; the idea is to go through the student's notes and pull words out. These activities don't have to be sophisticated; they simply need to help the student memorise the word and some aspects of its usage. Remember: recycling activities don't necessarily involve testing the student – recycling also includes looking at the new words or phrases to see all the various ways in which they can be used.

Here are some examples of how you could recycle the material in the box above:

- What kinds of things can *crumble*? (Elicit *cakes, buildings, relationships, empires.*)
- What is the opposite of a) *a shabby house*? b) *a shabby coat?* c) *He was dressed shabbily?*
- In which situations do people feel *overwhelmed*? What about you? (e.g. by *emails, work, emotions)*

- What do you think the following mean? a) *The carpet is worn out.* b) *I feel worn out.*
- Find a synonym for *It makes me very irritated.* (If you think the student will have difficulty remembering, give the first letters: *It d________ me c_________*. What drives **you** crazy?
- Is there anything in your life you would like to have done differently? Begin with *With hindsight, I would have (should have)…*
- How would you express *to let go of the reins* using different words? In which contexts would you use this expression? What other things can you *let go of*? (Elicit *someone's hand, a rope, a handle* (physically); *an employee, a relationship* (metaphorically).)

Example 2

Anke's teacher prepared exercises such as the following three to recycle new vocabulary. As the student was at a low level, they did not require much preparation time.

Word-building

Nouns	Verbs	Adjectives
Management	*to manage*	*Manageable*
	to control	
	to last	
	to condition	
	to cleanse	

Opposites

What are the opposites of the following?

- *easy to control*
- *manageable*
- *Too much silicone is good for your hair.*
- *hair with volume*

Sorting

Put the following adjectives into the correct boxes: *manageable, popular, long-lasting, controllable, coarse, well-known.*

Hair	Product

Vocabulary storage

Set aside time to look at different vocabulary storage techniques with your student, such as flashcards, vocabulary books (small ones which the student can put in a pocket or handbag are best) and storing the vocabulary in the computer. Make sure that the student notes down all new words, ideally in 'model' sentences related to his or her life: this will help him or her to remember the words more easily. At the same time, the student can also make a note of the word's syllable stress, collocations, grammatical structure, opposites, synonyms and so on.

Using authentic materials

Course books are unlikely to meet the requirements of students with very specific needs. In this case you may need to make use of authentic materials such as:

- materials the student brings with him or her (e.g. company reports, emails, brochures, catalogues, handbooks);
- articles from newspapers and magazines;
- song lyrics;
- advertisements;
- literature (e.g. short stories, poetry);
- off-air TV and radio recordings and video recordings of films;
- websites (the information can either be downloaded, or the teacher and student can look at the website together).

> **Yasu**
> Yasu is going to work in the Netherlands for nine months. The teacher has spent class time with him searching the Internet for information about life in Amsterdam, particularly accommodation. The printouts from the websites they visited then formed the basis for discussion and vocabulary extension. Yasu has also done role-plays based on talking to accommodation agencies.

Preparing authentic materials for use in class can be very time-consuming, so it is best to avoid producing detailed worksheets. What this means is that you need a general approach that you can adapt for use with most authentic materials.

It is essential to have a clear purpose in mind when using authentic material such as a newspaper article. For example:

- expanding vocabulary;
- improving reading skills;

- generating discussion;
- summarising information (e.g. ask the student to read and reproduce the main points of the article in a presentation);
- 'mimicking' what the student has to do in his or her job (e.g. skimming British financial press for relevant articles);
- comparing written and spoken English;
- transforming written English into spoken English.

Basic format for exploiting a news article

This assumes that the teacher has little time for preparing the article, and that the student does not want to do homework and agrees to read the article in class.

Pre-class preparation

- Allocate a couple of minutes for reading the article and highlighting interesting vocabulary. Number all the paragraphs in the article.
- Allocate five minutes for preparing up to five 'global' comprehension questions. These can be handwritten, or you can write them on the board.

In class – first reading

- Give your student a time limit within which to read the article quickly (this encourages the student to read for meaning rather than looking at every word). The student should read for 'gist' and may not consult a dictionary. While the student is reading the article, you can think of ways in which to focus on the key vocabulary you want to look at later in the lesson.
- Ask the student to give a brief summary of what he or she has understood, or ask some general comprehension questions which you have prepared in advance.
- Give the student a few more minutes for re-reading
- Then, either ask more detailed comprehension questions (you can prepare these while the student is reading), or start looking at the key vocabulary in the text.

Focusing on vocabulary in a text

All you need do is write down the key words you want to highlight and have your questions mentally prepared, for example:

- 'Can you find a word which means *famous* in paragraph 3?'
- 'Guess the meaning of *mind-boggling* in paragraph 5.'
- 'Find five different ways in the article for describing numbers (e.g. *Two-thirds did..., Seven out of ten said...*).'
- 'Find three examples of *essential spending* and *non-essential spending* in the article (e.g. bills, eating out.). Now do the same for *addictive behaviour* (e.g. surfing the Internet all night) and *addictive substances* (e.g. tobacco).'
- 'Give a definition for a *reluctant shopper* and an *indecisive shopper*.'

Case Studies

Peter wants to look at a government white paper on new healthcare initiatives. The teacher selects a section, reads it and writes down the key differences between the old system of the internal market and the new system of integrated care. Peter and the teacher then slowly go through these differences, discussing them. Peter then reads the relevant section for consolidation.

Coralie has a pre-intermediate level of English. The teacher decides to expand her vocabulary for describing people's personality and looks, using the 'personal advertisements' for individuals seeking partners. The teacher gives Coralie two columns of advertisements: one for men, one for women. Coralie has to give each advertiser a name (e.g. Reese; Martin) and then complete a table with sections for physical characteristics, personality traits, hobbies and interests, aspirations etc.

Once Coralie is familiar with the key vocabulary, she then reads another set of advertisements, this time commenting on them (e.g. "Perhaps he wants a 'serene' woman because his last girlfriend was very difficult...", "I suppose she says she 'loves champagne' because she is looking for a rich boyfriend...").

Speaking

Fluency is not one skill, but a range of skills. It encompasses:

- syntax and grammar;
- pronunciation;
- stress, rhythm and intonation;
- vocabulary;
- appropriateness;
- speed of response;
- quality of ideas;
- confidence;
- listening skills.

It is very difficult for learners to exert control over all these elements when verbalising their ideas. With one-to-one tuition you can focus on the student's individual speaking difficulties, so the objectives of speaking activities can be varied, and are not limited simply to developing accuracy, fluency or confidence.

Roger

Roger speaks extremely slowly and when asked a question takes a very long time to compose his reply. In order to improve his response time, the teacher gives him prompts to which he must give immediate answers. No other linguistic elements are assessed during these practice activities apart from the speed at which Roger a) responds and b) speaks.

Discussion activities

- **Prepared talks:** These can be less formal than presentations. In addition to giving the student time to prepare, you can provide language summaries giving useful vocabulary for the topic.
- **Unprepared talks:** To practise spontaneity, give the student a list of topics to choose from. The student has to talk about the topic for an allotted time, e.g. five minutes.
- **Articles:** The student can choose the article and lead the discussion.
- **Newspaper headlines:** The advantage of looking at headlines is that the student does not need to read anything. However, bear in mind that the student may lack the vocabulary for discussion that reading the whole article can provide.
- **Charts:** Newspaper and magazines publish 'charts' (e.g. beer consumption in Europe; obesity levels in the western world). These can be used to stimulate discussion.
- **Controversial statements:** e.g. *Management consultants are a waste of money*; 'MBAs help you get better jobs'.
- **Pictures or photographs:** e.g. take in ten pictures shortlisted for a competition; ask the student to comment on which one should win and why. Pictures are very good for stimulating conversation with lower-level students.
- **Themed language summaries:** Create a short language summary (similar to, but shorter than, the ones found in vocabulary books – and with no exercises) with discussion questions. For example, a language summary for personal finance could include vocabulary describing people's attitudes to money, methods of saving, investing and spending, together with questions for discussion.
- **Role-plays:** these give the student the opportunity to speak, but not for free expression – so be careful of using role-plays if your objective is to help your student improve his or her fluency.

Speaking activities for advanced speakers

You need to find ways of stretching advanced students' language. You can do this by choosing complex or controversial topics such as cloning; however, make sure the student has the appropriate vocabulary available for discussing the topic. You can also play 'Devil's Advocate', putting the student under pressure to defend his or her position. It is important to tell the student that you are just as interested in his or her ideas as in the language used; this should encourage the student to use these ideas and to 'stretch' his or her linguistic capabilities.

Listening

Listening is often thought of as a passive skill as opposed to the 'active' skill of speaking. In fact, listening is an active, dynamic process; the brain needs to decode incoming signals, which means it is actively engaged in constructing meaning from the sounds it receives through the ears. The ears simply pick up the sound; the brain makes sense of it. Students sometimes rely too much on their knowledge of the linguistic system to make sense of what someone is saying ('bottom-up processing'). However, they also need 'top-down processing'; this relies on the learner's non-linguistic knowledge to decode the speaker's message.

A successful listener:

- uses visual and environmental clues to help understanding;
- does not panic;
- does not try to understand every word;
- uses his or her knowledge of the world to construct meaning;
- uses his or her predictive skills to deduce what is going on from a few key words;
- guesses the meaning of words from the context.

One-to-one lessons present a good opportunity to work on any difficulties your student has with his or her listening strategies. However, if we ask our students to listen to an input without introducing the topic and setting the scene first, we are asking them to do something native speakers rarely do, i.e. listen to something with which they are completely unfamiliar, or about which they know nothing. In course books, and books aimed at providing listening practice, the listening tasks are designed to give the student maximum help in understanding the situation before he or she listens. The student then listens to try and catch the general meaning (extensive listening); this may be followed by detailed listening tasks (intensive listening).

If you use a piece of authentic listening such as a news bulletin or a film, you need to exploit the material in a similarly systematic way. Don't just ask your student to listen to five or ten minutes of video and then tell you what was going on; the student can improve this kind of listening strategy independently outside the classroom. It is your task to use the listening material in such a way as to a) check listening strategies, b) help improve strategies if they are not good, c) expand the student's language knowledge by focusing on the linguistic features of the input (e.g. vocabulary; sentence construction; phonology, cultural elements).

A procedure for listening

Warm-up

- Generate interest and motivate student.
- Set scene.
- Pre-teach vocabulary if necessary (i.e. specific words/phrases needed to complete the task).
- With video inputs, the student can watch without sound and predict what will be said.

Extensive listening

- Give the student an easy task based on getting the general meaning and building confidence.
- Play video or audio-tape.
- Check task.

Intensive listening

- Give the student a more detailed task.
- Play tape.
- Check task.

Typical extensive listening tasks

- The student has a list of words and ticks any that he or she hears.
- Give the student a list of sentences. Ask the student to tick any sentence for which he or she hears a sentence with a similar meaning.
- Give the student a list of 'true or false?' questions (based on the general 'sense' of the passage, rather than specific details).

If you don't have time to prepare any extensive listening tasks, simply ask the student to a) write down any words he/she catches, b) write down any facts or figures he/she hears, c) give a very brief summary of what he/she understood, or d) compare his or her predictions to what was heard.

Typical intensive listening tasks

- Specific comprehension questions (e.g. *What does the figure 3,345 refer to?*, *How many people live in Alabama?*, *Why is acquiring new skills so important?*).
- Listening 'word for word' – the teacher can write down a sentence from the video, with blanks to be filled in, e.g. *The government has ____________ that there will be no ______________________ in the _________ future.*
- Vocabulary work, e.g. *Listen for a word which means "extremely small"*; *What do you*

think the word 'virtually' means? Listen and see if you can hear the phrase "a hell of a problem".

- Phonological elements, e.g. *How is the phrase "It would have been better not to go" pronounced?*

If we are using authentic video with the student, we do not need to prepare the tasks in advance. For example, if you record the morning news for your student:

- Watch it quickly to identify stories which don't require too much background knowledge and which are at the right linguistic level for the student.
- Do any pre-listening activities necessary.
- While the student is watching for the first time, scribble down key facts and useful vocabulary.
- Ask the student some very general comprehension questions.
- Watch the video again, this time exploiting it intensively. The key facts you scribbled down can be the basis for comprehension questions which you ask the student.

Understanding rapid connected speech

If the student can understand general meaning, but has difficulty understanding detail, you can help by looking at the features of rapid connected speech that create difficulties for non-native speakers to understand, e.g. redundancy (i.e. the speaker uses words which are not necessary for understanding the message); false starts; repetitions; use of idiomatic language (e.g. *I blew it);* dialects. You can also introduce the student to the following phonological elements of the language:

Liaison Linking of words, particularly when the second word begins with a vowel (e.g. *at home*; *in a minute*). The sounds /r/, /w/ and /j/ can be inserted between words to improve liaison (e.g. *law and order*, *you are*; *she always comes*).

Weak forms Function words (i.e. words which have little meaning on their own, but which contribute to the grammatical construction – for example prepositions, modals and pronouns) are usually not stressed.

Vowel reduction Unaccented vowels are pronounced less distinctly.

Contractions e.g. *Why've you come? I'd've done it if I'd had time.*

Elision The loss of a sound or sounds, e.g. *next week* (*t* is lost); *old man* (*d* is lost).

Karlo
Unusually, Karlo has good productive skills but great difficulties with listening. He is unable to use visual clues to help him guess what is going on, nor does he use his knowledge of the world to make sense of what is being said. The teacher spends a lot of time doing 'predicting' work with Karlo. She also gives Karlo regular dictations to help his intensive listening skills. She is 'tough' with Karlo and will not help him if he asks her what a word means (unless it is difficult to guess the meaning from the context). The teacher has also told him he is to watch satellite TV at home for a minimum of one hour a week. She has stressed that it does not matter if Karlo understands little or nothing; the important point is to gain exposure to spoken English.

Dictations

Dictations can be used in many imaginative and interesting ways; however, many of these techniques are geared to group teaching. However, dictations can be very worthwhile in one-to-one classes for students who have difficulty decoding listening inputs and don't use their knowledge of the language system and of the world to help them; (e.g. they hear *festival* instead of *first of all* in a context where *festival* would not make sense). Dictations also aid the development of short-term memory, as the student must retain chunks of language in his or her head; they also help the student to improve note-taking skills.

You can involve the student by letting him or her choose the text; you can then add variety to the dictation by:

- asking the student to do a gap-fill, rather than asking him or her to write down every word;
- letting the student read the text in advance;
- varying the length of text segments (the longer, the harder);
- varying the type of text (e.g. using dialogues).

Sergei
Sergei is an elementary level student. The teacher writes short texts based on different aspects of Russian and British life, which she then uses for dictations. She includes in these texts grammatical structures and vocabulary that Sergei has recently been taught. A classic dictation procedure is used:

- The teacher reads the entire text; Sergei listens.
- She then reads the text in segments: each segment is read twice, and Sergei writes down the segments. (The teacher also asks him to put in the punctuation.)
- The teacher re-reads the text; Sergei checks his work.

- The teacher looks at his work, but makes no comment.
- The dictation is put to one side until the next lesson.
- The teacher re-reads the text (which is very short); Sergei now has the opportunity to make any further changes.
- Finally, the teacher and Sergei look at the original together.

The teacher does not pay attention to spellings as she is more interested in Sergei's listening skills and in the consolidation of the new grammar and vocabulary.

The teacher varies her approach to the dictations by using gap-fills and longer segments and by letting Sergei read more difficult texts in advance (see above).

Pronunciation

The one-to-one classroom affords the teacher the opportunity to 'home in on' the reasons why a student's speech can be difficult to understand or tiring to listen to. The student, in turn, can practise making the correct movements with his or her lips and tongue without the worry of looking foolish in front of classmates. Homestay teachers can even bring a mirror to the lesson so that the student can look at the movements of his or her mouth.

Identifying the problem

Making individual sounds:

e.g. the student cannot clearly pronounce /*b*/ or /*v*/ or cannot distinguish between these two phonemes, or has difficulty with a sound that does not exist in his or her own language.

Articulation:

e.g. the student does not open his or her mouth widely enough.

Intonation:

the student does not vary the pitch of his or her voice sufficiently to show meaning or attitude.

Syllable stress:

the student puts the stress on the wrong syllable (e.g. *Ar-se-NAL* instead of *AR-se-nal*).

Sentence stress:

the student does not give enough prominence to key words; e.g. *I DIDN'T forget to do it, It was TERRIBLY expensive.*

Liaison:
the student does not liaise words, and he or her consequently sounds rather 'staccato'.

Contractions:
e.g. the student doesn't use contractions, and sounds stilted as a result.

Rhythm:
this involves the use of contractions, weak forms, pausing and syllable stress (e.g. *It's BET-ter to DO it / at a-NOTHER TIME*).

You can record your student during pronunciation exercises or speaking activities in class. Introduce him or her to the language laboratory if your school has one. Encourage him or her to do as much listening as possible outside the classroom, as this will help with pronunciation; he or she should also take active notice of the kind of intonation patterns native speakers use, and try to copy them.

Reading aloud

Normally it is difficult to do this in a group class, as the group members are not willing to listen to each other. However, some students enjoy doing it and the one-to-one class gives you an ideal opportunity to practise the various elements of rhythm and intonation.

Take a short text; let the student read it first. Then together you can prepare the text for reading aloud by 'marking up' the following features:

- **Rhythm:** the student can identify the sense groups* before they read; e.g. *She found the shop assistants / extremely unfriendly / and decided / not to go there again. //* This is particularly good for students who tend to 'gabble'.
- **Liaison:** Before the student reads the text, you can practise liaison by highlighting all the words that will be linked, e.g. *…shop assistants / extremely unfriendly / and decided… not to… there again…* (ask the student to link the 's' and the 'e' and the 'y' and 'a' even though there is a pause between them).
- **Prominence:** The student can underline the words that should be given prominence.

* An explanation of 'sense groups' can be found at www.britichcouncil.org/languageassisstant/pdf/unit6.pdf

Note: occasionally, reading aloud distorts the student's stress, rhythm and intonation, which may be more natural when he or she is speaking normally.

Writing

As with speaking, writing involves mastery of different sub-skills such as spelling, the organisation of ideas, paragraph construction, the use of linking devices to show cohesion, punctuation, nominalisation (i.e. forming nouns from other parts of speech), the use of reference words, and an ability to manipulate the various types of clauses. Additionally, there are many different types of writing, ranging from emails to promotional letters, from essays to advertisements. An individual can learn to be competent in one particular area of writing, such as standard business letters, but this does not mean he or she will have the writing skills to tackle (for example) writing a detailed report. Also, more informal means of communication, such as email, don't require the full mastery of writing skills.

Writing in the one-to-one classroom is a lonely business: it cannot be done in pairs or small groups, and apart from the teacher there is no immediate readership for the student's written work. However, writing is a very beneficial activity for developing overall language skills: not only can the student improve his or her writing abilities, but writing also helps to consolidate the language he or she already knows and, in some cases, can help them extend their language.

Keeping a diary

This is an excellent way of reinforcing the grammar, syntax and vocabulary that the

Galina

Galina has a pre-advanced level of English. However, she has never learned to write in English and is very keen to do this; she also wants to improve her spelling. Together, Galina and her teacher work out a programme for improving her writing skills. The teacher starts by giving her very simple writing tasks so that she can focus on the form rather than the ideas. Galina uses the 'spell and grammar check' function on her computer to check her work; in class the teacher looks at cohesion, coherence, sentence structure and helps Galina to make her language more idiomatic (i.e. something a native speaker would write). Galina then moves on to doing more difficult, but still very structured writing tasks (e.g. writing answers to comprehension questions to a text). This does not allow Galina any scope for creativity, but she is happy with that as her aim is to improve her written fluency. Once Galina feels more confident and finds it quicker to put ideas on paper, she graduates to more complex themes. However, she and the teacher decide to focus only on writing narratives and not to explore other types of writing such as letters or 'for and against' essays.

student has learned. It forces the student to think carefully about how the language is constructed and to be precise with his or her use of language. Before the student starts the diary (which can take any form – daily, weekly – perhaps 'thoughts on the week' rather than a 'blow-by-blow' account of what he or she has done during that time), decide what kind of language he or she will use. For example, will a conversational tone be used or does the student prefer to practise a more formal written style?

Academic writing

Celita

Celita wants to improve her academic writing. She does not have much experience of this, so the teacher spends time looking at the features of this type of writing such as defining terms (e.g. I understand the term *constant innovation and change* to mean...), putting both sides of the argument and avoiding categorical statements (e.g. in most circumstances... experience shows...). Celita and the teacher discuss in depth how Celita will handle the essay topic, and what points she will make before she writes it. She is not allowed to give it to the teacher until she has edited it at least twice. The teacher then highlights any mistakes or slips and gives it back to Celita to correct. Celita is a careful and accurate writer; her main difficulty is knowing the best word to use and her use of linking words (e.g. *While several young people managed to persuade Bill Gates of the urgency to develop the software for Internet services. Finally, Bill Gates agreed to proceed.*) The teacher always makes comments on the quality of Celita's arguments before looking at any linguistic difficulties she may have.

Reading

Students normally want to focus on their listening and speaking, and are happy to work on their reading skills by themselves. However, some students recognise that they don't have the linguistic competence necessary to pick up the meaning of a text, and ask for the teacher's help in improving their reading skills.

There is an enormous variety of reading material that you can use in class, such as fiction, newspapers and magazines, business texts, reference materials, instructions, notices and catalogues. With one-to-one students you can concentrate on the types of material and the topics which interest them.

People employ different reading techniques for a variety of purposes, such as *skimming* (i.e. reading for general meaning), *scanning* (i.e. reading quickly to find a specific piece of information), *intensive reading* (shorter texts – usually for information) and *extensive reading* (longer texts – usually for pleasure), and they employ a variety of skills when reading, such as:

- predicting;
- deducing the meanings of unknown words and phrases;
- understanding both explicit and implicit information;
- identifying main points, and extracting them for summarising;
- understanding the way ideas are linked together within a sentence e.g. *due to…*, *resulting in…*;
- understanding relations between sentences;
- understanding reference words (e.g. *in such a way*, *despite this*, *this means*, *the ones*, *like theirs*).

Jakub

In his job Jakub has to skim the headlines of the *Financial Times* each day, identify articles of interest and read them. He currently finds this task time-consuming and would like to improve his reading skills. The teacher decides to make this the focus of his lessons and Jakub looks at the *FT* every day in class. Together with the teacher he identifies:

- typical grammar of headlines (e.g. *factory to close).*
- typical vocabulary (e.g. *row, ban, quit, woe, boom, aim, bid).*

Next, the teacher gives him techniques for getting the general meaning of an article in which he is interested:

- predicting what the article is about;
- reading the first couple of paragraphs;
- timed readings (i.e. he has to read the article quickly within a time limit);
- scanning exercises (i.e. looking for specific pieces of information within a time limit);
- highlighting certain words (e.g. all the linking words; all the words connected with money).

Then Jakub does more intensive reading tasks:

- he reads articles, identifies the main points and summarises the article for the teacher;
- he answers intensive comprehension questions;
- he practises deducing the meaning of unknown words and phrases.

Reading exercises

You can find various different types of exercise for exploiting texts (both intensively and extensively) in course books. The kind of exercise you use depends on your text. Examples which can be easily used in class with authentic materials are:

- completing tables: ask the student to look for facts and figures in the articles to complete a table.
- text rebuilding: provide key words from the text and ask the student to rebuild it in his or her own words.
- definitions and synonyms: ask the student to find words in the text which match the definitions and synonyms you give to him or her.
- 'true or false' questions: these can be used in both extensive and intensive exercises.

Creating a personalised grammar reference

Most course books contain grammar reviews at the back. These are very helpful for the teacher, but can sometimes be too technical for the student. You can help the student create his or her own personal grammar review by making sure he or she has model sentences (which can be based on the student's own life) for all the new grammatical structures learned. If you are making a self-study cassette (see below) for your student, you can even record these on to it.

Creating a self-study cassette

During the course you can make a self-study cassette for the student to take home after the course. This can include:

- model sentences;
- key pronunciations (i.e. words or phrases that the student has had difficulty in pronouncing);
- key vocabulary.

You can also help the student prepare a presentation which he or she records on to cassette to take away. This is particularly good for teenage students, who can take it back to show their parents.

Using the Internet

There are several specific books on the market on the subject of exploiting the Internet in the classroom, such as *Teaching English with IT* by Dave Smith and Eric Barber (Modern English Publishing) or *The Internet and Business English* by B. Barrett and P. Sharma (Summertown Publishing).

Conclusion

Many of the techniques for teaching groups can also be used in the one-to-one classroom; it is simply a question of tailoring these techniques to the student's needs, interests and wants. Preparing classes for individual students can be quicker and easier than for groups, because the student often provides the input for the lesson. In addition to using our students as a resource, we should help them build their repertoire of tools for self-study.

Chapter 6

Giving Feedback, Error Correction And Recycling Activities

One-to-one lessons allow you to address the student's specific linguistic difficulties, and to give very direct and honest feedback without worrying that the student will 'lose face' in front of other group members. In this chapter we will discuss the best ways of giving feedback, correcting errors and recycling language learned in a one-to-one context.

Providing feedback should be one of the most important components of the course, and you need to factor in sufficient time when doing your lesson planning. When giving feedback, we give comments about the overall success of the student's performance in a particular task. With error correction, we look at the linguistic performance in detail. Mistakes and errors are used by teachers interchangeably, but in fact we can differentiate between them:

'*Slips* can quickly be detected and self-corrected by their author unaided.
Mistakes can only be corrected by the person who makes them if their deviance is pointed out to him or her.
Errors cannot be self-corrected until further relevant... input… has been provided'.

(James, C: 1998: p.83.)

Errors can be classified into different areas:

- phonological errors;
- lexical errors;
- grammar errors;
- discourse errors;
- pragmatic errors;
- receptive errors (misunderstanding or misinterpretation of a speaker's meaning).

The teacher's approach to feedback

Even confident students can become easily disheartened by critical comments, so you need to take a very sensitive approach. Praise the student's work first, then give any negative feedback in a constructive way, and finally finish by praising again – this is what the Americans call the 'hamburger approach' (i.e. sandwiching the negative comments between the positive).

This basic approach is valid for all students. After that, how you handle feedback and correction will be influenced by the student's attitude to errors: some students are not interested in accuracy whilst others want *everything* corrected. In both cases you need to give the student a modified version of what he or she wants.

Course objectives

The student's course objectives affect your handling of mistakes and errors. If he or she is studying for an exam, then the emphasis will be on accuracy. With executive students, the focus is usually on the student's overall communicative effectiveness, unless lack of accuracy affects the communicative performance. For example:

Fluency practice

Raina will talk about different topics in order to improve her fluency. Feedback will focus on:

- pronunciation;
- stress, rhythm and intonation.

In Raina's case the overall target is to improve fluency, so you will pay much less attention to accuracy. The linguistic focus for the feedback is the phonological aspects of fluency.

Speaking

Axel wants to discuss different subjects in order to improve his overall accuracy. The topics will be simple to allow Axel to focus on his use of language. The feedback will pay particular attention to:

- sentence construction;
- translations from German.

Now let us take a Japanese student who tends to translate from his mother tongue, speaking a form of 'Japanese-English'. Feedback can be focused on helping the student to understand the differences between the way a native speaker constructs sentences compared to a Japanese speaker. (For example, the student says

His absent days from work are many, while a native speaker would say *He is often absent from work*).

Discussion

Yoshi will prepare short talks on different topics such as:

- football;
- sport in general;
- travelling.

Feedback will focus specifically on any use of 'Japanese-English'. The objective is to raise Yoshi's awareness of the differences between 'Japanese-English' and 'English-English'.

The task itself

The type and amount of error correction you give often depends on the focus of the practice activity which has taken place.

Sara

Sara is afraid to speak. You tell her that after the next speaking activity you will not give her feedback at all: the objective of the task is to encourage her to speak on a specific topic. The only feedback she will get is your facial expressions and typical 'listener feedback' such as *I see* and *Really*?

Javier

Javier is extremely inaccurate. Because of the volume and diversity of mistakes, the teacher has decided to target different kinds of mistakes on different days. For some activities the feedback will concentrate on a specific grammatical difficulty (e.g. comparatives and superlatives) and ignore everything else. At other times the focus for error correction will be another linguistic difficulty (e.g. Javier's habit of using nouns as verbs).

Giving feedback on the student's communicative performance

Before giving feedback on any activity, first ask the student to carry out some self-assessment. Did the student enjoy the activity? How difficult did the student find it to express himself/herself? What did the student think about his or her performance? Did he or she think it was a useful exercise?

Then you need to evaluate the students' overall communicative effectiveness. For example:

- Could you understand the student?
- Did he or she achieve the aims of the task?

In the classroom we sometimes react as humans first and as teachers second, which means that (in a discussion for example) we can find ourselves overlooking errors and mistakes if we are impressed by the quality of the student's ideas. In many circumstances outside the classroom, the quality of the student's ideas will be more important than his or her linguistic performance, so we should praise students for their ideas first of all.

Example

Imagine that your student has just enacted a work-related telephone call with you.

First of all, praise the positive elements of the telephone call from a business perspective:

- *You achieved your objective* (e.g. to make a complaint and request action)
- *You stated the objective of your phone call very clearly at the beginning.*
- *You spoke very clearly.*
- *You listened very carefully.*
- *You summarised all the key information.*
- *You didn't panic when you couldn't understand me.*
- *You structured what you wanted to say – which meant it was easier for me to follow your points.*

Then talk about any negative aspects of the student's performance:

- *You spoke very quickly sometimes.*
- *You sounded quite impatient when I said I couldn't give you a definite answer over the phone. Were you feeling impatient? You sounded as if you were!*
- *You used very informal, colloquial language. It wasn't appropriate for this call, which was quite formal.*

Once you have evaluated the student's business performance, you can then look at the linguistic elements – although it may not always be easy to separate the two. This is the age-old dilemma with business English: the language needed for performing a business skill, and the business skill itself, cannot always be clearly separated.

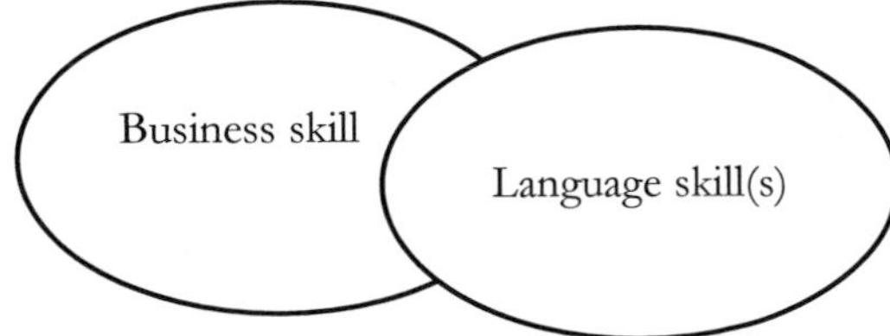

Behavioural aspects may also play a part. For example:

The student didn't listen:

Was that because she is not a good listener in her own language or because she was preparing what to say next?

The student sounded rude:

Was he intending to be rude or was there a socio-pragmatic failure? (i.e. a cultural difference concerning what is appropriate social behaviour)

The student did not speak concisely:

Is this because she is not concise in her own language or because she has difficulties with the language system?

Once you have given any negative feedback, make sure you remind the student of the positive aspects of his or her performance.

Reformulation

The term *reformulation* is used here to describe a technique whereby the teacher looks at what the student actually said or wrote and then reformulates the language into idiomatic English (i.e. something a native speaker would say). Reformulation goes beyond merely correcting: it involves changing the whole way the sentence is constructed.

For example:

Original: *We have no contact with the customer in the location of our company. We have a contact with the customer in the location of his or her company.*

Correction: *We have no contact with the customer on our premises. We have a contact with the customer on his or her premises.*

Reformulation: *We go to the customer. They don't come to us.*

Reformulation is useful for the following reasons:

- some language which students produce is impossible to correct; we have to change everything in order to achieve comprehensibility.
- if we simply correct the sentence, in some instances we may achieve something very stilted.
- the student is exposed to new language forms.
- it increases the student's overall awareness of how native speakers construct their sentences.

Reformulating individual sentences

The way of increase capital - I can't agree the way by public. I can only agree the way by private.
becomes:
I don't agree with floating the company. I think the company should remain private.

We are a safety company.
becomes:
Safety is our main priority. (We are a company which takes safety very seriously.)

You can stick to your clothes.
becomes:
You can keep your clothes on (when you go to bed).

...because of social contacts which expand... because of social contacts which are distant...
becomes:
...because people will have less social contact (with each other).

This is an evaluating problem.
becomes:
We have to evaluate this problem.

The meaning of his speech is quite clear for the fundamental ideas.
becomes:
I understand his main ideas.(I understand what he wants to say).

Reformulating chunks of language

In the following example, the student lacked the vocabulary he needed to talk about his country's economy.

Original version

In my opinion, this impact is strictly related to the fact in this situation there was no possibility of economical parameters, a constant increase in terms of products and consumption and we had some different fluctuations in all these parameters and the result of this was a sort of confusion in the conomy and you know that the investors want a situation that is under control.

The teacher and student changed this to:

> *Inflation is low, our exports are doing well, the balance of trade is good, but these figures don't necesarily mean a healthy economy and, as you know, investors want a stable situation.*

In the following example, Martin was a very fluent, confident speaker working in the UK, who classified himself as an advanced learner of English. He decided to take a group language course after he realised his colleagues had difficulties understanding him. His course also included four one-hour individual tutorials with one of his group teachers. In the group class he was resistant to the teachers' comments, but the one-to-one teacher had more opportunity to give him personalised feedback.

Martin's original version

> *So what does it mean to me? The meaning of life means the whole life starts with the birth and ends with the death – so – in life it's not all fine. You have, even with the birth there's some bad things with it and some with the death, sure, something bad too. So the meaning of life for me gives me, well, a mix of feelings between bad feelings and good feelings. In the childhood you have more good feeling, you have to have good feelings to went through your life in a better way. So when you have a luckier childhood, my belief your life after, after your adult 16-18, I think it's easier to live than if you have a childhood more or less – I take the word bad – and you have to think a lot about these things, these bad influences you get as a child. So I think when you have now this life from 18 till 75, I think it's easier to live this life, this part of the life than without a nice childhood.*

Teacher's reformulation

> *Your childhood has a profound influence on your later life. If you have a happy childhood, generally this will help you to be a happy adult. Of course, we can all experience unpleasant events in our life, but if we have had a good childhood, this will help us to manage the bad things in life.*

During the class, the teacher did not understand the point Martin wanted to make, so after the lesson she wrote a transcript of the recording she had made. Martin was not aware of why he was difficult to understand, or of the full extent of his language difficulties, until he saw the transcript. After this, he became more ready to accept the recommendations of his group teachers and responded well to the activities in his individual classes targeted at improving his accuracy.

Different methods of giving feedback

Oral correction

This is useful when the teacher wants to intervene quickly and supply the student with the correct word or structure. It can also be used for persistent mistakes. However, if the error is 'fossilised', the student may not respond, so if it is not impeding communication or irritating the listener, you may have to give up. It is best not to correct the student on the spot if it will interfere with his or her train of thought.

You can use other techniques for drawing the student's attention to slips, such as gestures or facial expressions (e.g. look puzzled) rather than correcting orally.

Correcting persistent mistakes

- Hold up a card every time the student makes a persistent mistake (e.g. *I think...* for a student who persistently says *My meaning is…*)
- Write crosses on the board to indicate every time the student makes the mistake. The number of crosses are counted at the end of each lesson.

Audio-recording the student

This is essential in any situation where you have to concentrate on the content of what the student is saying, such as complex role-plays or discussions. It is difficult to keep large chunks of language in your head and you may have forgotten what the student said before you have a chance to write it down. As the activity is taking place, take a note on the cassette dial of any kind of difficulty the student is experiencing, and listen to that part of the cassette at the end of the activity, giving the student time to self-correct. Using the cassette recorder allows you afterwards to write down word for word what the student says, which is very useful for reformulation. It also allows you to illustrate any phonological difficulties that the student has.

Video-recording the student

You can video-record your student performing any output activity (although this may be difficult in a small classroom). It is particularly useful to video-record the student making a presentation or prepared talk. If the recording is short, you can look at all of it afterwards with the student; otherwise you can use highlights.

Feedback sheets

Feedback sheets give the student a written record of what he or she said, together with the changes and improvements which the teacher and student make when going through the sheets together. They are an excellent method of expanding the student's linguistic knowledge and provide a resource to be exploited after the course has finished.

Together with the student, you can look at the mistakes and errors chronologically. Alternatively, you can work through them according to:

- gravity (i.e. the ones you think are the most serious);
- type (e.g. if the student made three mistakes of the same type, you can group them all together);
- the ones which created difficulties in the communication;
- the most 'interesting' ones;
- the ones which illustrate something that the student has previously learned.

Normally it is best to let the student identify the mistakes and make the corrections as far as possible. However, sometimes time is at a premium. If this is the case, write the corrections or comments next to the transcript of what the student said on the feedback sheets. Ask your student to look at the sheet(s) in his or her free time, and then at the next class you can go over them to see if the student has any questions.

Example feedback sheets

Below is an example of a 'blank' feedback sheet.

Name: Silke **Date: 13th June** **Activity: Fluency**	
Mis-pronunciations 1. 2. 3. 4. 5.	New vocabulary: 1. 2. 3. 4. 5.
You said:	You should have said:

In the following feedback sheet, a Swiss student gave a presentation to show how hydro-power is generated. This student was very fluent and confident, with excellent presentation skills, but very inaccurate.

Name: Beat	**Date: 29th April** **Activity: Presentation**
Mis-pronunciations 1. Valley 2. Cubic metre 3. Spiral 4. Multiply 5. Fluctuate	New vocabulary: 1. To drain 2. To build UP a relationship 3. A bird's eye view 4. To build a power plant
You said: ■ I will inform you according to your huge demands to know hydropower works... ■ Contacts here for the first time of the blades with the water ■ The costs go up and the state of the art changes… ■ Without to get… ■ You have so many barriers.. ■ That gives you an idea how long does it take.	You should have said: ■ [*Demand* = request] ■ You asked me to explain how hydropower works… ■ You wanted to know how hydropower works… ■ You were very keen to know how hydropower works… ■ The blades make contact with the water here for the first time ■ …the technology changes… ■ Without getting… ■ 'Barrier' is OK, but 'obstacles' or 'hurdles' would be better words in this context ■ …how long it takes (This is NOT a question)

The following shows a typed feedback sheet with the various errors, mistakes and teacher's comments arranged in an orderly fashion (shown in italics).

Feedback sheet after a meeting role-play

Good language use

It's in our interest to save the Japanese customer… This critical situation…
I come to the conclusion… We have to go into details…

Pronunciation (syllable stress)

Per- so –nnel Re –dun- dancy

Intonation

I want to give you another option you can think about it before the next meeting.
Teacher's comment:
You need to show the end of one sentence and the beginning of another sentence very clearly;
The voice drops *at the end of a sentence and starts* high *at the beginning of a new sentence, e.g.: 'I want to give you another option – you can think about it before the next meeting'.*

Vocabulary

We have to evaluate these special options to get over the overdraft.
… for paying back the overdraft.
The first proposal is to cut off the costs.
…is to cut costs.
(To cut off the gas, electricity, telephone, relations, money supply)
Maybe we can mix up options 2 and 3.
Maybe we can combine options 2 and 3.
(A mix-up = *a confused situation;* to mix up = *to confuse)*
If the Japanese customer breaks down…
If the Japanese customer goes bankrupt…
It was just another puzzle piece.
It was just one other option.
We should give some pressure to the customer…
…PUT some pressure ON…

Register

Thank you for your attention.
Thank you for your ideas/ co-operation. (Thank you for coming.)
('Thank you for your attention' is very formal. It also makes more sense to use it at the end of a formal presentation when you need the audience's attention rather than in a meeting when you need the participants' ideas and opinions.)
Yeah but…
I understand what you're saying, but… I see your point, but…
('Yeah, but…' is OK in an informal situation, but not so suitable for a formal meeting.)

Students recognise the usefulness of these feedback sheets and most are happy to go through them, making notes and checking vocabulary in the dictionary. You can suggest different ways in which they can be exploited:

- Transfer the language pointers on to their home computers.
- Create language summaries.
- Create flashcards.
- Stick pieces of paper with key language onto walls and cupboards at home.
- Allocate five minutes a day for reading their language summaries.

Recycling feedback sheets

These activities can be as simple as the teacher repeating what the student said in the previous lesson (as written down in the error sheet) and asking him or her to correct it:

Teacher: *You said 'Products which are quite more successful...'*
Student: *'...much more successful.'*
Teacher: *Good. 'The situation is not satisfying.'*
Student: *'The situation is not... satisfied?'*
Teacher: *What about beginning the sentence with 'I'm...'?*
Student: *'I'm not satisfied with the situation.'*

Writing recycling exercises on the computer can be time-consuming although the student will be impressed and find them very helpful. In fact, it is quite sufficient for the teacher to allocate fifteen minutes before the start of the class, take some paper and prepare the recycling activities by hand. After a while, you can do it spontaneously in class without preparation.

Recycling activities – Master Template

Name: **Date:**

Exercise 1 – Idiomatic language

Change the following so that they sound more idiomatic (i.e. more English sounding):

My fear is very high.
Who is responsible for the control of the achieving of these objectives?
(and so on...)

Exercise 2 – Grammar

Correct the grammatical mistakes in the following:

It's not quite expensive.
Are the farmers you mentioned possible to deliver to all 30 supermarkets?
(and so on...)

continued...

...continued

Exercise 3 – Vocabulary

Change the words in italics:

We can get a *credit* from a bank.

It depends on the *spirit* of the person.

(and so on...)

Exercise 4 – Prepositions

Complete the blanks with the correct preposition:

They don't pay attention _______ foreign news.

It's _____ our interests to do it.

(and so on...)

Exercise 5 – Opposites

Find approximate opposites for the following:

Our computer system is *up-to-date.*

He's very *thin.* (Don't use the word *'fat'.)*

(and so on...)

Exercise 6 – Synonyms

Find two synonyms for each of the following words:

Big a)_____________________ b) _________________________

Approximately a)_____________________ b) _________________________

(and so on...)

Exercise 7 – Rewriting

Rewrite the following sentences using a verb construction:

There was a slight increase in sales. *Sales* ________________.

There was a substantial fall in demand. *Demand* ________________.

There was a steady growth in turnover. *Turnover*________________.

(and so on...)

Exercise 8 – 'Odd man out'

Which of the following can you NOT say?:

I do it quite often.

I like him quite a lot.

There is quite a little money left.

There were quite many people at the party.

(and so on...)

continued.../

...Continued.

Exercise 9 – Vocabulary

What do the following words and expressions mean?:

hindsight – He's very mean – I'm broke – complacent – a high flier

(and so on...)

Exercise 10 – Definitions

What are the meanings of the following words? How do we use them?

Moral v. Morale

Final v. Finalise

Well-educated v. Highly-skilled

(and so on...)

Exercise 11 – Word Partnerships

Find verbs which partner the following nouns:

To ________________ a comment

To ________________ a question

(and so on...)

Find nouns which partner the following verbs:

To carry out ________________

To provide ________________

To fulfil ________________

(and so on...)

Exercise 12 – Pronunciation

How do you say the following words?:

promise	weight	moral	morale	to analyse
an analysis	strength	a subsidy	half	legible

(and so on...)

Conclusion

Make sure you are always positive when handling feedback and error correction. Constantly remind your students of what they can do well; make them aware of the progress they are making. If the student lacks confidence, be very judicious with your error correction.

Chapter 7

Teaching Business English

Business English is not some separate entity from general English. Executive students and other individuals who want to study business English all need to speak, listen, read and write in English to a greater or lesser extent, use grammar, and pronounce words correctly, just as any other student of English. The language skills for business English are the same as for general English; it is simply that the contexts for using the language are different. In this chapter we will discuss the teaching of business English in further detail.

When teaching business English, we distinguish between students who already are in work and those who have not yet started their careers (the latter are known as *pre-experience students*). It is much more common for students already in jobs to take one-to-one lessons as they generally have specific needs and are often in a hurry.

Occasionally teachers think that there is a point before which a student should not attempt to learn business English (e.g. elementary level). In practice, an individual can begin learning the English needed for his or her job from day one. However, unless they only operate within an extremely narrow field, they will still need to learn the vocabulary connected with everyday life.

	Pre-experience students	Students in work
Work experience	No	Yes
Needs	General needs	Usually have very specific needs connected with their work
Knowledge of business concepts	Depends on age	Yes
Understanding of business skills (e.g. meetings)	Usually not – depends on age	Yes
Business skills training courses	Usually not	Sometimes
Communication skills training courses	Usually not	Sometimes
Motivation for learning	Usually want English to improve their prospects in the job market	Usually have very specific reasons connected with their current or new jobs
Objectives for the course	Usually general objectives	Specific objectives
Expectations	Can range from high to low	Can be extremely high due to time pressures
The four skills (reading, writing, speaking, listening)	May want to focus more on written English than students already in jobs	Emphasis on speaking and listening
Age	Young	Usually 25+
Time pressure	Usually not	Yes. Many feel under pressure to make progress quickly
Working to objectives	Not used to working to objectives	Used to working to objectives
Autonomy in the classroom	Have few problems with the teacher being in the 'driving seat'	Some students are used to being in control and have difficulty in relinquishing it to a teacher

Business skills

A business English course can include all the language elements such as listening, speaking, pronunciation and grammar, together with various business skills. These refer to what students actually do in their work, and include:

- presentations
- telephoning
- meetings and discussions
- negotiations
- socialising
- writing (e.g. emails, letters, reports, contracts, manuals)
- reading (e.g. business pages of newspapers; reports; manuals; contracts)
- interviews (e.g. job/appraisal/grievance)
- other (depending on the student's job)

It is unlikely that pre-experience students are familiar with these skills even in their *own* language, so you need to devote time to exposing them to the skills and sub-skills involved, not just the language associated with them. Students in jobs are normally experienced in the various business skills, although you should not assume that the student is necessarily good at them in his or her own language. You need to make sure you have a good basic understanding of the business skills yourself, otherwise it will be difficult for you to teach your students with confidence.

If you need to improve your understanding of business skills, there are plenty of books on the market which briefly and simply cover all these topics as well as many other useful business concepts such as team-building, project management and leadership. *The Sunday Times*, the Institute of Management and the Institute of Personnel Management all offer these easy-to-read guides. There are also books aimed at the EFL market which cover the type of language needed for meetings, presentations, negotiations and so on. For example:

- *Business Skills Series* (Laws, A., Summertown Publishing)
- *Down to Business Minimaxes* (Dignen, B., York Associates)
- *Business Builder Modules 1-9* (Emmerson, P., Macmillan ELT)
- *Double Dealing* (Schofield, J., Summertown Publishing, due 2004)

Business concepts

A *business skill* refers to what the student actually uses language for in the work place. A *business concept* is the idea that the business-related words describe; for example, *a market economy*, the *stock exchange*. How much a pre-experience student knows about business concepts will depend on his or her age; there is a big difference between a seventeen-year-old and a twenty-three-year-old. It is unlikely that pre-experience students will be familiar with all, or even many, of the business concepts that are implicit in the language you teach, so you may need to spend a significant amount of time teaching the concepts as well as the language.

Vocabulary

Business vocabulary is often seen as an integral part of business English. For some pre-experience students, business vocabulary represents what they want to learn on a business English course. Students in jobs, however, normally know the specific language needed for their work interests; even elementary students who do not have the grammar to string sentences together may know the words for their job-related vocabulary in English.

What is business vocabulary? One way to look at it is as a continuum where the words and phrases become progressively more and more specialised, as shown in the example below.

JOB-SPECIFIC VOCABULARY ➔		➔	GENERAL VOCABULARY	
Job-specific	Industry-specific	General business	General with business applications	General
e.g. a metalworker	*e.g. papermaking*			
a bolt guide	a pulp mill	turnover	a decision	a flat
spring	a continuous grinder	an invoice	a deadline	narrow
a feeler gauge	a waste water pump	a subsidiary	to work out	to persuade
halves of a screw die		a managing director	to over-spend	
		a sub-contractor		
		to invest in		
		to de-regulate		
		to out-sell		

Life has become much easier for the one-to-one teacher as there are now many more books for specialist vocabulary areas, covering subjects such as computing, technical English, tourism, law, marketing, medicine, military English, banking and finance, telecommunications, and Human Resource Management. And, as we have seen earlier, we can use the Internet to research topic areas which do not have EFL books dedicated to them, such as logistics management and spectacle design.

Effective communication

Part of the role of the business English teacher is to give feedback to the student on his or her overall communicative effectiveness. This is not solely language-related: if the student is a good communicator in his or her mother tongue, they will be able to transfer these skills to English. Communicating effectively includes:

- speaking clearly, at an appropriate speed and volume;
- checking, clarifying and summarising frequently;
- listening carefully;
- using objective language (e.g. *I think this proposal has some disadvantages* instead of *This proposal is no good*);
- structuring your arguments (e.g. *I'd like to make two points. Firstly, I don't think… Why not? Well, mainly because..., OK, that's all for my first point. My second point is…*);
- using clear, short, simple sentences to convey meaning (KISS principle – see below);
- using language which is appropriate for the situation (e.g. informal language for informal situations);
- preparing difficult topics in advance'
- giving feedback to the speaker to show they are listening (e.g. *Mmm…*; *I see*; *That's interesting*);
- not dominating the conversation.

The KISS principle (Keep It Short and Simple)

Most business English trainers are familiar with the KISS principle, and it is a very handy acronym to convey to our students the idea that they need to avoid over-long, complicated sentences.

However, students can be confused when you reformulate something they say and the end result is longer than their original utterance. If this occurs, you need to explain that the KISS principle is an over-simplification, and is just a way of putting complex linguistic notions into an accessible form for the student.

For example:

Student's original version

I will use this approved discussed data in my secondary analysis.

Reformulated version

I would like to discuss this data with you and later I will use it in my secondary analysis.

Cultural aspects

It is part of the Anglo-Saxon communication style to want to present information in a simple, clear, systematic way. So we could ask ourselves: are we imposing our way of communication on our students? Possibly, but students in multi-cultural groups appreciate it when the speaker follows these precepts, and they are ready to give negative feedback to the speaker for not doing so.

Multi-lingual group classes provide opportunities for students to learn about other cultures and communication styles. However, individual students (particularly executive students) sometimes ask to look at culture and cultural differences. There are some books on the market specifically targeting these areas, which can be used in class, for example:

- *Culture Pack : Inter-cultural Communication Resource for Trainers* (Utley, D., York Associates)
- *Intercultural Business Communication* (Gibson, R., OUP)

When you give feedback to the student on his or her overall performance in a speaking or business skills activity, you can highlight any areas which you think illustrate a cultural difference between the student's culture and native English-speaking cultures.

Using the student as a resource

Executive students provide ideal resource material. You can, for example, base telephone role-plays on the calls your student needs to make for work; enact meetings and negotiations as they actually occur in the student's job; practise the presentation that the student is going to make the following month; role-play the job interviews he or she is going to carry out in Malaysia; and have the student write emails based on the ones he or she sent in English the previous week. But there's one problem with all of this. Some students adore having their job and workplace as the basis for all business skills activities and discussions. Others are bored by it and enjoy looking at other business areas. You must always have up your sleeve a repertoire of good quality meeting-related, negotiation-related, telephoning and writing tasks, as well as socialising role-plays, in case the student does not want to use his or her work situation as the basis. Business English course books and books specifically covering business skills can be an excellent source of role-plays, although it is much harder to find challenging material for advanced levels.

One useful idea is to keep a 'bank' of all the situations you practise in class with your one-to-one students, based on their work contexts. Then you can transform these into role-plays that you can use with subsequent students who do not want to use their own work context for practice activities. You will find some examples of these later in this chapter.

How to teach business skills: an overview

Minimal input:

keep input to a minimum.

Learning by doing:

give the student maximum opportunity to learn through doing (i.e. in the output stage of the lesson, such as role-play activities). This also allows you to find out where his or her strengths and weaknesses lie.

Feedback:

give lots of constructive feedback, looking at the communicative performance first and the linguistic performance second.

Work diagnostically:

if you think the student can cope, use the *Test-Teach* method (i.e. getting the student to perform a task, evaluating his or her performance and then deciding if any remedial work is needed) instead of presenting the language first and then getting them to practise it.

Elicit language from student:

with a higher level student, elicit the target language from the student instead of presenting it.

(NB: for a reminder of the difference between role-play and enactment, see 'Definition of Terms' on page 2.

Presenting information

This can cover all types of presentations, but it can be far more wide-ranging and also include *giving explanations* – something which is required in many contexts, (e.g. explaining why staff turnover increased last year; explaining on the phone to your manager why you have not written the report by the requested deadline; explaining why you are late…).

The elements of a good presentation

Preparation:

Know your audience;
Develop clear objectives.

Organisation:

Create a clear structure;
Develop visual aids.

Delivery:

Use of notes;
Eye contact;
Body language.

Speed of delivery:

Use of pausing;
Stress, rhythm and intonation.

KISS (Keep it short and simple) **principle**

Use of restatement;
Use of clear language for showing the organisation of the information;
Define unfamiliar terms.

Personalisation

Use examples/analogies/stories.

The following is a classic structure of a presentation.

Greetings:	Greet the audience and introduce yourself.
Introduction:	1. Give the objective(s) for your presentation.
	2. Outline the points you plan to cover.
	3. Mention your timing and distribute handouts (if applicable).
	4. Propose a procedure for questions.
Main body:	Communicate your message.
Summary:	Summarise and briefly restate main points.
Closing:	Thank the audience for listening; invite (further) questions.

Most EFL books which cover presentations include some or all of the following elements:

- Opening the presentation.
- Giving the introduction.
- Changing topic.
- Referring to visuals.
- The language of trends.
- Summarising and concluding.
- Work on phonological elements such as stress, rhythm and intonation.

Students usually request presentations because a) they regularly present information in their job, or b) they are preparing for a specific presentation in the near future. If the student has previous presentations on his or her laptop, you can work diagnostically with those, as well as preparing any that he or she may have to make in the immediate future. The student can make mini-presentations (based, for example, on charts or graphs from newspapers or magazines), present newspaper articles or explain an aspect of his or her job. Higher-level students can prepare their presentation by themselves in their free time, although it is always a good idea to keep a careful eye on their preparation so you can spot any potential problem areas before the student delivers the finished product – thereby minimising negative feedback. With lower-level students, you can guide them while they prepare their presentations.

Miroslaw

As Miroslaw was a confident upper-intermediate student, on the first day of the course the teacher asked him to give a diagnostic presentation on a very familiar subject in order to find out where his strengths and weaknesses lay. The teacher gave him time to prepare in class. Miroslaw worked as financial director for the Polish subsidiary of a German company, and he decided to use his annual presentation to the parent company where he explained his budget for the following year and justified his figures. The teacher played the role of the German financial director who asked as many difficult questions as possible in order to put Miroslaw under pressure.

Klaus

Klaus worked for a top American management consultant firm, specialising in the automotive industry. He was preparing to go to the Far East, where he would be based for the next few years. Klaus had lived in the United States and was extremely fluent, with a terrific vocabulary and range of idioms. However, he spoke much too fast, made many grammatical slips and very often misused the vocabulary he knew; the focus of his course was therefore to improve these areas. Klaus used presentations that he had previously made to car manufacturers for practice in class, and the feedback focused on improving his accuracy.

With students in jobs, you will usually be working with situations related to these jobs. However, with pre-experience students who do not have specific topics for their presentations, there are many fun alternatives:

- *Presenting a narrative*: e.g. the student can recount a short story or a novel that he or she has read; non-fiction can also be used.
- *Persuasive presentations – presenting a product or activity:* e.g. ask the student to think of

one product which he or she finds particularly useful (such as an electric toothbrush) and then do a 'sales' presentation where they extol its features and virtues. It need not be a product – it could also be an activity (e.g. taking Aikido classes). Or you could ask them to make a presentation on a surprising topic such as 'Why chocolate is good for you' or 'Why saving money is a waste of time'.

- *Presenting a process:* e.g. how to cook something; how to keep your brain in good working order in middle age.
- *Presenting a place*: e.g. the student chooses a place that he or she would (or wouldn't) like to visit, or a place he or she has visited and been particularly impressed by.
- *Presenting a person*: e.g. a famous person the student would like to meet, and why.

Ideally, you will video- or audio-record any presentations the student makes and go through highlights with him or her.

Meetings

There is an infinite number of types of meetings, ranging from short informal discussions between two people to formal affairs with a chairperson and many participants. This means that the term *meetings* encompasses all kinds of activities, from managing conflict to rubber-stamping decisions. When teaching meeting skills to groups, you give them meeting-related role-plays with scenarios which may have nothing to do with the actual meetings they attend, but which you hope will appeal to them and which you feel will generate the kind of language they will need in a meetings context. With one-to-one students, however, you can work with the student's exact meetings situation, allowing him or her to use the language they need in real life.

Elements of a successful meeting

Performing successfully in a meeting requires the participants to use the elements of effective presentations that we looked at on page 109. It also includes:

- good preparation;
- clear objectives;
- a clear agenda;
- an effective chairperson;
- minimal interrupting.

The student should have equal opportunity to 'learn through doing' and to learn from the feedback after the 'doing'. So a typical scenario could be:

- Language input (0-10%) ⇦⇦⇦⇦
- Setting up a role-play (10-15%) ⇧
- Doing role-plays (50%) ⇧
- Feedback (20-30%) and diagnostic work ⇨⇨⇨⇧

If the student is a low level, you need to pre-teach some basic language for structuring a meeting, such as opening and closing a meeting and changing topic. Simple language for making proposals, and asking for and giving clarification, is also very useful.

The details of the role-play can be based on the student's own situation, which he or she can then enact with you (in stages over a number of lessons if necessary – you do not need to have a full-length 'meeting' in one lesson). You play the other role(s) and take down notes for the feedback. The lower the level, the more time you will need for setting up and preparing the role-play. You also need to allow plenty of time for giving feedback, always remembering to look at the overall communication and business performance first, then the specific linguistic items.

Yves
Yves frequently faced conflict situations in his job in the mergers and acquisitions department of a large accountancy firm. Together with the teacher, he enacted several situations he had recently experienced which had involved conflict, such as having a meeting with a colleague who refused to co-operate with him.

Thomas
Thomas was a lawyer working in a large multi-national. He often had to chair meetings where the topic was the acquisition and disposal of subsidiaries. Together with the teacher, he practised the chairman's role: opening the meeting, stating the objectives and going through the agenda based on meetings he had in the last few months. The teacher then typed up these introductions so that he had a language summary to refer to when he was preparing for meetings in his own country.

Negotiations

A negotiation is a specific type of meeting, which means that all aspects of language used in meetings are also relevant for negotiations. Although there are cultural variations in the ways in which people from various nationalities tend to negotiate, the basic skills (e.g. beginning by setting out one's requirements, not putting one's best offer on the table straight away) are the same from country to country. You need to have a basic understanding of the various elements of negotiating in order to be able to work confidently with your student. Once you have that, you can learn the details from your students, many of whom will be skilled negotiators.

The stages of a negotiation

These may vary according to the type of negotiation, but below is a typical sequence.

The preparation stage:

The parties carefully prepare their positions.

The negotiation itself:

Stage 1: Relationship building.
Stage 2: Giving the background to the situation and establishing an agenda.
Stage 3: Exchanging information - stating your requirements; asking about the other party's requirements.
Stage 4: Exploring the various possibilities.
Stage 5: Making concrete proposals.
Stage 6: Bargaining.
Stage 7: Reaching agreement.

The 'win-win' approach is a very common approach in negotiations today. This moves away from the idea that one party wins at the expense of the other to a more co-operative approach whereby both parties benefit.

Negotiators need to decide their objectives in advance. *Minimum objectives* refers to the minimum that you are prepared to accept from the negotiation (e.g. £1000 for selling your car). Your *desirable objectives* represent more than the minimum, but less than you would ideally like. Your *ideal objectives* represent what you ideally wish to achieve from the negotiation (£1,800 for your car). Realistically speaking, it is almost inevitable that you will need to compromise on some of your objectives.

Generally speaking, it is best to avoid the language and behaviour below unless absolutely necessary.

Language	**Behaviour**
■ 'You must...' (*We must...* is OK) ■ 'You should...' ('*We should...*' is OK) ■ 'We want…' ■ 'That's impossible.' ■ 'We can't do that.' ■ 'You're wrong.' ■ 'No! No! We can't accept that.' ■ 'That's out of the question.' *(Of course, this language sounds much less confrontational if you say it with a friendly intonation.)*	■ Interrupting (unless to clarify) ■ Making threats ■ Using aggressive or subjective language; or using intonation which indicates impatience or irritation ■ Using confrontational body language

Below/on the following page are two examples of negotiating situations based on the student's jobs.

Example 1

The student was Hungarian and worked for the subsidiary of a large multi-national company. Every year he negotiated trading terms with one of his company's Czech clients, an international supermarket chain.
The international supermarket bought many products from the multi-national, but in this negotiation only margarine and tea were discussed. Points to be negotiated included payment terms, minimum quantities, promotional activities, delivery points and new product listings.

The student spent one lesson discussing with the teacher what had happened in the previous year's negotiation, and making sure that the teacher fully understood the situation. The teacher then typed up the main components for the negotiation, checked with the student that the details were correct, and then this was used for the basis of the negotiation in the next lesson, with the teacher playing the role of the supermarket.

Example 2

The student was a Human Resource Manager responsible for recruitment in a large bank. The bank used a large number of employment agencies for its recruitment needs. However, it wanted to find one large agency which would cover most of the bank's requirements. The teacher played the role of the

continued...

...Continued.

representative and the student helped her with all the details she needed to negotiate sensibly. Points for discussion were the agency's ability to cover the whole country, its ability to find specialists (e.g. IT specialists, accountants), the use of sub-contractors for any part of the work, administrative procedures, and the fees. Before the negotiation, the teacher typed up a summary of the kind of language the student would need for this specific situation and gave it to the student to prepare for homework.

Telephoning

Strategies for effective communication are even more important for telephoning, as there are no visual clues to help the person at the other end of the line. It is crucial to state the objective of the call very clearly, to summarise all new information, to give the speaker feedback that you are listening or that you have understood (e.g. 'I see', 'Mmm') and to structure what you say.

A typical call may include some or all of the following:

Opening the call
Asking for the person we are calling
Introducing ourselves
Telling the other person how long the call will take
Pleasant exchanges (if we know the person well)
Giving the objective of the call
Main body of the call
Changing topic
Clarifying, checking & summarising
Closing the call
Summarising the information exchanged
Clarifying any points which are not clear
Promising action
Saying when the action will be taken
Thanking the other person for (help)
Promising to call again
Saying goodbye

If the student is at a low level, you will need to input typical phrases for doing the above. With higher levels, you can check their use of 'telephone language' during the role-plays. As with all role-plays and enactments, you need to allow sufficient time in class to set the situation up before the student actually makes the call.

Stage 1 – Set the scene
Together with the student, decide the topic of the call, ideally based on a call the student made or received recently, or based on typical kinds of call which feature in the student's work life. (Alternatively, you can use role-plays from published materials.)

Stage 2 – Prepare
Give the student time to prepare the call. If appropriate, prepare the call with the student using the whiteboard or a piece of paper.

Stage 3 – The role-play
Depending on the context, the role-play can be done using mobile phones, internal phones or interphones (phones which work by being plugged into the electrical circuit). It is a good idea to record the call.

Stage 4 – Feedback

Oscar
Oscar had sent an email to another manager. The other manager disagreed with the comments and suggestions Oscar made and sent an email back. This email was very direct and the manager made his disagreement clear. The manager sent copies of his email to other people, thereby publicising his disagreement with Oscar. Oscar rang the manager to express his annoyance and to make sure the manager did not repeat this in the future.

Raina
Raina had been asked to go on an international training course for a new SAP release. However, she did not think she was the best person to go on the course, as the training would demand specific know-how on the current SAP operation, which she did not have. She rang the training manager to suggest that her assistant should take her place.

Socialising

Socialising is defined here as covering a wide range of social situations, such as dealing with a visitor, making small talk, inviting someone out, and complaining politely. In addition to all these situations, the student needs phrases to respond to what other people say or do (e.g. someone sneezes, falls over, looks worried, gives you good news). You can use the student's own work situation or, if that is not appropriate, there is a mass of published material with practice activities.

Example practice activities

1. The teacher creates a pack of cards with instructions written on them. The teacher follows the instruction on the card, e.g.: *You have a terrible headache. Ask if anyone has an aspirin.* The student has to make an appropriate response such as *Bad luck. I'm afraid I don't have any aspirin – but I'll ring my colleague – she may have some.*
2. *Vocabulary Games and Activities for Teachers* (Peter Watcyn Jones, Pearson Education/Longman) has mini-dialogues on pp.46-47 where the teacher reads out a statement or question (e.g. *Another drink, Paul?*) and the student has to choose the correct response (*No, not just now, thanks.*).
3. You can write your own short role-plays.

1. Role-card A
You are with a supplier. You are sure he or she will ask you to dinner tonight. You like all food except Indian and Chinese.

Role-card B
You are with a client. Invite him or her to dinner tonight. Suggest going to a very good Indian restaurant which is nearby. There is also a very nice Chinese restaurant near the office.

2. Role-card A
You have a client staying with you for a two-day meeting (Thursday and Friday). You know that after the meeting is finished your client is staying on for the weekend, and that his or her partner is coming along. Invite your visitor and his or her partner to dinner on Saturday evening. If that doesn't suit him or her, suggest taking them sightseeing on Saturday morning and having lunch together

Role-card B
You are visiting a supplier for a two-day meeting (Thursday and Friday). You are staying the weekend in your supplier's city to do some sightseeing. Your partner is joining you on Friday evening.

You are looking forward to having a relaxing weekend alone with your partner after a very busy week. You plan to do some shopping and a little sightseeing on Saturday. On Saturday evening you want to go for a romantic dinner. Your flight is at 1830 on Sunday evening.

3. Role-card A
You are having a meeting with a colleague from an overseas subsidiary. You have flown over to your colleague's country for the meeting. It is the first day of a two-day meeting.

It is getting late (1845) and you would like to finish the meeting now and go back to the hotel. Your hotel is ten minutes away. You have covered eight out of ten topics on the agenda.

Suggest discussing the other two points tomorrow. You can begin the meeting thirty or forty-five minutes earlier – at 0815, for example.

Role-card B
A colleague from your company's headquarters has flown over to your country for a meeting with you. It is the first day of a two-day meeting. It is getting late (1845). You have covered eight out of ten topics on the agenda. You think it will only take about thirty to forty-five minutes to discuss these two points.Suggest staying late tonight so that you can do so.

You would prefer to work late tonight than to start early tomorrow because you do not like getting up early. You do not want to start earlier than 0900. Your colleague is staying at a hotel ten minutes away from the office.Start the conversation by saying 'It is now 6.45…'.

Email and letter writing

Establish with the student that although emails can be similar to spoken English in tone, and often use much more informal language and vocabulary than a letter, *initial* contacts by email should be formal or semi-formal. It is very useful for the student to know a range of neutral phrases and expressions that can be used in different situations, both formal and informal (e.g. *I would be grateful if you could…*).

Find out when the student prefers to do the writing tasks – for homework or in class. You can construct the writing tasks by:

- using the student's own work situation;
- basing the emails on any telephone calls you may be working on with the student;
- creating short writing tasks.

Work diagnostically: give the student a task to complete, then gauge from the results what language you need to input (although it is helpful to give the student a summary of useful language to refer to as he or she writes).

Sample email writing tasks

1. You have just visited a client in Hungary. Write an email to summarise the main points you agreed on and to thank him or her for the wonderful hospitality you received.
2. You are the team leader. One member of your team is not working as hard as you think he or she should be. Write a short, polite but clear email asking him or her to contribute more to the team's activities.
   Below is an example of an email based on student's own work situation. The teacher typed up the original, giving a copy to the student and keeping one for her materials bank.

```
To:       Francesca; Paolo; Gustavo; Roger; Elisabeth; Antigoni
From:     Jean.Schmidt@supernet.com
Subject:  Monthly report
At our last meeting, we agreed that you would write the report of
your monthly activities before the 5th of every month. I explained
that I base a significant proportion of my monthly report on the
information I get from you - so your reports are vital for me. It
is now 7th June and I haven't received any of the reports - which
means I'll miss my deadline. I appreciate that you're all very
busy and I understand that it is difficult to find time to do
everything. However, the monthly report is a priority and you all
agreed that the 5th would give you adequate time to do your
preparation. Please ensure that you meet the deadline for July.

I expect the information by Thursday at the latest. If you can't
make that date, please call me. Thank you for your co-operation.
```

Report writing

A report can vary in length from half a page to a mini-tome. Some reports (such as a monthly sales report) have fixed structures. Normally the student will either have brought reports along for you to go through in class, or be able to give you the context in which he or she needs to write reports.

There is some published material for report-writing (e.g. *Business Builder* (Emmerson, P., Macmillan ELT), modules 4-6) but you may find the best way to do the language input is a) diagnostically (based on the material the student produces, b) through brainstorming and writing key phrases on the board which the student can use in the report-writing task he or she is about to complete.

Example of student's report

Department	January – June 2003	3 June – December 2002
Finance	4	1
Sales & Marketing	3	0
Production	3	1
Administration	3	4
	17	**6**

If your student needs to write reports, but cannot provide a work-related situation

Staff turnover June 2003

We have experienced an unusually high staff turnover since the beginning of the year.

All employees were interviewed in depth to find out the reasons for their resignations; however, we have been unable to detect a clear trend for the staff turnover. Staff gave many reasons for their decisions to leave the company. These include:

1. Partner relocating (2 employees)
2. Wish to reduce workload (2)
3. New job more conveniently located in relation to employee's home (2)
4. Family illness (1)
5. More money in new job (2)
6. Better prospects in new job (2)
7. Return to full-time study (1)
8. Need for a change (3)
9. Starting own business (1)
10. Early retirement (1)

We are particularly concerned by points 6 and 8. As yet, we are in an exploratory stage; we need to find out more before drawing any conclusions. We are currently working on this and will report back at the end of July.

Recruitment

It has proved more difficult to recruit staff this year. In fact, the high staff turnover may be a symptom of the increasing difference between supply and demand; job opportunities in this area have expanded noticeably in the last two years.

for you to use, you can invent a task. For example, you can take a simple case study from a meetings-based role-play book and, instead of using it as a basis for discussion, ask the student to write his or her recommendations. An example is given below.

> Your company would like to introduce more flexible working. It envisages a significant percentage of the workforce working from home part of the week. This would allow the company to move to smaller premises. Write a report outlining the advantages and disadvantages of working from home.
>
> Use the structure below. Invent any details necessary.
>
> - Results of staff survey regarding flexible working *(invent this)*
> - Technical aspects *(equipment needed at home; space needed; helpline for technical problems)*
> - Social aspects *(feeling isolated; needing to come to the office regularly);*
> - Financial aspects *(costs of equipping staff; savings on rent)*
> - Type of person suited to flexible working *(self-motivated; disciplined; good at time management)*
> - Conclusion

Writing your own role-plays

As we have seen, not all students want to base the practice situations on their own job contexts. This leaves the teacher having to find suitable role-plays from somewhere. Published materials are one source, but it is a good idea to build up a bank of your own role-plays based on the situations presented by your previous one-to-one students.

The following telephone role-play is based on a letter which a one-to-one student wrote in class with the teacher. The teacher took the situation and transformed it into a telephone role-play.

The supplier – Felco Fabrics

- You are a textile manufacturer based in *(decide country)* called *Felco Fabrics.*
  You supply *Turbo Clothing,* a manufacturer based in Manchester.
- You have been working with *Turbo Clothing* for the last two years. *Turbo Clothing* represents one percent of your sales. They place approximately 4 orders a year with you.
- Recently *Turbo Clothing* sent in a claim about some fabric you supplied three months ago. According to *Turbo Clothing* the jeans material you provided contained defects. The value of the order is £15,000.
- As far as you are concerned, it is now irrelevant whether the jeans material contained defects or not since *Turbo Clothing*'s claim has arrived too late. According to your contract, *Turbo Clothing* needs to make any claims against defects within eight weeks of receiving the goods.

 Call *Turbo Clothing* to tell them that you cannot accept their claim.

The manufacturer – *Turbo Clothing*

- You are a British clothing manufacturer based in Manchester. One of your regular suppliers is *Felco Fabrics* with whom you have been doing business for the last two years. You place orders approximately 4 times a year with *Felco.*
- You received a consignment of jeans fabric from *Felco* three months ago. When you came to use it you discovered that it had defects. Consequently, you have put in a claim against *Felco.* The value of the order is £15,000.
- You were late putting in the claim. This is because, unusually, you did not use the fabric immediately as you changed your manufacturing plans at the last minute and therefore did not need the material. However, when you came to use it, you discovered the defects. Once you noticed them, you immediately put in a claim.

 You will receive a phone call from *Felco Fabrics* regarding your claim.

Job Talk

Course programmes for executive students sometimes contain a section entitled *Job Talk*. This is a part of the lesson where the student explains different aspects of his or her job; the teacher provides any missing vocabulary and gives feedback on the other linguistic elements. For students who are interested in talking about what they do, this can provide hours of material for the lessons and greatly help the teacher to expand his or her knowledge of the business world.

Conclusion

Executive students are normally short of time and need to use their lessons in the most effective way possible. By giving your student plenty of opportunity to 'learn through doing' and by providing good-quality feedback, you can help your student to maximise the time spent in his or her one-to-one lessons. With pre-experience students you need to be prepared to be more than a simple language teacher, and to be able to explain the new concepts and skills in an accessible manner.

Chapter 8

Homestay Teaching

Homestay teaching, also known as home tuition, involves teaching a student in your own home. Many one-to-one courses are conducted n this manner. In this chapter, we will dicuss the pros and cons of homestay teaching and how to make it a positive experience for both student and teacher.

Although most homestay teaching is one-to-one, some courses have two, or even three, students. The course is usually dedicated to studying English, but there can also be non-EFL components. Teachers are normally TEFL initiated (i.e. a holder of a Certificate in TEFLA issued by RSA/Trinity or any other accepted equivalent validating authority). Other relevant professional qualifications (or relevant experience in the case of ESP) are acceptable for teaching young learners.

You can find an overview of what is required to be a homestay teacher in the Homestay Providers' Association (HPA) Code of Practice (www.h-p-a-org.uk). This is based on the criteria set out in the British Council Accreditation scheme. Homestay teachers are normally homeowners with good quality homes (i.e. comfortable with all the basic necessities), ideally near a means of transport. If not, the teacher needs to be prepared to offer lifts. The house should have a quiet room allocated to teaching. Executive students should get executive quality accommodation, which normally means their own en-suite bathroom. The most common reason for a teacher's house failing to meet the necessary standard is the general condition of the house (e.g. not decorated to a high enough standard, too small, dirty or disorganised). Very often the quality of the bathrooms leads to the prospective homestay teacher being turned down.

Students usually get full board (three meals a day) and always eat with the teacher and/or family. They get their own room where they can relax, study and sleep. Students will have access to most of the facilities in the home; the guidelines that a good homestay organisation will send to a student in advance will make it clear to him or her which facilities can be used.

The minimum length of stay is normally one week, with most students staying for one to four weeks. Students can choose a variety of programmes (e.g. from two hours a day to seven hours a day Monday to Friday), although a teacher can vary those hours and days in agreement with the student.

Organisations providing homestay tuition can be broadly categorised into three types:

- Home tuition organisations (including language schools for whom homestay is an add-on, as well as organisations dedicated solely to home tuition).
- Homestay accommodation agencies (which specialise in providing accommodation with private hosts).
- Independent host teachers.

Students can be offered varying standards of service. One organisation provides four different levels: prestige (including pre-course aperitif and four course dinner), executive, standard or young learners. They can also choose to do two-centre stays (e.g. spending two weeks in the countryside and then moving to London for two weeks).

Independent teachers have complete autonomy, but have to deal with the administrative work which would otherwise be taken care of by a homestay organisation, such as arranging visas and insurance, meeting the legal requirements for having juniors in their homes, dealing with complaints and claims for refunds, and arranging transfers to and from the airport.

Advantages of homestay for students

Full immersion experience

The student is surrounded by English, and the time outside the lessons is as valuable as the time spent in class, with organised social activities and excursions provided by the homestay teacher.

Effective way to learn

Homestay courses appeal to a wide range of students who are short of time, such as executives, exam students and anyone who wants to maximise his or her learning experience, both in the classroom and in a comfortable social environment.

Cost-effectiveness

Homestay courses are good value for money (e.g. they represent a significant saving for a company compared to the cost of accommodating an executive student in a hotel – although this is unlikely to be the only reason for choosing a homestay course).

Safe environment

Children who are too young to study in a language school can be safely be sent abroad to learn in a homestay environment. Homestay courses also appeal to timid, introverted students who are looking for a safe, secure environment.

Speaking only with native speakers

Some students do not want to be exposed to 'wrong' English, so actively avoid other students and seek immersion with only native speakers.

No travelling between host family and school

This is good for younger students, busy people such as executives, and students on a low budget.

Home environment

Some students do not like being in a school environment. The homestay house also provides a place for an executive student to set up a mini-office or business link using Internet access.

Disadvantages of homestay for students

Pedagogical

Homestay teachers do not have access to the same resources, pedagogical support, and training and development as teachers working in a school; their teaching skills may be less up-to-date and their use of materials less varied.

Isolation

Homestay students miss out on the socialising that takes place in a school environment.

Difficult to complain

The student may not want to offend his or her host and if the homestay teacher is not affiliated to a homestay organisation, there is no Director of Studies for the student to contact.

Teenagers and young children

Homestay is very attractive for parents wanting to send their children on courses. Students as young as eight can be sent to do homestay classes, although it is often unclear why children of such a young age are doing a language course; it can seem like an expensive form of child-minding. Normally, juniors are placed in families with children of similar ages.

However, in the busy summer period, the supply of families with eight-year-old children can run out, making it difficult to place juniors in families with children of the same age. This age group can suffer badly from homesickness (it is often not their choice to do a language course) so part of the homestay teacher's role is to cope with this.

The teacher may be relieved when the student goes to his or her bedroom, but the student may be sitting there alone and homesick. The teacher has to make a big effort not only to integrate the student into the family, but to provide opportunities to meet people outside the immediate family. Younger children are particularly labour-intensive (e.g. you can leave a sixteen-year-old in the High Street for half an hour, but not a twelve-year-old).

Advantages of homestay teaching for teachers

Flexibility

Homestay teaching is ideal for anybody who needs flexibility. It tends to be attractive to people such as the following:

- People raising young families;
- Retired people;
- People supplementing their incomes (e.g. actors; piano teachers; market researchers; part-time office workers);
- People who are studying;
- People who don't need the income, but who do it as a kind of hobby.

Job satisfaction

Homestay teaching is holistic in that you cover all aspects of the student's learning programme from start to finish, and continue teaching them outside the classroom hours. You get to know your students in great depth and your teaching has the potential to be more effective than in a school, because the emotional response the students have in a successful homestay situation makes the learning experience more memorable.

Variety

Because of the fluctuations in work, homestay teachers are less likely to limit themselves to one particular age group or speciality. Homestay teachers also have the opportunity to take the student out for all kinds of visits and excursions. They can also get involved in courses which offer more than just language tuition. (See *English Plus* courses on page 134).

Autonomy

Homestay teachers do not have a Director of Studies physically close by, checking their records of work, timekeeping, course programmes and course content – although sometimes that autonomy is more of a perception than a reality, as good homestay organisations have procedures for maintaining academic standards.

No travelling to work!

Disadvantages of homestay teaching

Isolation

You are isolated in terms of materials, resources and pedagogical support. You have to be very self-motivated and dedicated to trying out new ideas and materials, and it is easy to become set in your ways.

Materials

If you work independently, you need to provide all the resources needed for your classes, which can represent a large investment (although self-employed teachers can offset expenses against tax). Even if you work for a language school, getting materials to and from the school is logistically difficult unless you live nearby.

Training and development

You do not have the same opportunities for training and development as other teachers. Attending training courses means that you often miss out on work.

Lack of support network

There are no other teachers with whom to trade ideas, or to whom you can voice your grievances.

No escape from work

Homestay teaching is tremendously demanding work, as you are on duty twenty-four hours a day. You cannot become complacent, however easy-going your student is, and it can be extremely difficult if there is not a good rapport between you and the student. For many teachers the biggest problem is the non-teaching time. Some students are self-sufficient and independent, whilst others want constant attention and are unable to occupy themselves. The weekends can be the worst. What do you do with the student who arrives early on Sunday when it is pouring with rain? One advantage of executive students is that they usually come on Sunday evening and leave on Friday. They can also be more independent when they go out and are less reliant on the homestay teacher for their entertainment outside of class.

Pay

The homestay teacher provides classes, accommodation, food, comfort and social interaction; the pay does not reflect the reality of the amount of work you do.

Fluctuations in work:

you can be inundated in summer and have nothing in winter. Consequently, it is unwise to rely on homestay teaching as your sole source of income.

Encountering the unexpected

Homestay, more than any other type of teaching, exposes the teacher to the unexpected. Living 'cheek by jowl' with your students, you see all kinds of behaviour that would be hidden in other circumstances, such as eating disorders and alcoholism. Homestay courses can be a way for parents to get a difficult child or teenager – even ones with personality disorders – out of the way. Students may behave in a manner that you are not willing to accept in your own home (e.g. students treat your home as a hotel, coming home late; parents may declare that their child does not smoke or drink alcohol, but the child can arrive with other ideas).

Addressing problems

Work for a reputable organisation

A good homestay organisation will:

- have policies and procedures for all aspects of the homestay course, including clear guidance for you as a homestay teacher and guidelines for the student on what to expect;
- offer advice on pedagogical questions;
- offer you a few training days a year;
- observe you if practicable;
- offer you the chance to observe teachers teaching on their premises;
- give the student the opportunity to come into the school to meet the Director of Studies;
- show an interest in the student (e.g. phoning the student weekly to check that he or she is happy with all aspects of the course);
- support you if you have problems;
- organise social events for homestay teachers;
- give you the opportunity to meet, or put you in touch with, other homestay teachers employed by the organisation.

The British Council runs an accreditation scheme for organisations offering homestay programmes. Working for a British Council recognised organisation will assure the homestay teacher of certain pedagogical and administrative standards (e.g. arrangements for the induction and monitoring of new teachers; signed contracts or letters of agreement; prompt payment; an adequate range of resources available for students and teachers). This may result in a substantial amount of paperwork for the teacher, but the reasons for this are self-evident.

Some homestay teachers want to maintain their independence and deliberately keep the student at an arm's length from the Director of Studies. However, in this way, they deprive themselves and the students of a useful resource. Use your organisation: do not be tempted to isolate yourself by revelling in the freedom from administrative 'interference' that homestay teaching brings. A sympathetic Director of Studies often acts as a 'conduit of pain' – somebody you can turn to if your student is causing you grief – and a supplier of advice for managing difficult students or situations.

Resources

You can exploit the enormous amount of ELT and non-ELT material available on the Internet, which is often under-used by teachers in schools. You can use authentic materials such as newspapers, magazines and recordings of TV programmes. You also have added resources in the form of your house, friends and immediate environment, all of which you can make use of. All the time spent outside the classroom can be a source of material for use in the classroom (e.g students can recount their visits; summarise what they have understood from the news; do projects based on the local area).

Create banks of lessons

You need to systematically develop a portfolio of lessons and course materials which you can adapt to each student's individual circumstances.

Clarify expectations on the first day

Start the first day by finding out what the student expects from you and establishing what you expect from him or her. The student can make a list: *The teacher should...* and you can do the same. This should help you to establish ground rules of behaviour in your home and to find out how you can fulfil your student's expectations.

Time management

Experienced homestay teachers work out strategies for allowing themselves breaks during the week and ways to give themselves time to prepare lessons (such as preparing their classes while their students do self-study activities or review their notes).

- Remember – the student also needs time to himself/herself.
- Work out a timetable which gives you time to do the things you need to do during the day without letting the student feel abandoned.
- Discuss with the student how he or she will spend free time, so that there are no unfulfilled expectations on either side.
- Make a classroom/home 'contract' with the student. In the 'contract' you and the student define what will be covered in the classroom, in the time spent together outside the classroom and in the time spent individually.

One London-based homestay organisation pays for other people to take the student out three evenings a week; it is part of the package offered to the student, and the cost is included in the price of the course.

Income

It is best to work for several homestay organisations in order to secure a steady supply of work, or have a part-time job that you can fit around your students. Bear in mind that it is much more difficult to rely on homestay work for a steady income if you live outside a big town.

Involve family and friends

The ideal situation is when both husband and wife are involved in ELT. Then the husband can take over from the wife, and vice versa, giving both partners a break from the student from time to time. If the student is the same age as your children, they can involve the student in their activities (e.g. another person to play Monopoly with or to involve in the football team). If you see that your children are contributing to your student's successful stay and your employability as a homestay teacher, then you might think it worth discussing this with them, and maybe even passing on some of your earnings if they are particularly helpful.

You can also take students with whom you get on particularly well to any social events that you organise with your friends, such as going to the theatre or cinema or restaurant (although you need to check with your friends first!).

Broadband Internet access

It is a good idea to provide a computer with broadband Internet access for the student outside classroom time. This gives them the opportunity to write their emails and to search the Internet for any project or class work they have to prepare, and gets them 'out of your hair'. If you do not want the student to use your computer, let them know about any nearby Internet cafes.

External visits

There are an enormous range of visits and excursions that you can offer to your students: trips to the cinema, theatre, museums, historic buildings and theme parks; any kind of sporting activity; taking them along to any groups you attend (e.g. Women's Circle, yoga classes). Some students are very independent and are happy to visit different places by themselves. If you have children yourself, you can ask to have younger students in the school holidays when you need to entertain your children anyway. You can also get the students to research any visits they make – this is a way to keep them busy when you need time for yourself. Younger students can write up the details of their visits and take the text home to show their parents.

Complaints

Explain clearly to the student at the beginning of the course that he or she can contact the Director of Studies in the event that he or she is not happy with any aspect of the course. In reality, students sometimes complain *after* the course, often at the suggestion of a family member, when it is too late to do anything. It is a good idea to emphasise how important it is to solve problems as soon as they arise, rather than waiting until the student is back at home.

However, often it is not the students who complain about the teacher, but the teacher who is unhappy about the less than desirable behaviour of his or her guests (e.g. drunk/spoilt/naughty, even amorous, students). In a reputable homestay organisation, the students receive guidelines on how they should behave in their homestay family and what they can expect from that family.

'English plus…' courses

Some homestay organisations offer other activities as part of the English language learning package. These are courses where part of the time is spent on language learning while the other element is an activity in which the student has a particular interest. For example:

- English + scone-making
- English + flower-arranging
- English + shopping
- English + British customs
- English + gardening
- English + sightseeing
- English + antiques
- English + football, golf, tennis, etc.

The homestay organisation can invite teachers to propose different courses according to their personal interests. For example, if you live in London and enjoy going to the theatre, you can propose 'English + theatre' although you need to check if the student's interpretation of 'theatre' doesn't exclusively mean 'musicals', for example. These courses can be very attractive to the teacher, although the main criterion is to share the interest that you are offering as the 'plus' side of the course. In the best case scenario, it is the equivalent of doing something you enjoy and being paid for the pleasure of doing it!

However, these courses can be a cause of dissatisfaction if students do not feel they are getting what they want. They often have expectations that are far higher than they would be for a normal course, which can mean either a lot of extra work for the teacher, or a dissatisfied student. You therefore need to be very clear about the aims of these supplementary activities:

- The activity must have some linguistic content (i.e. the student has the opportunity to speak and interact with the teacher).
- The student needs to do something or produce something.
- The student should be pro-active.
- The teacher should accompany the student on any visit related to the supplementary activity.

With activities such as English + tennis or English + golf, students are unlikely to complain because the activity which they are doing is so clearly defined. Other activities are not so clear-cut. In addition to this, it can be very time-consuming to arrange the activities. If you want to get involved in these kind of courses, you have to weigh up whether the extra money is worth the extra stress.

Advice for teachers thinking of become homestay teachers

Provide a professional service.

- Enjoy having people in your home.
- Make friends with other homestay teachers so that you have a support network.
- Be ready to cope with the different aspects of humanity you will encounter.
- Make sure your children understand why you are doing it (i.e. to give them nice things like skiing holidays), otherwise they might resent it.
- Choose your organisation(s) carefully. Getting a high level of support from an organisation is often better than working for one which offers higher levels of pay.
- Take advantage of the support an organisation can offer you.

Conclusion

Homestay teaching takes over your life. The teaching is the nice part; the question is, can you handle the rest? If you need a lot of time and space to yourself, then homestay teaching is unlikely to suit you. Even if you are suited to homestay teaching, this does not necessarily mean that your partner or the rest of the family will be pleased to have students living with them. Your family should enjoy it too, and it can be difficult if one of them feels resentful.

Homestay teaching flies in the face of the adage *'Don't mix business with pleasure'* – only do it if you love it!

9

Chapter 9

Teaching Children and Teenagers

Teaching the younger age groups can be a daunting prospect for teachers who have had no experience of this age group, or who have no children themselves. However, if you have an empathy with children and exploit the mass of materials and pedagogical advice available for teaching the younger age groups, it can be very rewarding. In this chapter we will discuss the various aspects of teaching these younger students.

Definition of age groups

There are various categorisations for young learners. The website of the IATEFL Special Interest Group for Younger Learners divides its material into three broad categories:

- Very young learners (younger than seven years old)
- Primary (seven to twelve years old)
- Secondary (thirteen to seventeen)

There is obviously a big difference between a seven-year-old and a twelve-year-old, or a thirteen-year-old and a seventeen-year-old. Macmillan's OneStop English website (www.onestopenglish.com) also divides its material for young learners into three groups: four to six years old, seven to nine and ten to twelve. There can be big differences between children of the same age too: factors such as family background, education, cultural background, and previous learning experiences all affect the child's maturity.

Teaching children and the law

The 1989 Children's Act legislates for children under sixteen (under eighteen if disabled). The 1999 Protection of Children Act defines a 'child' as a person under eighteen.

The definition of 'child' is currently unclear in relation to language schools. Anyone hosting under-sixteens is 'in loco parentis' and must know where the child is at all times. It is important that anyone coming into contact with children aged fifteen or younger obtain Criminal Records Bureau clearance. (www.crb.gov.uk). For young people aged sixteen to seventeen it is also advisable to obtain clearance. Homestay providers are recommended to let their Local Authority know that they are hosting foreign students. Host families hosting under-sixteens for longer than 28 days should register as foster parents.

Teaching children (7-12)

It is quite unusual to find a younger learner (e.g. under the age of twelve) taking private lessons in his or her own language unless having special needs lessons or taking extra coaching of some kind. One-to-one lessons for children often take place in a homestay context – an ideal learning environment for a child – and most of the learning will take place informally outside the lessons. On this kind of course the child needs mothering, and the bond you develop with the child will help in his or her learning.

Teaching children one-to-one can be very hard work. Children have very short attention spans and you need to create a very active environment in order to maintain their interest. On the other hand, they have not yet developed inhibitions and can be easier to teach than adults. There are none of the barriers that can exist between adults in the classroom: you don't need to pretend to be polite, the child has no ego and has no worries to bring to the classroom. A child's attitude to learning English very much depends on whether they like the teacher or not, as they are too young to see the actual need for learning it.

Children are:

- keen to learn;
- unselfconscious;
- curious.

They:

- absorb things quickly, but also forget them quickly;
- remember better through doing;
- learn holistically; general meaning is more important than individual words.

They have:

- strong imaginations and enjoy stories and fantasy;
- lots of energy;
- short attention spans.

Choosing the right level activities

Children are still learning their own language and developing their knowledge and understanding of the world. You can find a good overview of how children learn at different stages of development at the website:

www.onestopenglish.com/News/Magazine/children/Children_animal.htm.

This looks at the characteristics, implications and needs of three different age groups from four to twelve, together with suitable activities. You need to be constantly aware of how advanced your student is (or is not) in his or her social, cognitive and emotional growth, and then make sure that the material you use is pitched at the right level. You don't want to use activities that your student finds childish; nor do you want to initiate activities which are cognitively beyond him or her.

Materials

The following are all useful:

- Scissors
- Colouring pens
- Tape recorder
- Drawing paper
- Drawing pins
- Prompt cards
- Glue
- Paints
- Flash cards
- Realia
- Access to a laminator
- Board games
- Masks
- Puppets

Activities for young children

- Drawing
- Colouring, labelling, cutting, sticking

- Stories
- Games (e.g. for learning numbers and colours)
- Songs
- Poems
- Rhymes and chants
- Making things (e.g. greeting cards)
- Quizzes
- Tongue twisters
- Miming
- Learning by heart (poems, rhymes, etc.)
- Doing puzzles

Useful websites

www.onestopenglish.com
This has both material for use in the classroom and methodology.

www.learnenglish.org.uk/kid_frame.html
The British Council's KidsZone has quizzes, print-and-do activities, stories and songs.

www.countryschool.com/ylsig
This is the website of IATEFL's special interest group for Young Learners. It has a very large list of Internet EFL/ESL resources for Young Learners.

www.ajkids.com
Ask Jeeves Kids.

www.longman-elt.com/young_learners

www.storyarts.org
A complete website devoted to storytelling.

www.enchantedlearning.com/Dictionary.html
A fun American online dictionary for young learners.

Repetition

Children love routine, so you can keep to the same lesson format or repeat games and activities that they enjoy. Stories can be told and retold, illustrated, and acted out.

Movement

The class needs to include plenty of movement and total physical response activities, so you need a classroom with space. Don't give children activities which require them to sit still for any length of time.

Energy levels

Know which activities will excite children and which ones calm them down. Don't start the class with high energy level activities.

Stimulate all the senses

Children need a lot of visual stimulation, but don't forget to exploit the other senses such as touch and smell.

Variety

Introducing variety into a lesson by doing a range of activities on different topics is not necessarily a good idea: the child can become confused if the lesson jumps from one topic to another. Instead, you can keep to the same topic, but vary the activities. (See *Teaching English in the Primary Classroom* by Susan Halliwell, Longman 1992, pp 28-35, which shows an hour's varied lesson for beginners based on just five colours).

Speaking and listening

The child will still be developing reading and writing skills in his or her own language, so the classes should concentrate on speaking and listening.

- *Listening*: The teacher is an important source of listening (e.g. telling stories). Formulating responses to comprehension questions is taxing for the child, so let him or her respond non-verbally or with minimal language.
- *Speaking:* This can be more difficult than listening: a child's receptive skills are always better than his or her productive skills. It is important to remember that accuracy is not the aim.

Vocabulary

Learning vocabulary is made easier as the words which young students need are concrete, and there are many games you can play with them to reinforce the words.

Learning chunks of language

'Children learning a foreign language often use complete phrases of language they have picked up from someone else e.g. "*I don't know, Knock it off...*" Children may not have been taught these chunks formally, but they help them to communicate when they have very little language.' (Moon: *Children Learning English*, Macmillan ELT, 2000, p.6.)

Songs, rhymes and poems are a good way of learning chunks of language.

Recycling

Children forget things quickly, so you need to be constantly recycling.

Video

Any children's programme will be good for classroom use, particularly the more educational ones. Disney films have the advantage that the child may have often seen the film in his or her mother tongue. Teenagers can also watch material aimed at younger children: although they are more mature, the language content will challenge them.

Interest and motivation

As with all one-to-one teaching, be ready to change activities instantly, if the child is not interested.

Feedback

Be extremely encouraging and give the child a lot of praise. You do not want to discourage the child or make him or her anxious about language learning early in life.

Displaying the child's work

The child is usually more interested in the end product than the topic itself, so make sure the child can display whatever he or she makes (e.g. a picture, book or models), and prepare scrapbooks for the child to take back to show his or her parents.

Sergei

Sergei is a ten-year-old Russian boy doing a homestay course. He has four lessons a day, from 0915 to 1245. He always goes out for his third lesson to do something practical, e.g. going for a walk with the task of looking at certain trees and buildings; taking measurements around the house to practise numbers. The fourth lesson is spent following up the activities of the third lesson. Sergei enjoys looking at and talking about different picture books in English (designed for native speakers), particularly the ones with humour.

Activities outside the classroom

For children doing a homestay course, the time outside the classroom is often more important than the lessons themselves. Not only can you involve the child in what you do in the home, but you can exploit all kinds of visits for language learning purposes: any kinds of sports activities, shopping, walks, visits to the leisure centre, visits to families with children of a similar age.

Hana

Hana is a nine-year-old Russian girl, doing a one-month homestay course. The teacher treats her as she treated her own children when they were young. Hana does not want to sit down and do her lessons, so the teacher has decided to focus on the activities in the home as a means of improving her English. Everything she does together with the teacher can be used for learning purposes (e.g. looking at recipe books together to decide what to have for supper; talking to other children when the teacher takes her for a swim at the leisure centre). Hana is very enthusiastic about England, especially the shops, and she loves buying things. The teacher asked her to hand over her money on the first day to stop her spending it all at once. This resulted in a few tears but now Hana's money will last her the whole month. Hana adores the family's cat and dog and the total attention she receives from the teacher and her partner. She is not particularly interested in meeting other children as she is happy to have the adults' attention. The teacher has taken over the mother role and gives Hana the discipline that she sometimes needs (e.g. making her go to bed when she does not want to).

Teaching teenagers

Children develop their intellectual, motor and social skills and learn more about the world as they get older. You can use a much wider range of topics with older children, and you can now introduce reading and writing into the classroom. Maturity levels vary: you may have an eighteen-year-old who is very independent but who displays the maturity of a thirteen-year-old in certain contexts. Younger teenagers can find the informality of the one-to-one classroom challenging. They are used to a classroom setting, usually working in a formal context. They have probably never learned English in a one-to-one situation before and they may be shy and insecure.

If you are a homestay teacher and have children of a similar age, your teenage students can become involved in your children's activities.

Attention span

Teenagers have longer attention spans than younger children, but they don't have the concentration of adults so give them plenty of short breaks. However, if your student lacks interest or concentration, don't automatically assume that it is anything to do with you. For example, has the student had any breakfast? Has the student had a row with his or her boyfriend/girlfriend? It is important to know what's going on in the student's life, relationships and even eating habits, particularly since personal relationships can play such an important part of your classes with him or her. If your student seems distracted, allow an opportunity to get it off his or her chest before going on with the lesson.

Motivation

Teenagers can be more difficult to teach than young learners. It is unlikely to have been the teenager's decision to take the language classes: parents normally arrange one-to-one classes because they think that their son or daughter is a) not performing well enough at school, and/or b) needs to get a head start in English. Sometimes the teenager has been sent to do a course to get them out of the parents' way. Some teenagers have been 'turned off' language teaching because they are in large classes in their own countries, and have not been able to keep up with the rest of the class, so they may be coming to the classroom with negative attitudes. It is a great opportunity for you to boost the student's morale and allow their language learning abilities to blossom in a way he or she would have little chance of doing in the large classes where they learn English at school.

The teacher's listening skills

More than any other age group, teaching teenagers involves listening carefully to the student. By careful listening you can discover what motivates them: sometimes you discover that they are interested in something that would never have occurred to you. It is also important to treat them as equals and avoid playing on your status as the teacher; your lessons may be the first time that an adult has treated them as an equal. While you can develop close relationships with adults, it is unlikely that you will become their confidant(e), but this can happen with teenagers, who may even tell you things that they would not dream of telling their parents.

Exam preoccupations

Many teenagers take one-to-one lessons in preparation for exams and they can become obsessed by this. If you do something that they don't feel is directly relevant for their exams, you need to explain the rationale for doing it very clearly, otherwise they may not make any effort. In terms of lesson content, you may have to restrict yourself to what they are doing at school. It is a very good idea to ask a teenage one-to-one student to bring a copy of his or her school book with them. Your task is to work on the basis of the school book and expand and consolidate the language taught therein, making it interesting and motivating for the student. However, not all students want or need to work from their school textbook and this gives you much more scope. Some feel that as they are paying a lot of money for their lessons, why go over something that they can do at school?

Po-Chih

Po-Chih is a fifteen-year-old boy living in Malaysia. He greatly objects to spending his time outside school on extra English lessons and has proved a nightmare to teach. His teacher has spent time finding out what he is interested in talking about and has negotiated a compromise with him: in exchange for being able to discuss the topics he likes for part of the lesson, he will work with the school textbook for the rest.

Achievable tasks

Teenagers are very self-conscious and get discouraged if you give them activities that they cannot do. Pitch your lessons very carefully, always making sure they can succeed well at the tasks. They can give up easily if faced with something difficult, so you need to use your powers of persuasion to convince them that they can achieve the task. You also need to handle correction very gently.

Reassure

The teens are a very insecure time. Teenagers need reassurance, and it is important to praise them a lot and to give them a personal boost with your praise, which need not be limited to language learning matters.

Eva

Eva is an eighteen-year-old Polish girl with upper-intermediate level English, but with intermediate level speaking skills. She is very quiet and it is very difficult to get her to communicate. It is also tricky to find subjects she is interested in. However, when the teacher finds topics that Eva wants to talk about, she can be animated. She has made enthusiastic presentations about the Polish education system and Polish literature, which she researched on the Internet; she has also talked with passion and at length about her beloved cat. She is very keen on Harry Potter and is currently reading the latest book (nearly 800 pages in English) which has provided an excellent source of discussion.

Topics teenagers can relate to

Teenagers are interested above all in the things that relate to their world, especially their relationships: with their parents, siblings, boyfriend/girlfriend, friends (and enemies) at school. Music, sport and film are other topics that usually stimulate them, together with issues such as the environment and drugs. They are also often interested in things that will be useful for their future careers. You may find, though, that they are not interested in current affairs, and may not even know much about what is going on outside their circle of family and friends.

Using published materials

It can be very challenging to find the right published materials for an individual teenage student, simply because the teenager market is a very difficult one for materials writers to target. Teenagers often dislike course books, particularly the routine of using a book where all the units follow the same format. Trends change quickly, so authentic materials are ideal for tapping into the things that are popular in a teenager's world.

Antoine

Antoine is a fifteen-year-old French boy. He is very bright and a natural linguist. He enjoys reading newspaper articles and comparing broadsheets with tabloids. He too is currently reading the latest Harry Potter book. Antoine has looked at JK Rowling's biography and read several interviews with her for discussion in class.

Practical suggestions for teaching teenagers

Structured talks

Teenagers are still developing their opinions, and it can be difficult for them to talk spontaneously or at any length on subjects outside their own world; any speaking activity with them should be well-structured.

Role-plays

This age group can be embarrassed by role-plays. This is less so in a one-to-one class than in a group where they are performing in front of their peers, but it is still important to bear this in mind if you want to do a role-play with the student.

Current affairs

Some teenagers are very interested in current affairs, but may not have developed their opinions yet, so you may need to help them formulate these.

Presentations

Get the student to prepare a topic for a presentation.

Songs

Choose a song that the student likes and then download the lyrics from www.lyrics.com, www.lyricworld.com or www.getlyrics.com.

Listing activities for songs include:

- *Songs with language input*: You can find songs which contain language or structures that you want the student to learn.
- *Pairs of words which sound similar:* The teacher prepares pairs of words. The student listens to the song and decides which word in the pair they hear.
- *Reactions to songs*: Choose a piece of music or a song which is mood-provoking. Present the student with a selection of six random pictures and ask the student to choose two pictures which he or she thinks fits well with the song, and explain why. Here, his or her reaction to the song is more important than any specific language work on the lyrics.

Readers

These are good for expanding vocabulary, improving reading skills and helping students become more aware of how the language is constructed. Many graded readers come with cassettes and worksheets which you can download from the publishers' websites. The aim is for the readers to be read as real books. Forget the comprehension questions and find other ways to exploit the material. For example:

- Choose events in the story that are mentioned but not fully described, and ask the student to fill in the details.
- Write a letter of advice to one of the characters, suggesting what he or she should do.
- Bring in half a dozen pictures and ask the student to choose one that in some way represents the student's overall impression of the story. The student might say that none of them do, or they might pick the picture representing the sky and create a long story as to how the picture reminds them of elements in the book.

You will find teacher's guides to using graded readers at the website: www.macmillan.cz/img/readers.pdf and www.cambridge.org.elt/readers.

Video

Mr Bean videos are always popular for their visual humour, and the students can provide a running commentary (see comments for using video with children on page 146 above). How to handle listening is covered in Chapter 5, *Teaching Techniques For One-to-One Classes.*

Writing

At school teenagers are often asked to write very dry, serious pieces of text, so you need to avoid this kind of writing. Journal writing is a good idea; ask the student to write the journal in class to begin with until he or she gets used to it, after which it can be written in his or her free time. Ask the student to write about anything for ten minutes, writing as much or as little as he or she wants. Tell the student that you are going to respond to it, but will not correct it. The student might write 'I hate this lesson'. The teacher can write back 'I'm sorry to hear that. What exactly don't you like?'

Games

Most teenagers still love games such as *Scrabble*, *Snakes and Ladders* and *Monopoly*.

Authentic materials

Teenagers can be very motivated by authentic materials such as catalogues, magazines, newspaper articles, website printouts or off-air video recordings. (See Chapter 5, *Teaching Techniques For One-to-One Classes.)*

Using the Internet

See Chapter 13, *Visits And Project Work.*

Conclusion

When teaching children, remember that you are focusing on the child's whole development, not just his or her language development. Keep your lessons very simple and minimise lesson preparation by varying the activities, not the topics.

With teenagers, treat them as equals and listen to them even more carefully than you would with older students. Stick to subjects they are familiar with and have shown an interest in. With both age groups, by sensitive handling of the classes, you can help them develop a positive attitude to learning English.

10

Chapter 10

Lesson Planning

This chapter discusses lesson planning for one-to-one classes. One-to-one lesson plans are not fundamentally different from those you would use for a group except that you have none of the problems of group management to worry about. Another difference is that you can do more esoteric activities than is generally possible in group lessons (e.g.discussing cooking methods with a pastry chef, reading poetry, visiting hair salons for your student's research).

Experienced teachers normally carry their lesson plans in their heads or, at most, limit themselves to a few jottings on a piece of paper. Less experienced teachers, however, need to plan their lessons carefully in order to feel confident about what they are doing and to give their classes structure and coherence.

The lesson plan should include the following:

- The objectives of the lesson.
- Timings in minutes.
- The various activities that will be covered in the lesson.
- An appropriate balance of input and output.
- The materials to be used (e.g. books, videos, audio-cassettes, Internet articles).
- The hardware to be used (video recorder; OHP).
- Clear stages to provide variety and a clear record of what the student has learned.
- The teacher's assumptions (e.g. *The student will not remember the new vocabulary from the previous day).*
- Anticipated difficulties (e.g. *Oscar will have more difficulty with the listening activities than previously).*

There are various formats for lesson plan documents, although they should all include the above elements. If you are preparing a lesson plan for your Director of Studies because you will be observed, the format will look something like the example opposite (top):

However, if the lesson plan is for yourself, then you can work with a blank piece of paper like the example opposite (bottom).

Examples of a lesson plan

Name of student	
Length of lesson	
Aims	
Materials	
Stages and timings	
Assumptions	
Anticipated problems	

Lesson plan for Catharina

[Catharina is using 'Proficiency Gold', Longman]

1. Intro topic 'Machines' (Speaking) p.148 ex. 1 & 2
   5 minutes ~ *Force her to speak!!!!*
2. Exam focus 'cloze' question
   P. 152 ex. 1,2,3,4
   35 minutes ~*Easy for her. Do it orally to make it more interesting*
3. Revision – reflexive verbs/sentence transformations
   P.153 ex. 1,2,3
   30 minutes ~ *Be careful here – don't make a big deal about the grammar or she'll get nervous. She can redo the ones she has problems with for homework.*
4. Speaking exam practice
   P. 133 ex.1, P. 186 ex.2
   20 minutes ~ *She hates speaking!! (Give her strategies for dealing with the speaking part of exam).*
5. Feedback –
   5 minutes ~ *5 minutes should be sufficient – she won't make many mistakes*

Stacks of material here – but she's so good we might get through it all. Do it orally – any bits she's not certain about she can redo for homework

Catharina is taking one-to-one classes in order to prepare for her Cambridge Proficiency exam. Ultimately she would like to become an English teacher. She is almost bilingual, having spent several years living in the USA. However, she does not know formal grammar, and grammar rules scare her.

Objectives

The 'Aims' part of your lesson plan should clearly state what you want your student to be able to do with the language or skills by the end of the lesson. The number of objectives you should include per lesson will vary depending on the student. (See examples on opposite page.)

Variety

The number of different activities to include in a lesson, and the length of time you should spend on them, depend upon the student's attention span and level. You could work on the principle of a maximum of 30-45 minutes for one activity, although heavy input sessions should be much shorter than this.

The term 'variety' includes variety of:

- *Method of input* (e.g. reading texts; eliciting; listening);
- *Activity* (e.g. free discussion; structured role-play);
- *Language skill* (e.g. listening, speaking);
- *Business skill* (e.g. presentations, meetings);
- *Method of feedback* (e.g. feedback sheets; gestures; on-the-spot correction).

Timings

Normally it is advisable to do heavy inputs when the student is fresher (i.e. at the beginning of a lesson or early in the day). Do open-ended activities at the end of a class so you can finish on time.

Deviating from the lesson plan

With one-to-one students you have more flexibility than with groups, and can abandon or deviate from your lesson plan when necessary. Be ready to jettison or re-jig your lesson plan if:

- your student is tired;
- your student seems bored with the activity;
- the material is too easy or too difficult;
- the material doesn't work with your student;
- you find unexpected mistakes or problems with the material.

You will not lose face if you openly admit that an activity or piece of material suddenly seems unsuitable. On the contrary, the student is likely to admire your flexibility. The key is to have other activities up your sleeve to take their place. However, just any old activity will not do; it should be something that meets the

Example 1: Aims and Objectives

Roustem (ninety-minute class)

Roustem is a pre-advanced student who wants to improve his overall speaking skills through reading and discussing newspaper articles. He wants to spend the whole lesson speaking, with feedback and error correction from the teacher.

Aims for the class

- To recycle new vocabulary.
- To give Roustem the opportunity to speak about topics which motivate him and stretch his English.

Activities

Recycle new words and phrases from previous class (five important ones – a couple of other less important ones).

Roustem summarises two articles he has chosen and read before the class, and then gives his personal comments.

Teacher gives feedback on his summaries and his subsequent discussion. Roustem looks at headlines in the newspapers and finds some for discussion.

Feedback from the teacher and error correction with Roustem.

Example 2: Aims and Objectives

Eugenio (sixty-minute class)

Eugenio is a pre-intermediate student with a good grammatical knowledge, a limited vocabulary, and a very strong Spanish accent. He also lacks fluency.

Objectives

- To recycle new vocabulary.
- To improve Eugenio's fluency and to encourage him to use the language he already knows more effectively.
- To expand his vocabulary.
- To do a little pronunciation work.

Activities

Recycle a couple of new words quickly.

A few minutes of pronunciation work, taking a key sound in English which creates difficulties for Spanish speakers.

Topics for discussion based round units from vocabulary books such as *English Vocabulary in Use: Pre-intermediate and intermediate* or from language summaries prepared by the teacher for various subjects such as 'personal finance'.

Feedback and error correction.

student's needs, lacks or wants in some respect.

If you are working in a school or homestay context, do not be afraid to leave your classroom to go and quickly prepare something else for your student. If you do not have anything you can give them to do while you are out of the room, you can make up the lost five or ten minutes at another time.

Digressions

Some students are happy to follow the lesson plan but need frequent digressions, either for a few minutes of free conversation or to discuss language points. This is part of their learning style and you need to accommodate them – although it will affect the timings of your lesson (See Chapter 12, *Troubleshooting*).

Here are some sample lesson plans.

Example 1: lesson plan

Length of lesson	60 minutes
Name of student	Lily
Level	Pre-advanced
Teaching point	1. Listening (and vocabulary expansion) 2. Vocabulary expansion: describing economies
Source material	1. Watch stories from CNN news 2. Describing economies – exercise written by teacher 3. Reading – one-paragraph inputs from *The Economist* (with accompanying charts) on American, Swedish and Brazilian economies
Assumptions	The material will be the right level for Lily We will be able to complete all the tasks within the 60 minutes
Anticipated problems	Some of the vocabulary for describing economies will be unfamiliar and we will have to spend time recycling it
Additional information	Homework → Lily will read www.bbc.co.uk article on the Chinese economy Follow-up for next class → Lily will talk about the Chinese economy

Example 1: Stages of the lesson

Timing	Aim	Activity
30 minutes	Improve Lily's extensive and intensive listening skills; expand her vocabulary	**STAGE1: Video listening** We will watch the news headlines from CNN. We will look at: 1. The headlines 2. 1 or 2 business stories All new vocabulary will be recorded in the *Word Bank*
20 minutes	Introduce Lily to the key vocabulary for describing economies	**STAGE 2 (A): Vocabulary exercise:** `Describing economies` We can do the exercises altogether. I anticipate that she'll know about 50% of the vocabulary and the rest should be new
10 minutes	Reinforce the new vocabulary; show Lily how the vocabulary is used in real life	**STAGE 2 (B): Reading** *(seeing the vocabulary in context)* 1. I will give Lily the extracts from *The Economist* – three short paragraphs plus accompanying charts describing the economies of Brazil, America and Sweden 2. Lily can use her highlighter to underline any key vocabulary for describing economies + Homework

Example 2: Lesson plan

Name	Date	Time	Level	Materials
Virginie	Wednesday 4 June	0900 – 0950	Advanced	Virginie's latest essay

Virginie is an advanced speaker of English who is preparing to do a part-time MBA. She is taking one-to-one lessons to improve her writing skills. She emails essays on various business topics to the teacher, who then looks at them at home and emails Virginie back with comments on a) overall impression (i.e. coherence, cohesion, strength of arguments, logic) and then b) highlights specific language points for Virginie to look at, (but does not give the corrections). The teacher uses the *Tools* –

Track Changes option in Microsoft Word. Virginie and the teacher then discuss the essay in class and Virginie self-corrects as much as possible. The hours the teacher spends at home working on the assignment are deducted from Virginie's overall hours.

General aims

1. To go through Virginie's most recent essay
2. To isolate and correct any slips she has made
3. To improve her use of linking words

Language focus/input

Virginie is not familiar with more sophisticated linking words such as *in the event that; arguably; surprisingly; in that.* She also has problems using reference (e.g. *in this way; doing so; at such a time).*

Skills focus

1. Speaking
2. Vocabulary expansion

Materials

Collins CoBuild English Guides 9: Linking words Exercises 9-13 p.186-195

Stages of the class

5 mins	Teacher discusses overall impression of assignment
10 mins	Virginie self-corrects as much as possible
15 mins	Go through exercises (probably covering exercises 9-10 ; Virginie can do the rest for homework)
15 mins	Virginie and teacher discuss possible topics that she can write a short essay on. Virginie will talk through the kind of ideas she will include in the essay
5 mins	Teacher to go through any spoken errors Virginie makes during the class

Homework

1. See above
2. Finish the *CoBuild English Guides 9: Linking Words* exercises

Possible problems and solutions

The teacher has not taught this kind of language and is a little unsure of the best way to handle the exercises, so will spend more time preparing the class than usual.

Personal aims

The teacher does not often have the opportunity to teach this kind of language, so finds it interesting to work out different ways of presenting and practising it.

Example 3: Lesson plan

Name	Date	Time	Level	Materials
Miroslaw	Friday 6 June	1530 – 1700	Strong intermediate	*Market-Leader intermediate unit 7* pp 54-55

General aims

1. Give Miroslaw an opportunity to use the language he already knows in conversation
2. Activate vocabulary which he already knows
3. Do not tire him too much

Language focus/input: Vocabulary
Skills focus: Speaking

Stages of the class

1. **Warm-up (10 minutes)**
   Ask him to name different inventions and inventors
2. **Speaking activity (15 minutes)**
   Page 54-A *What inventions or innovations do you associate with these names?*
   Briefly give an example of an invention/innovation that I personally couldn't live without at home/work. Ask him to do the same (p54 B)
   p54-C Look at vocabulary in box (I'm sure he'll know it) nb. Skip p54-D
3. **Feedback on speaking (5 minutes)**
4. **Vocabulary activity (15 minutes)**
   p55-B Vocabulary for describing inventions or new ideas. Which ones have a positive meaning? Which negative?
   (Brainstorm opposites to these words)
5. **Speaking activity (35 minutes)**
   p55 Strange inventions – read about the real inventions and innovations below. What is your opinion of each one? (He'll love this)
6. **Feedback (15 minutes)**
   Go through feedback sheets

Homework - No!!

Assumptions

He will be very chatty about this subject.
He will know most of the vocabulary already

Anticipated problems

He may be exhausted – too tired to even talk. In that case, we could simply go for a walk like yesterday or we could watch a *Mr Bean* video and I could get him to comment on what's going on.

Example 4: Lesson plan

Name	Date	Time	Level	Materials
Saltuk	29th Oct	1400 – 1515	Pre-intermediate	A handout with the structure of the report (prepared by teacher) and key vocabulary for each stage of the report

General aims

1. To recycle vocabulary from previous lessons for describing hotels and their facilities
2. To give Saltuk the opportunity to practise report writing skills

Language focus/input

Vocabulary for describing facilities in a hotel

Skills focus

Writing

Assumptions

- Saltuk will be quite quick at writing
- We will have enough time to write at least a substantial part of the report (if he keeps it very simple)

Anticipated problems

He may want to make the report more complicated than necessary

Example 4: Stages of the lesson

1. Brainstorm vocabulary for describing hotels and their facilities. Write on board.
10 minutes

2. Tell Saltuk that he is going to write a brief report about a new hotel that has opened up in his city. Ask him what information he would like to include in the report.
10 minutes

3. Give Saltuk the structure of the report:
   a) Objective of report
   b) General details (location; price category)
   c) The rooms
   d) The public areas
   e) Restaurants and bars
   f) Other facilities
   g) Overall impression

5 minutes

4. Ask Saltuk to tell you verbally what he will say for each stage of the report. Input useful vocabulary, phrases and whole sentences where necessary.
10 minutes

5. Drafting first version of the report.
25 minutes
   a) Ask Saltuk to start writing the report, stage by stage. He can use the teacher as a resource, asking questions about things he is uncertain about. Remind him to keep it very simple.
   b) If he doesn't finish it in class, he can finish it for homework.
   c) Teacher to give initial feedback as Saltuk does first draft of the report. No corrections – simply feedback. Encourage Saltuk to correct himself.

   If the timings are right, there should be 15 minutes left before the end of the class. Use it for free conversation and talking about the next class. If Saltuk gets tired, get him to write the report in the next class (or for homework).

Course programming vs. lesson planning

The course programme shows the objectives for all or part of the course and is aimed at the student. A lesson plan is for the teacher only.

A course programme:

- gives the overall objectives for the course (based on the needs analysis);
- does not usually mention materials;
- should not include ELT jargon such as *controlled practice* or *lexis* which the learner will not understand or be interested in.

Consider the two extracts on the opposite page. The first is a lesson plan for telephoning, and the second represents telephoning in the course programme.

Lesson planning for a telephone lesson

Aim	**30 minutes** 1. To give Hideyuki the opportunity to practise his telephoning skills To identify any problems Hideyuki has with telephoning in English
Materials	■ blank pieces of paper ■ audio-cassette to record the call ■ telephones
Stages 10 minutes	**Stage 1: Set up situation for a telephone role-play** ■ Ask Hideyuki to choose a phone call he has made recently to enact in class ■ Hideyuki to explain the situation and what was said during the call ■ Teacher to check own understanding of situation and clarify own role in the phone call
5 minutes	**Stage 2: Structure the call** Teacher and Hideyuki to work out a structure for the call and to predict type of language needed
10 minutes	**Stage 3: Make phone call** Teacher to use extension on first floor. Hideyuki to use one in coffee lounge. (Record phone call)
5 minutes	**Stage 4: Feedback** NB: Teacher to check if Hideyuki wants to do any more phone calls in subsequent lessons
Assumptions	We can complete everything in 30 minutes
Anticipated problems	Hideyuki finds making phone calls very nerve-racking He is a weak lower-intermediate level – he may have some difficulties explaining to the teacher the situation to be enacted in the telephone role-play

'Telephoning' for a course programme

Language input

Nadia to study useful language for a variety of telephone situations, e.g.:

- Giving the objective of a telephone call
- Clarifying, checking and summarising

Output

- Role-plays of different types of telephone calls (including Nadia's work calls)
- Feedback and error analysis

11

Chapter 11

Evaluating Progress And Making Recommendations For Future Study

We give our students feedback daily on their performance after any kind of activity; for example *your listening has improved! I've really noticed it today*, or *you try to use your new vocabulary. That's excellent.* However, more structured feedback is also required. In this chapter we will look at the various ways of providing this feedback and helping the student to build on his or her progress in the future.

Progress

Your student's textbook may have tests or revision units to measure progress, but otherwise progress measurement often relies upon how your student feels and what you have noticed. Very often the main achievement of the course is to increase the student's confidence. Additionally, the student may have improved his or her language awareness, learning strategies, overall communicative ability and motivation, or activated passive knowledge of the language. In other words, the student may have consolidated his or her current level rather than made linear progress.

Learning strategies

Discuss your student's learning strategies with him or her, and highlight the things he or she should be aiming for in the following areas:

- *Speaking strategies*: e.g. the student does not get blocked when facing a difficult situation; does not panic when under stress; is not afraid of making a mistake.
- *Listening strategies:* e.g. the student uses visual clues to guess what is happening; tries to understand the overall meaning.
- *Reading strategies:* e.g. the student guesses the meaning of words from the context; does not try to understand every word.

- *Vocabulary strategies:* e.g. the student writes down whole sentences and phrases in his or her vocabulary book, rather than just individual words.
- *Phonological strategies:* e.g. the student notices the lip movements of native speakers; notices and tries to copy intonation patterns he or she hears.

Communication strategies

We have mentioned the importance of the student's overall communicative abilities in other parts of the book. (See Chapter 6 – *Giving Feedback, Error Correction And Recycling Activities* and Chapter 7 – *Business English.)* These include speaking slowly and clearly, listening carefully, structuring an argument, checking and clarifying.

Study strategies

Highlight the study strategies your student should be aiming for in the following areas:

- *Note-taking:* e.g. the student needs to take notes (although not too many) and write down new words in a vocabulary book.
- *Dictionary use:* ideally the student will have an EFL English-English dictionary appropriate to his or her level, in addition to one in English and his or her own language.
- *Participation in class:* e.g. the student should be encouraged to ask the teacher questions and to let the teacher know when there is something he or she does not understand.
- *After class:* e.g. the student should revise using his or her notes; watch TV, go to the cinema or read a newspaper, book or graded reader in English.
- *Socialising:* students on overseas courses should use breaks and lunchtimes to practise English with their fellow students and to join in the social programme.

Planned tutorials

Informal reviewing of the student's progress in each lesson is very important, but it is no substitute for a formal review of the student's progress. It is important to include regular tutorials into the course programme for this purpose. (See the example tutorial plan on the next page.)

You should also talk about:

- motivation;
- confidence;
- strengths and weaknesses;
- progress made;
- socio-linguistic competence.

The tutorial is done collaboratively with the student; you can also ask the student to write a short self-assessment before the tutorial in order to increase his or her participation. As with giving any kind of feedback (see Chapter 6), you need to

Student tutorial

Name: **Date:**

- Level
- Overall communicative effectiveness
- Language skills
- Business skills (e.g. *telephoning, presentations*) if appropriate
- Learning strategies
- Ideas on how to continue learning after the course
- Comments on any other aspect of the course (*administration, accommodation, social programme)*

You can add sections depending on the student's circumstances, e.g.:

- How to make the best use of your time in the UK, as well as in the classroom.
- Recommendations for the next stage of the course.

Teacher's signature: **Student's signature:**

emphasise the positive aspects of the student's performance. It is also a good opportunity to find out if the student is experiencing any kind of problem, because students sometimes wait until the course is finished before complaining. This means that if the student makes a complaint after the course, the language training organisation can point out that nothing was mentioned during the tutorial.

Level

Two of the main level scales used in Europe are the English Speaking Union nine-level scale and the five-level ALTE (Association of Language Testers in Europe) which correspond to those in the Council of Europe's Common European Framework of References for Languages. You can find information about the worldwide ELT/EFL ESL LEP ESOL scales and test charts at the website: www.geocities.com/esolscale/4html.html.

You may know your student's level because he or she has taken your organisation's placement test, or the student may be studying for an exam (e.g. Cambridge First Certificate) which gives you an indication of his or her level.

Computer-based tests

There are various computer-based tests, such as the Council of Europe's diagnostic language tests, available on the Internet free of charge (www.dialang.org) and the Business English Language Testing Service (BULATS) – although this is aimed more at group testing in organisations. ARELS (Association Recognised English Language Schools) offers placement tests in writing and listening for ELT organisations.

Subjective judgements

Unless your student has recently taken a valid and reliable exam or test, you will have no means of establishing an objective level for them. If you evaluate them yourself, explain that you are giving them an impression, i.e. a subjective judgement made only on the basis of your experience of the student's performance in class; you also need to explain the level scale that your organisation uses. In the example below/overleaf, a pre-advanced level is described (level 7 on a nine-level scale).

Level 7

Pre-advanced

Speaking: Able to participate effectively in most language situations using appropriate style and register.

Listening: Able to understand everyday conversation on a wide range of topics with confidence. Is developing reasonable level of competence in dealing with more specialised language. Can cope with listening situations in which part of the message is distorted.

Reading: Able to understand general and some specialised text types. Can sustain concentration on reading tasks over a long period.

Writing: Able to write coherently and accurately on a wide range of topics, using appropriate style and register.

> 'One needs to remember that levels only reflect a vertical dimension. They can take only limited account of the fact that learning a language is a matter of horizontal as well as vertical progress as learners acquire the proficiency to perform in a wider range of communicative activities.'
>
> Council of Europe *Common European Framework of Reference for Languages: Learning, teaching, assessment:* 2001, p 17

Writing reports

The report is also a public relations document and should look professional. Language learning organisations will have their own report formats with guidelines on how to write them. The report can include the following:

- Student's level at arrival; evaluation of student's language skills at arrival.
- Overall course objectives.
- Work covered during the course (*this should be brief*).
- Participation in class.
- Attitude.
- Confidence (*on arrival and at end of course*).
- Evaluation of progress made.
- Specific language recommendations and information on how to achieve them.

There are a number of things to watch out for with report writing. Firstly, reports often include subjective evaluations and consequently can be a potential source of conflict among teachers, or between teachers and the Director of Studies. Secondly, reports need to be sensitive: while it is easy enough to make mildly negative comments, it is difficult and possibly counterproductive to say anything hard-hitting. Finally, teachers often have neither the time nor the inclination to write long reports; it is also time-consuming for the Director of Studies to edit them. Tick box systems with a short space for the teacher's comments are the best.

Opposite is a blank report form, followed by a completed one.

Blank report format

Name:
Level:
Course Dates:

Language skills

Speaking
Listening
Reading
Accuracy
Pronunciation
General vocabulary
Specialised vocabulary
Communication strategies
Learning strategies
(Teacher writes in grade for each of these)

Communication skills

Teacher inserts the communication skills studied as appropriate, e.g.:
Telephoning
Socialising
Presentations
Meetings
Negotiations
Business writing
Business reading

Comments

Course Director's signature:

Definitions of grades

A = Excellent; **A/B** = Very good; **B** = Good; **B/C** = Adequate;
C = Needs further training; **C/D** = Needs further training;
D = Needs further training; **N** = Not included.

Evaluate the student within his or her overall level. For example, you may give your student an overall upper-intermediate level, but within that level they may achieve an intermediate level for speaking and a pre-advanced level for listening and vocabulary.

Example of a completed report

Name: Massimo
Level: Intermediate
Course Dates: 23-27 June

Language skills

Speaking	B	General vocabulary	B/C
Listening	A/B	Business vocabulary	A/B
Reading	B	Communication strategies	B/C
Accuracy	A/B	Learning strategies	C
Pronunciation	A/B		

Communication skills

Telephoning	N	Meetings	B
Socialising	N	Negotiations	N
Presentations	A/B	Business writing	N
		Business reading	N

Comments

Massimo's objectives for his one-week course were to improve his speaking and listening skills in English and to practise his language skills in the context of presentations and meetings. Massimo's lack of vocabulary frustrated him in all activities practised in the classroom, as did his lack of confidence in his language skills. However, it became apparent that Massimo's difficulties lay less in his limited vocabulary and lack of confidence than in his communication strategies and language learning techniques. In fact, once he has acquired these strategies, Massimo has the potential to become an excellent communicator. For the future, we recommend that he continue with systematic language learning, either through self-study or with a trainer. We also gave him specific advice on how to expand his vocabulary, such as reading newspaper articles. The more Massimo uses English for his work, the more significant progress he is likely to make. We would welcome him back to the ABC school of English at any time.

Course Director's signature:

Definitions of grades

A = Excellent; **A/B** = Very good; **B** = Good; **B/C** = Adequate;
C = Needs further training; **C/D** = Needs further training;
D = Needs further training; **N** = Not included.

Example End-of-course report

Name: Laura * *(Laura is aged 12)*
Course: One-to-one
Level: 6 (Upper-intermediate)
Date: 11-13 June

Language skills	**Grade**	*KEY*
1. Oral communication	A+	A = Excellent
2. Listening	A+	B = Good
3. Reading	A+	C = Satisfactory
4. Writing	A+	D = Fair
5. Grammar	A	E = Poor
6. Pronunciation	A	
7. Vocabulary	A	
8. Participation	A	**Course Grade = A**

Attendance record	
1. Attendance	A
2. Punctuality	A

General Comments

Laura was an enthusiastic student with real ability in English. She worked hard and had no trouble producing the language learned in class. Her speaking is at an exceptional level for someone of her age, and as she expands her grammatical knowledge and vocabulary, it will continue to improve. For the future we would encourage her to read more books in English, and to watch films and television in English, as this will expand her vocabulary immediately. With further study and development we have no doubt that she will become an extremely competent user of the language. We have enjoyed teaching her and wish her well for the future.

Teacher: **Course Director's signature:**

Above is an end-of-course report based on a different format.

Before writing the report, show your student a blank report form, discuss what you will say and then, if possible, show him or her your draft. Get his or her approval before the final, official version is written up. Remember not to use EFL terminology in the report such as *syntax* or *lexis;* it needs to be accessible for the student and for other potential readers such as training managers.

Recommendations for future study

(You will find further details at the back of the book in *Recommended Resources.)*

Reading

- *Websites*: e.g. the student can download an article a day from www.bbc.co.uk or any of the sites for English language newspapers. Also you can give the students the addresses of good quality EFL sites such as www.bbc.co.uk/worldservice/learningenglish
- *Newspapers and magazines:* Some students prefer to buy a newspaper or magazine rather than reading them online.
- *Graded readers*: Most publishers have a series of graded readers ranging from elementary (approximately 200 words – depending on the publishers) to advanced (approximately 3000 words).
- *Books for native speakers:* The student should read a few pages before buying, to check that the book is at the right level. Recommend that the student reads on subjects he or she is passionate about, or looks for titles he or she wants to read in the native language.
- *Reference books:* Recommend reference books (e.g. advanced learners dictionaries; dictionary of collocations; pictorial dictionaries; thesauruses; online dictionaries; dictionaries with CD-ROMs; grammar reference books).
- *Language learning magazines:* Suggest your students subscribe to a language learning magazine such as *Modern English Digest,* aimed at elementary and intermediate level learners (www. modernenglishdigest.com). There are many English language learning magazines in different countries, specially adapted to their market with explanations in the mother tongue. These are usually available on subscription or from newspaper kiosks. German speakers, for example, may be familiar with the English teaching magazines *Spotlight* and *Business Spotlight* (spotlight-verlag.de).

Listening – Material designed for native speakers

The student can make use of the following material designed for native speakers.

- *DVDs.*
- *Talking books*: These are cassettes designed for native speakers who are visually impaired, but are also bought by many people with perfect sight as an enjoyable way to listen to a story.
- *Videocassettes*: e.g. films and many BBC programmes such as documentaries and classical drama series. (Be aware that videos come in three formats, which creates compatibility problems – PAL videos will not play on NTSC videos in Japan, nor SECAM videos in France).
- *Listening on the web*: e.g. at www.bbc.co.uk/radio/

Listening – Material designed for language learners

- *Audiocassettes and CD-ROMs.* The student can listen to these in the car or on a personal stereo.
- *Listening on the web:* e.g. at www.englishlistening.com.

Vocabulary

All reading activities will expand the student's vocabulary. In addition, they require good dictionaries and need to organise their vocabulary learning. They can buy self-study books (e.g. topic-based; books covering idioms or phrasal verbs) to help them in this area.

Speaking

- *On the job*: If the student needs English for his or her job, he or she should take every opportunity to use it. If the student works with other English speakers, native or non-native, he or she should copy useful phrases and expressions from them.
- *English-speaking clubs.*
- *English 'lessons' with friends:* The student can find a friend who is at approximately the same level and have regular 'lessons' with that person. They can use a text book, choose a newspaper article or do exercises for part of the lesson, and use the rest for free conversation. Although there is no teacher, the reference books they consult to answer their language questions perform a 'teacher' role.

Writing

- *English spelling and grammar check:* Students can check any writing they do on the computer (e.g. writing a diary) by using the English spelling and grammar check facilities.
- *Pen pals (www.penpals.com):* See the comment on pen pal projects (page 189 in Chapter 13, *Visits and Project Work*).

Feedback sheets

Encourage the student to review and make use of his or her feedback sheets after the end of the course. (See Chapter 6.)

Goals

Give the student something to aim for, such as studying for an internationally recognised qualification, for example these recognised qualifications:

Cambridge ESOL Examinations

General English

- Key English Test – KET
- Preliminary English Test – PET
- First Certificate in English – FCE
- Certificate in Advanced English – CAE
- Certificate of Proficiency in English – CPE

Business English

- Business English Certificate – BEC

Modular Assessment

- Certificate in English Language Skills – CELS

Young Learners

- Cambridge Young Learners English Tests – YLE

Academic English

- International English Language Testing Service – IELTS (jointly run with the British Council and IELTS Australia: IDP Education Australia)

London Chamber of Commerce Examination Board (LCCIEB)

Business English

- Business for English (Levels 1,2,3,4)
- Business for Commerce (Levels 1,2,3) – more academic than EFB
  (Both exams have optional oral tests (but not for level 1))
- Spoken English for Industry and Commerce – SEFIC (Levels 1,2,3,4)
- English Language Skills Assessment – ELSA

ARELS/Oxford exams

Oxford and ARELS exams are designed primarily for students interested in studying at a British university. The Oxford exams make up the written component, whilst the ARELS ones deal with spoken communication.

- Oxford Preliminary
- Oxford Higher
- ARELS Preliminary
- ARELS Higher
- ARELS Diploma

TOEFL

This is an American test, geared towards overseas students wanting to study at colleges and universities in North America.

TOEIC

This is also used by students wanting to study in English-speaking countries, and by corporations and government agencies, to assess the English ability of their employees.

Conclusion

It is important to include regular tutorials in your course programme, and to end the course on a positive note in your final report. Many students learn their English through self-study, so giving your student the widest range of possibilities for learning independently is essential.

12

Chapter 12

Troubleshooting

In this chapter we will discuss potential problems that may arise in your one-to-one classes, and how to address them.

Potential problems in class

The student	**The teacher**
The student may be: ■ unmotivated; ■ not talkative; ■ stressed; ■ anxious; ■ lacking in confidence; ■ suffering from culture shock; ■ suffering from homesickness; ■ very tired by the lessons; ■ demanding; ■ rude; ■ obsessive; ■ arrogant. The student feels a loss of control (e.g. executives who are used to being in the 'driving seat'). The student expects to be 'spoon-fed'. You are not the kind of teacher he or she wants or expected.	You may not have established a good relationship with the student. You may find the student: ■ tiring; ■ boring; ■ intimidating. You feel sleepy in class.

You need to avoid or minimise problems as far as possible, and there are several ways you can do this.

Explain clearly what the course will entail

Explain clearly to the students on the first day what the course will entail, what kind of teaching methods you will use and how much progress they can expect to make. The beginning of the course is also a good moment to ask the student directly about his or her motivation levels and what he or she expects to achieve. It is also important to know what the student expects from the teacher. If the student comes from a culture where the teacher is always in full control of the class, he or she might feel that you are abdicating responsibility if you allow a lot of autonomy or ask his or her opinion about what activities to do in class, so it may be a good idea to explain why you are doing this.

Gain the respect of the student

- Be well prepared.
- State the objectives of the class at the beginning of each lesson.
- Regularly check with your student that he or she is happy with the content and style of the lessons.
- Be interested in your student. (This sounds like elementary advice, but it may be something you need to work at quite hard if your student is not very inspiring.)
- Don't talk too much; your role is that of listener.
- Recognise your limitations. If your student clearly wants someone to entertain them and that is not your forte, be ready to accept that you are not the ideal teacher for that student and try to compensate in other areas.
- If the student gives you negative feedback (e.g. *This exercise is not useful*; or *I don't like that activity*), react positively and work out with the student what exercises and activities would be more suitable.
- Be flexible, e.g. change or adapt your lesson plan if you don't think it suits the student's mood or energy levels.
- Dress appropriately, e.g. dress smartly for the first few lessons in order to create a professional image in the student's mind.

Once your student respects you professionally, they will accept more easily any experimenting you do in class.

Adapt to the learning style of your student

It is critically important to understand how your student likes to learn. There are various ways of classifying learners according to their learning style, such as the four types identified by Honey and Mumford in their book *Manual of Learning Styles*, 1992 (the activist, the theorist, the pragmatist and the reflector), or categorising students according to whether they are visual, auditory or tactile/kinaesthetic learners. In fact, we do not need to decide which of these categories our students fit into; they will be a mixture of these different types anyway. The point is not to know the theory about learning styles, but simply to be aware of how our student likes to learn and then to take steps to respond to that style.

For example, you can ask yourself these questions:

- How much imagination does the student have?
- What's the student's attention span?
- How systematic is the student? (e.g. Do they take notes? Do they review their notes?)
- Does the student state explicitly when he or she does not like something, or is it up to you to read between the lines?
- What activities does the student clearly enjoy in the classroom?
- What activities does the student clearly *not* enjoy doing?
- How much of a risk-taker is the student?
- How much autonomy can the student assume?
- How does the student view the teacher?
- How much theory can the student take?
- How quickly does the student get tired?
- How long can the student tolerate an activity before they need some kind of light conversational interchange?

At the simplest level, you need to be aware of how the student reacts to the various activities you do with him or her. If they do not like an activity, then you should a) avoid it, b) minimise it, or c) explain very clearly the rationale for the activity and win over the student's co-operation.

Obviously you need to adapt to the student's learning style, but this does not mean you have to change your *teaching* style. It is worth remembering that students

Fabrizio

Fabrizio was a Public Relations Director for a large Italian multinational, and had a particularly idiosyncratic learning style. Fabrizio's attention span lasted about ten minutes before he would waylay the teacher with a digression of some kind. However, without apparently doing any work in class (more time was spent in impromptu coffee breaks, on the phone or in diversions from the objectives of the class), Fabrizio managed to learn an impressive amount and he performed well in the output activities. He subsequently did several other courses, creating great frustration for teachers who did not adapt to his learning style. However, with the couple of teachers who understood how he liked to learn, he was a charming and enjoyable student.

appreciate having teachers with different teaching styles. If they prefer one teacher to another, sometimes it is due to the *content* of the lesson rather than the personality or teaching abilities of the individual.

Your image

It is also worth asking yourself about the image that you are projecting in the classroom. You may see yourself as an easy-going, motivating individual; your student may see you as an over-serious slave driver. Such glaring mismatches in perception are rare, but variations in how the student perceives the teacher and how teachers perceive themselves are common.

One of the best ways to find out how your student sees you is to look at his or her course feedback comments.

Learning from the student's feedback at the end of the course

Students normally complete a course evaluation questionnaire at the end of their lessons. Depending on where the course took place, the student may be asked to evaluate the pre-course information, teaching, materials and equipment used in class, social programme, accommodation and administration of the course. These feedback sheets are a valuable learning tool for the teacher, and some language learning institutions give their teachers access to them. If you are not able to look at the student's evaluation after the course, ask your Director of Studies to let you know if the student made any specific comments on your teaching style or manner in the classroom.

Many teachers find this very hard to do, and are sensitive to any negative comments the student may make. However, if you can, bite the bullet and read what your student has to say about you. If the student makes constructive comments (or if you can interpret negative comments constructively) and you then implement changes into your teaching style or manner in the classroom, you will improve as a teacher.

Dealing with difficult situations

Tired students

Learning English one-to-one can be immensely tiring. This is particularly true if the student is taking an intensive course, and it is not just low-level students who can get exhausted: very advanced students who are learning something new (e.g. accounting vocabulary) can get worn out too. And students who are studying abroad not only have to cope with the language, but also have to acclimatise to the new culture.

If you realise that your student is becoming tired, you can:

- take a break;
- go out of the building with the student – for a walk, to a coffee shop or whatever is appropriate;
- introduce physical movement in the classroom;
- think about re-arranging the programme.

If you want to prevent your student getting tired:

✗ **Don't Do This:**
- cram in as much as you can;
- be afraid of silence;
- be afraid of silent reading in class.

✓ **Do This:**
- understand clearly what constitutes a tiring activity, and which activities are less demanding;
- give your student time to think (which entails silence);
- give your student time in class to prepare any activity that needs preparation;
- take frequent breaks if your student tires quickly;
- change the activity if you see your student getting tired;
- over-estimate the time it will take for you to complete a task; you can always have a few five-minute fillers up your sleeve in case you finish early;
- aim to finish a few minutes before the end of the class.

Tiring activities include:
- dense input sessions (grammar, vocabulary, pronunciation, meetings language – whatever the topic);
- controlled practice activities;
- challenging listening activities.

Less tiring activities include:
- speaking (although it depends how challenging the topic is);
- fun activities (e.g. games);
- easy listening activities.

Anxious students

There are many reasons why a student might be anxious: for example, he or she may not think enough progress is being made, have difficulties with the learning process, be about to start a new job, or be worried about exams.

Ideally, your student will talk to you openly about his or her concerns. In addition to encouraging this, you can make the classroom a relaxed, pressure-free environment by:

- giving the student achievable tasks;
- being positive, cheerful and encouraging;
- explaining how progress works, e.g. that it is not linear, and that sometimes it's difficult to notice progress until the end of the course – or even some time after that;
- giving very positive feedback;
- not putting pressure on the student;
- being relaxed yourself.

The student lacks confidence

You can handle this situation using the same techniques as for dealing with anxious students.

The student is rude

Students can sound rude when it is not their intention. This could be due to linguistic and cultural misunderstandings. For example:

- interference from mother-tongue intonation patterns;
- poor level of English;
- cultural differences over what is appropriate social and socio-linguistic behaviour in certain settings (e.g. requests in their language sound too direct compared with English).

During the feedback sessions, you can draw their attention to these points – it opens up the potential for interesting discussions on cultural differences between your student's culture and British culture.

Personality clashes

Sometimes it can be difficult to create a rapport with your student; one step on from this is having a student with whom there is the potential for a personality clash. In this situation you need to subsume your personal feelings about your student and just get on with your job. Every teacher gets bad feedback from a student at one time or another because the personal chemistry between them was not right; Directors of Studies are usually able to distinguish between negative feedback due to poor teaching and that which occurs as a result of a bad personality match.

Culture shock

If the student goes to an English-speaking country to do his or her course, they not only have to contend with speaking a foreign language, but also get used to the climate, dress, food and social behaviour of that country. This can lead to culture shock for some students. Students taking an intensive one-to-one course are at particular risk because there are no other classmates to distract them.

Homesickness is an aspect of culture shock, and can be experienced by adults as well as children and younger people. Not only do students miss their families, but they may also find their new circumstances intimidating, especially if they study in a big city like London. All this will detract from their ability to learn efficiently and effectively.

Get the student to talk about it

Get your student to describe what he or she finds surprising about Britain, and to talk about how British life differs from life in his or her country.

Distract the student

If you are in a school, you need to make sure that your student gets to know the other students and is included on any social programme that may exist. In a homestay context, you can make sure your student is fully occupied with activities outside the classroom by taking them on trips and visits, and giving them the opportunity to meet other people outside the homestay family. (This is covered more fully in Chapter 8 *Homestay Teaching*.)

Make the classes fun

Provide activities that you are sure your student will enjoy.

Obsessiveness

Students can be obsessive about various aspects of the language learning process – for example, they may look up every word in the dictionary to the detriment of the flow of the lesson, or be obsessed with learning grammar, or want you to correct every single mistake they make. You can try to persuade them that it is not in their best interests to study in this way, but often the best strategy is to give them a diluted version of what they want rather than fighting them.

Lack of motivation

Sometimes students are unmotivated because they have been sent on the course by their parents or company. If this is the case, get them to talk about it and then discuss how best to motivate them. Students can be stimulated by your enthusiasm and by your careful choice of classroom activities.

You find your student tiring

This can happen for several reasons, e.g. they start and restart sentences very frequently, or speak very fast and make many mistakes. You can try the following strategies:

- Admit you're tired! Suggest taking a brief break.
- Introduce movement to the classroom.
- Do some work on the offending linguistic fault.

Students are often afraid that they are tiring the teacher. If you find them less tiring in subsequent lessons, praise them for that.

You find your student boring

First of all, are you sure your student is not equally bored with you? If you are sure this is not the case, then tell your student that in a group class he or she would need techniques for holding the attention of the other students, and that this is exactly the same in the one-to-one classroom. If you do it humorously (and your student has a sense of humour), he or she will generally respond positively to this approach.

The student is very demanding

During the needs analysis is the right moment to explain clearly to the student what the course can and cannot provide, thereby making sure he or she has realistic expectations. If your student is too demanding, firmly explain why you cannot meet all his or her requirements.

You feel sleepy in class

One of the problems of the static classroom is the 'afternoon dip'. Teaching after lunch can literally be painful if your body is timed to expect a sleep after lunch. With group teaching you need to be more active, so this is less likely to be a problem.

- If you are sleepy, be upfront and tell the student. (He or she will probably be sympathetic, and may very well be suffering from the same problem.) If you can, take a brief coffee break together with your student, or go and get a cup of coffee and bring it back to the classroom.
- Stand up and move around the classroom. Of course, this is difficult if the classroom is as small as the classrooms allocated for one-to-one teaching tend to be – but physical movement is one of the reasons why it is much easier to stay awake in a group classroom.

Dealing with problem students

Look at the following examples and think of ways of dealing with the students in question. You will find suggested answers on the following pages.

Beatrice

Beatrice is a French teenager doing a homestay course while her parents are on holiday. She is unmotivated and grumpy in class. She is preparing for her *baccalaureate.*

Anastasia

Anastasia is a fifteen-year-old. She has arrived for her morning class clearly worried about something.

Michael

You are teaching Michael in-company. He is taking lessons in preparation for an advanced English exam. He is prone to asking you awkward linguistic questions and you suspect he does not fully trust you to be the best teacher to help him.

Günther

Günther is on a one-week course. He is very keen to study the present perfect, but you have told him that on such a short course and with his particular needs it should not be a priority. He has subsequently been difficult with you in class.

Bruno

Bruno, an Italian businessman, constantly questions your pedagogical and linguistic judgement. He is considerably older than you and obviously thinks you are too young to be teaching him.

Joao Alberto

Joao Alberto is an eighteen-year-old Brazilian from a wealthy family. He is taking six weeks of very expensive classes. However, he arrives late for all lessons and sometimes does not show up at all. He does not take the classes seriously and you find him very difficult to teach.

Miroslaw

You have two hours of one-to-one tuition with Miroslaw in the afternoon. You find his way of speaking exhausting; this is partly due to his accent, partly to his stress, rhythm and intonation and partly to the fact that he makes so many mistakes when he speaks.

Vaclav

Vaclav, a former university professor, now runs a German subsidiary in the Czech Republic. Vaclav uses overlong, over-complex sentences, and when you comment on this he seems reluctant to accept it. He often makes subtle remarks about being more intelligent than other people and you suspect he may talk in this way because he wants to be seen as an intellectual. The atmosphere in the classroom is slightly tense.

Jin Sung

For some reason Jin Sung, a Korean twenty-one-year-old, has taken a dislike to you. You do not know what you have done and you are trying your best to please him.

Yayat

Yayat takes lessons once a week in his lunch hour. He always keeps you at the end of the class by asking last-minute questions, and seems reluctant to let you go. The class usually over-runs by fifteen minutes. You let him do this because you worry that he is not getting value for his money in his sixty-minute lesson.

Paola

Paola is an Italian housewife. She has been taking classes with you for several months now and is intending to continue studying. She only wants to practise speaking, but has no ideas and nothing to say. You do your best to encourage her to speak, but with no success.

Teng

Not only is Teng a complete beginner in English, but he has never been introduced to the Roman alphabet and so cannot read or write. He was not able to survive in the group elementary class, so he has been given one-to-one lessons to get him to a level at which he can go back to the group.

Andreas

Andreas is a pre-intermediate student in his late fifties. His company has recently been restructured and it was decided that all staff should take English classes. Andreas is in a senior position in the company, does not understand why he has to take the lessons and is very unmotivated. When asked to talk about his job, he says *It's too complicated.*

Jean-Paul

Jean-Paul is a nineteen-year-old doing a three-week homestay course in your house. He gets up very late in the morning and seems completely 'out of it' in class. You later realise that he smokes dope every evening.

Jeanette

Jeanette is a wildly attractive, long-legged, unattached, thirty-year-old business English teacher. Male students ask her out constantly. She finds it very difficult to say no although she never wants to go out with them.

(See the next page for suggested ways to deal with these problems.)

Suggested answers

Beatrice

Put the ball back in Beatrice's court. Say to her: 'You're obviously concerned about doing the exams. What do you think is the best way to handle this?' Beatrice may be thrown by this approach, but will appreciate being treated like an adult. In fact, when you ask teenage students directly what the problem is, it may be the first occasion that an adult has really listened to them and you may discover more than you anticipated (that they hate their parents, are serial shop-lifters, etc.)!

Anastasia

If a teenager is worried about something, it is usually a good idea to find out what the problem is. Perhaps Anastasia has had a quarrel with her boyfriend and is dying to contact him. If this is the case, tell her to take a break and call him – otherwise nothing will get done in the classroom.

Michael

If you are an experienced teacher and have no problems handling Michael's questions, he will come to trust your pedagogical judgement in time. If he intimidates you, the Director of Studies might be able to give him a more experienced teacher. If there is no possibility of changing teachers, make a note of all the questions he asks you and tell him that you will have the answers the next time you see him, or that you will email him the information before the next lesson.

Günther

It is not worth fighting Günther. Teach him the present perfect in its simplest form possible and cross your fingers that this will keep him happy.

Bruno

Before you dismiss Bruno as being arrogant, is he right in any way? Perhaps the activities you are doing with him are not the best suited to his needs, but he is unable to tell you this graciously. If he does not believe your linguistic judgement, you can show him the evidence in a reference book. Be good-humoured when he questions your judgement, but make it clear to him that, while he may be expert in many different areas, in the classroom you are the linguistic expert.

Joao Alberto

It is important to 'cover your back' in this type of situation, in case Joao Alberto's parents come back to your organisation complaining that you have not taught him very much. Ask your Director of Studies to remind Joao Alberto that he is wasting his parents' money by not taking the classes seriously. If he continues to behave in the same way, tell him that you will not be responsible for any complaints his parents may have. Explain to him that you are having a hard time teaching him, and discuss with him different activities you could do in class which he would find more motivating.

Miroslaw

Tell Miroslaw that you find him tiring, but that you are working to reduce this problem by a) focusing on his phonological difficulties and b) getting him to slow down his delivery so that he has time to think about what he is going to say. Tell him that, as you find it tiring to listen to him, you will talk a little more than you would normally do in order to give your brain some 'breathing space'.

Vaclav

Record or write down Vaclav's overlong, complicated sentences as before, but don't make any comments about them. Just ask him to look at the sentences and see if there are any changes he would like to make. Don't say 'simpler sentences are better'; he will not be pleased to hear that as it conflicts with his views.

Jin Sung

Tell your Director of Studies about the problem. He or she should then talk to Jin Sung to find out what is troubling him. If it is a simple personality clash, perhaps the Director of Studies can move you to another student.

Yayat

You need to be very ruthless with your timekeeping. Start getting ready to finish the lesson a good five minutes in advance. Tell him that you have to finish exactly on time because you have a meeting/are expecting a phone-call/need to go to your next class, etc. Make sure you have a different excuse for each lesson. DON'T let yourself be waylaid.

Paola

Suggest to the Director of Studies that Paola would benefit from a change of teacher. If that is not possible, explain to Paola that you find it hard work teaching her because she does not talk enough. If that does not lead to any improvement, make sure you give her very structured speaking activities (e.g. describing a picture; answering a long list of questions on a discussion topic) which don't require her to be creative.

Teng

Use techniques for teaching young children.

Andreas

Break down Andreas's job into all its different parts and get him to explain it to you step by step. Very gradually, start filling in the details of his job. Recycle the new words and phrases so he gets a chance to explain the same things again, but in a slightly different way. Once he realises that he can talk about his job successfully, he will be pleased by the progress he has made.

Jean-Paul

You could:

a) pretend you have not noticed and wait until his supply runs out;
b) explain to him that you were not informed in advance that he would be smoking dope and that you are not willing to tolerate it;
c) tell him he can continue with the same behaviour, but you must inform his parents in case they complain later than he has not made enough progress.

Jeanette

She could:

a) wear trousers and minimal make-up to work;
b) invent a live-in boyfriend and make sure she mentions him in class;
c) go on an assertiveness training course to learn to say 'no';
d) ask the Director of Studies to give her female students only.

Chapter 13

Visits and Project Work

In this chapter we will discuss the various issues related to planning external visits to places of interest and how the student can obtain the maximum benefit from such visits. We will also examine the various types of project work which your one-to-one student could undertake.

Visits

One of the advantages of teaching one-to-one is that you can take the students out for visits without having to consult anyone else. You can go anywhere that is logistically possible and which appeals to the student. This can include activities such as beach walks; bird-watching; visiting parks, leisure centres, historical monuments, football clubs and museums; going to the cinema and shopping. First of all, establish what kind of place or activity would interest your student. This may be very different from what you expect. You can also give the student autonomy in deciding the details of the excursion: let them go to the tourist board (physically or online) and find out places to visit. Then they can plan the whole visit, work out how to get there, how long it will take, what to see and so on.

With both formal and informal trips you can divide the visit into a) pre-visit preparation; b) the visit; and c) follow-up activities. In a homestay situation the student can write a guide for any place visited, for the benefit of any subsequent students who come to the homestay family.

Projects

Projects are ideal for groups: the collaboration with other students is one of the advantages of this type of activity. However, they seem less applicable to the one-to-one situation: these types of lessons are very expensive, the student is usually studying for a limited period and time is precious.

Visit to the Royal Courts of Justice

Paolo is a law student who is doing a short course in the UK. The teacher plans a trip to 'legal London'.

Pre-visit preparation

The teacher and Paolo look at:

- the structure of the courts in England and Wales (e.g. magistrates courts; county courts; high courts; up to the European court of justice and the European court of human rights);
- the development of the British legal system;
- history of the buildings and surrounding area;
- the court dress of the legal profession;
- who's who in court.

The visit

The Old Bailey, the Royal Courts of Justice and, depending on time, a quick walk around Middle and Inner Temple, and Lincoln's Inn.

Follow-up

If he wishes, Paolo can write about an aspect of the day that struck him as particularly interesting.

However, projects also have a place in the one-to-one classroom, especially if we use a very loose definition of the word. Here, it is defined as meaning anything which involves the student doing research – usually outside the classroom, but not necessarily outside of lesson time – with an end result. Under this definition, 'projects' and 'visits' can merge into each other. A project can also overlap with a presentation; in this case, the researching aspect of the presentation is as important as the presentation itself. Projects tend to be more suitable for teenagers and children, but can work very well for adult students doing a long-stay course (e.g. an intensive course of six weeks). The important point to remember is that the 'project' can be very simple: the criterion is the quality of the language it generates.

Compared to project work in groups, projects for one-to-one students have the following advantages:

- They can be tailored to the student's own interests.
- The student can 'own' the project – the teacher does not have to take responsibility for everything.
- They can give a homestay teacher a breather if the student is preparing the project outside lesson time (although with fifteen-year-olds and younger you will have to accompany him or her, and if you live outside a city the student is dependent on you for transport).

- They are by necessity less logistically complex than for groups, and so are less daunting for the teacher.

The student can benefit from having the chance to use his or her English to actually do something, and from the opportunity to develop independent learning skills. Projects can be enjoyable for the teacher too, although you have to bear in mind that these kinds of activities can be time-consuming (even if they appear superficially simple). Don't embark on a project unless you have clear objectives, are well-organised, and are willing to do the extra work and research the activities could entail.

Obtaining information	**Skills**
■ Internet searches	■ Reading and extracting information
■ Telephone enquiries	■ Speaking
■ Using reference books	■ Listening and taking notes
■ Interviewing people	■ Analysing
■ Visiting places	■ Writing
	■ Presenting information

Questionnaires and interviews

Devising a questionnaire can be a challenging but worthwhile activity for the student. However, you need to be realistic: how easy is it for your student to interview people outside the school or homestay context?

If your student is attending one-to-one classes in a school, he or she can interview other students, preferably during lunch or coffee breaks. The questionnaires don't have to be oral; they can be answered in writing. If there are other one-to-one students, you can arrange with their teachers for your student to come into the classroom to conduct the survey. Interviews are easier in that the student only needs one or two people to interview. Once the survey or interviews are done, the student analyses the findings and writes up or presents the results.

Using your local library

In addition to books, videos and audiocassettes, libraries contain information on the local community, its history and local facilities, newspapers, magazines and journals, brochures, pamphlets and noticeboards. A lesson in the library is also a nice change from the usual teaching area for homestay students, especially during winter and rainy days when you cannot go outside. You will have to whisper, or not talk at all, so prepare activities that don't require too much communication between you and the student.

Projects for children

Projects are particularly good for children, as they help the child develop other skills as well as his or her English. *Projects in Britain* (Michael Lewis 1993 LTP) has some simple but good ideas for short questionnaires such as:

- *Traditions:* The student has a list of ten questions linked to stereotypes of British people and customers, e.g. *Do you drink a lot of tea? Do you often have bacon and eggs for breakfast?,* with some extra questions specifically designed for finding out about traditions in Britain, e.g. *At what special times of year do you send cards to other people?*
- *How much do British people know about your country?:* The student has to devise a questionnaire first.

All of this presupposes that you can find at least a small population for your student to interview (your partner, children, neighbours, willing friends).

Attila

Attila is a sixteen-year-old who expresses a desire to visit Madame Tussauds. The teacher takes him along with her own teenage son. Photographs are taken of Attila in different poses with the waxworks that have the most appeal for him. Once the photos are developed, Attila researches the biographical details of the waxworks in the pictures and writes a short description for each of them. Attila has an enjoyable day out with an interesting linguistic follow-up.

Madame Tussauds is expensive, but there are lots of museums which are free.

Projects with teenagers

Teenagers can enjoy projects a lot, but if you let them work on the Internet you have to be careful that it does not become the lazy person's way of doing no work: the student presses a button, prints out a lot of pages connected with the topic and then fails to do anything creative with the information. This is not very productive for the teacher and does not involve language learning for the student. Instead of working on the Internet, the student can prepare a highly personalised topic which cannot be researched on the Internet. For example:

- Creating profiles for five of his or her closest friends.
- Creating a family tree with notes on each family member.
- Describing two possessions which are important to the student; if applicable, he or she could design an advertisement for them.

If you want to let the student conduct research on the Internet, make sure the activity is structured and that he or she has a clear task. You can get the student to research a country which you want to visit or which he or she wants to visit, plan a dream trip, prepare a presentation on his or her own country, or research an aspect of British culture.

Pen pal projects

You can either ask friends teaching abroad if they have any students looking for pen pals, and try to match the students up, or you can use one of the following websites:

www.epals.com;
www.penpals.com;
www.teaching.com/KeyPals.

It is important to start by giving the student guidelines on how to structure his or her emails. Once they have got into the swing, you can let them get on with it. If the student becomes very interested in his or her pen pal, he or she can do a project on the pen pal's country.

Supermarkets

Foreign supermarkets are a source of great interest to some students. You can exploit this by going with your student to a good quality supermarket; if this takes place in Britain, the student can take notes in order to make a comparison between British supermarkets and the ones in his or her own country. The student can:

- describe the supermarket as you walk around;
- look at the labels on the products and compare them to the labelling in his or her country;
- discuss the various products.

This is a very simple activity, but that is the whole point: very simple activities can generate a great deal of linguistic output and, for the student who is interested, will be very involving. Any kind of shopping is suitable.

Projects for business English students

You can ask your student to research a company, or compare company websites. *Teaching English with IT* by David Smith (Modern English Publishing, 2005) or *The Internet and Business English* by B. Barrett and P. Sharma (Summertown Publishing, 2003) both have a variety of activities for exploiting company websites, together with company website evaluation sheets.

Newspaper-based projects

You can look at the layout, content and political approach of one newspaper in detail, or you can buy a selection of tabloid and broadsheet newspapers and get the student to compare and contrast. You will need to do language input in advance to make sure the student has all the terminology necessary (e.g. columnist; editorial; print size).

Polina
Polina loves films, so the teacher arranges for her to see a film of her choice. Before she goes to see it, the teacher writes a worksheet for her to read before the film and to fill in after seeing it. The teacher hasn't seen the movie himself, but he has read some reviews and knows the story. The teacher's questions focus on the images, ideas and techniques of the film, rather than simple comprehension. Then the teacher asks Polina to read a couple of reviews of the film which he found in newspapers and on the Internet. Once Polina has done this, the teacher asks her to give her reaction to the film and the reviews.

Sara
Sara, who has an intermediate level of English, works for a company producing upmarket costume jewellery. The company is planning to expand the business in Europe.

The teacher makes sure Sara has the vocabulary for describing jewellery. This is a big area and requires looking at catalogues, doing Internet searches for costume jewellery and working with the *Oxford-Duden Pictorial Italian-English Dictionary.*

Sara visits several shops to conduct a survey of what the shops are offering. The teacher chooses small independent shops, where Sara can create a relationship with the owner or manager during her visit.

Sara then rings the owner/manager of one of the shops, to see if she can set up a telephone interview to find out what criteria the shop uses when buying its jewellery.

Sara writes a report about her (small) survey of the British market.

Linguistic elements of project work

Exploit the linguistic possibilities of the activity as much as possible:

- The student should record important new vocabulary and phrases on to cards or write them in a vocabulary notebook.
- You need to monitor his or her language, make notes and give feedback.
- At the end of the activity evaluate what the student has learned.

Conclusion

If you decide to do any kind of activity outside the confines of the classroom, whether it be a project or a visit, make sure you have clear objectives as to what you want the student to get out of it. Prepare the student both in terms of the content and for any language work they may need to do; then do follow-up activities. Remember that the 'project' can be very simple: what is important is the student's interest in it and the language it generates.

Recommended Resources

ELT Websites

www.bbcworldservice.com/learningenglish
This has a wide range of activities for learners of English such as vocabulary exercises, quizzes, listening and topical news-based activities.

www.teachingenglish.org.uk
This is a site run jointly by the BBC and the British Council. It has lesson plans, articles on methodology and questions for discussion, plus other material. It also has good links to other organisations.

www.onestopenglish.com
This is Macmillan's website which is full of information and activities for both teachers and students. It also has *Guardian Weekly* articles with comprehension questions at three levels.

www.english-forum.com
This has a novel of the month together with a dictionary look-up and a list of online study resources.

www.english-to-go.com
This has resources based on Reuters news articles: ready-to-use articles and on-line interactive self-study exercises.

ELT Organisations

www.arels.org.uk
ARELS (Association of Recognised English Language Schools)

www.iatefl.org
IATEFL (International Association of Teaching English as a Foreign Language)

www.baselt.org.uk
BASELT (British Association of State English Language Teaching)

English language teaching magazines and newsletters

EL Gazette
A monthly newspaper for the EFL industry.
www.elgazette.com

ELT Journal
Quarterly journal for ELT teachers and researchers.
www.eltj.oupjournals.org

English Teaching Professional
Leading practical magazine for English language teachers.
www.etprofessional.com

Modern English Teacher
Quarterly journal for English language teachers.
www.onlineMET.com

Examinations

CambridgeESOL
www.cambridge-efl.org.uk
University of Cambridge, ESOL Examinations, 1 Hills Road,
Cambridge CB1 2EU
Phone: ++44 (0) 1223 553355
Fax: ++44 (0) 1223 460278
Email address: helpdesk@ucles.org.uk

City & Guilds / Pitman
www.pitmanqualifications.com
Exams for various levels, including young learners and business English.
City & Guilds Pitman Qualifications.1 Giltspur Street, London EC1A 9DD
Phone: ++44 (0) 20 7294 3500
Fax: ++44 (0) 20 7294 3502
Email address: infor@pitmanqualifications.co.uk

ETS (TOEFL, TOEIC)
www.ets.com / www.toefl.org / www.toeic.org
This has an online writing practice facility for students; the students can get

immediate score feedback on their essay responses and receive general suggestions for improving their writing skills.

Flo-Joe
www.flo-joe.co.uk
Practice activities for FCE (First Certificate Examination) and CAE (Cambridge Advanced Examination). For both teachers and students.

Fullbright
www.fulbright.co.uk
US Education Advisory Service – TOEFL.
The Fulbright Commission, London WC1N 2JZ
Phone: ++44 (0) 20 7404 6994

IELTS
www.ielts.org
British Council (IELTS Enquiries)
Bridgewater House, 58 Whitworth Street, Manchester M1 6BB

LCCIEB
www.lccieb.com
LCCIEB (London Chamber of Commerce and Industry Examinations Board)
Athena House, 112 Station Road, Sidcup, Kent DA15 7BJ
Phone: ++44 (0) 20 8302 0261
Fax: ++44 (0) 20 8302 4169
Email address: custserv@lccieb.org.uk

Trinity Exams
www.trinity-london.co.uk
Trinity College London, 89 Albert Embankment, London, SE1 7TP
Phone: ++44 (0) 20 7820 6100
Fax: ++44 (0) 207820 6161
email: tesol@trinitycollege.co.uk

Testing

www.dialang.org
This is a European project for the development of diagnostic language tests in fourteen European languages. Tests are available on the Internet free of charge. It offers separate tests for reading, writing, listening, grammatical structures and vocabulary. Its proficiency levels are based on the Council of Europe's scales, which are part of the Council's Common European Framework of reference.

Media

www.bbc.co.uk
This covers TV, radio and the World Service.

www.cnn.com
CNN news plus radio and video.

www.education.guardian.co.uk/tefl
The *Guardian's* TEFL pages.

www.ft.com
The *Financial Times'* website; this is useful for specialised areas, although you need to subscribe to get access to most material.

www.guardian.co.uk
This gives access to both the *Guardian* and the *Observer*.

www.thebigproject.co.uk/news/
Links to all UK national newspapers plus the main regional newspapers, TV and news agencies, minority newspapers and business news websites.

www.thisislondon.co.uk
Evening Standard website with useful London information.

English language learning student publications

www. modernenglishdigest.com
This is the website for the English language learning magazine *Modern English Digest*, aimed at elementary and intermediate level learners.

www.spotlight-verlag.de
German speakers may be familiar with the English teaching magazines *Spotlight*, *Business Spotlight* and *Spot On* for young learners. Their website is also very helpful.

Business English

www.bized.ac.uk
This is a service aimed at students, teachers and lecturers of business, economics, accounting, leisure and recreation and travel and tourism. The site contains Internet resources, learning materials such as company information and current topics.

www.besig.org
BESIG (Business English Special Interest Group) – see IATEFL

This gives information about BESIG conferences, workshops, news and forum and has a forum for discussion. It also has a regular newsletter for IATEFL members who join BESIG.

www.businessenglishonline.net
Macmillan's business English website.

Teaching children and teenagers

www.ajkids.com
Ask Jeeves for Kids.

www.countryschool.com/ylsig
This is the website of IATEFL's special interest group for Young Learners. It has a very long list of Internet EFL/ESL resources for Young Learners.

www.learnenglish.org.uk/kid_frame.html
The British Council's KidZone.

www.longman-elt.com/young_learners
This is full of useful activities and tips with resources for teachers and learners.

www.onestopenglish.com/children/childrenmain.htm
This has both material for use in the classroom and methodology.

www.thesite.org.uk
For teenagers and young adults.

www.storyarts.org
Aids for storytelling.

www.yahooligans.com
Version of Yahoo aimed at children.

Homestay

www.h-p-a.org.uk
Homestay Providers Association

British Council Recognised homestay organisations

Regent Language Training
12 Buckingham Street, London WC2N 6DF
Phone: ++44 (0) 20 7872 6620 Fax: ++44 (0) 20 7872 6630
Email address: homestay@regent.org.uk

International House
106 Piccadilly, London W1J 7NL
Phone: ++44 (0) 20 7518 6950 Fax: ++44 (0) 20 7518 6951
Email address: info@ihlondon.co.uk

Bookshops

www.amazon.co.uk

www.bebc.co.uk

www.ebcoxford.co.uk

www.eflbooks.co.uk

www.keltic.co.uk

www.lclib.com

Publishers

In addition to information about publications, the major publishers have on-line material to accompany their course books.

ABAX ELT Publishers www.abax.co.jp

Adams & Austen Press Publishers www.aapress.com.au

Addison-Wesley www.awl.com

Alta Book Center Publishers www.altaesl.com

Barron's www.barronseduc.com/english-language-arts.html

Beaumont Publishing www.beaumont-publishing.com

Cambridge University Press www.cup.cam.ac.uk

Crown House Publishing www.crownhouse.co.uk

Delta Publishing www.deltabooks.co.uk

Dymon Publications www.dymonbooks.com

DynED International www.dyned.com

Encomium Publications, Inc. www.encomium.com

Express Publishing ELT Books www.expresspublishing.co.uk

Full Blast Productions www.fullblastproductions.com

Garnet Education www.garneteducation.com

Georgian Press www.georgianpress.co.uk

Griffith Books www.griffith-books-ltd.sagenet.co.uk

HarperCollins Publishers www.harpercollins.com

Heinemann www.macmillaneducation.com

Heinle & Heinle Thomson Learning www.heinle.com

Hodder and Stoughton www.madaboutbooks.com

Houghton Mifflin www.hmco.com

John Benjamins Publishing www.benjamins.com/jbp

Longman English language Teaching www.longman-elt.com

Macmillan English www.macmillanenglish.com

Marshall Cavendish ELT www.mcelt.co.uk

McGraw-Hill Companies www.mhhe.com/catalogs/hss/esl/

Modern English Publishing www.modernenglishpublishing.com

New Readers Press www.newreaderspress.com

Oxford University Press www.oup.co.uk

Peter Collin Publishing www.bloomsbury.com/reference

Pro Lingua Associates www.ProLinguaAssociates.com

Publishing Choice www.publishingchoice.com

Richmond Publishing www.richmondelt.com

Summertown Publishing www.summertown.co.uk

Prentice Hall Regents www.phregents.com

York Associates www.york-associates.co.uk

British culture and life

www.britcoun.org
The British Council 10 Spring Gardens, London SW1A 2BN
Phone: ++44 (0) 20 7930 8466 Fax: ++44 (0) 20 7930 6347

www.visitBritain.com
Travel guide to Britain

www.open.gov.uk
This has links to hundreds of government ministries and departments, town and city councils, universities, together with statistics and news from the government

Games and activities

www.puzzlemaker.com

Jobs

www.edunet.com

www.jobsunlimited.co.uk

www.tefl.com

Encyclopedias

www.britannica.com

http://encarta.msn.com

Penpals

www.teaching.com/KeyPals

Glossary

A

Accuracy The ability to produce grammatically correct sentences (*Longman Dictionary of Language Teaching and Applied Linguistics*).
Active vocabulary The ability to use vocabulary actively in speaking and writing, as opposed to the passive understanding of vocabulary in listening and reading.
Appropriateness The use of language which is appropriate for the situation for which it is being used, e.g. not using informal language in a formal context.
Articulation The production of speech sounds in the mouth and throat *(Longman Dictionary of Language Teaching and Applied Linguistics).*
Authentic materials Materials which are designed for native speakers, not for language learners.

B

Bottom-up processing The student relies on knowledge of the linguistic system to make sense of what someone is saying, rather than non-linguistic knowledge (e.g. general knowledge). (See *top-down processing.*)
Business skill In business English, *business skills* usually refers to presentations, meetings, negotiations, telephoning and any other activity for which a student uses English in the workplace, such as interviewing or reading company reports.
Business concept The idea(s) that a business term describes, e.g. a market economy; high-risk investment,

C

Coherence The underlying logical connectedness of a text, whereby concepts and relationships are relevant to each other and where it is possible to make plausible inferences about underlying meaning.
(www..lancs.ac.uk/wbsnet/providertoolkit/glossary.htm)
Example: A: 'How are you?', B: 'I'm fine thanks' is coherent, while A: 'How are you?' B: 'The pound has risen against the dollar' is not.
Cohesion The grammatical and/or lexical relationships between the different elements of a text. This may be the relationship between different sentences or between different parts of a sentence *(Longman Dictionary of Language Teaching and Applied Linguistics).*
Example: Borrowing money on a credit card is very expensive. This does not deter many people

from doing it. (There is a link between borrowing money and this.)
Collocation The words most likely to be associated with another word; e.g. *to run a risk*; *a high-risk strategy*; *commercially viable* (see *Word Partnership*). Collocations include adjective+noun, verb+ noun, noun+ verb, adverb+adjective, verb+adverb partnerships.
Communicative methods Methods of teaching English which focus on improving the student's ability to communicate, rather than the student's knowledge of the language system.
Communicative performance The student's linguistic performance analysed in terms of the success of the overall communication, rather than simply on the student's use of the language system.
Controlled practice Practice activities which control the output of the student in order to reinforce a language structure. Controlled practice does not give the student the opportunity for free expression.
Course programme A document given to the student which visually represents the objectives of the language course. The content of the course programme is based on the results of the needs analysis.

D

Diagnostic grammar Teaching grammar according to the student's needs rather than following a prescribed syllabus of grammatical structures. The teacher then looks at the grammatical areas with which the student has difficulty, rather than pre-teaching grammatical items.
Diagnostic work Doing language work with the student according to the student's needs rather than following a prescribed syllabus.
(See *Diagnostic grammar*.)
Director of Studies The person in charge of the academic aspects of a course.
Discourse error An error which refers to a larger unit of written or spoken text, such as a paragraph or a conversation, e.g. a paragraph which lacks linking words which could aid the reader's understanding. Problems with coherence are discourse errors.

E

Elicit To manage to get information or a response from someone. (*Macmillan English Dictionary for Advanced Learners*)
Elision The loss of a sound or sounds, e.g. '*next week*' ('*t*' is lost); '*old man*' ('*d*' is lost).
Enactment Where the student acts out a situation encountered in his or her daily life, such as a weekly team meeting.
Error A mistake which results from incomplete knowledge (*Longman Dictionary of*

Language Teaching and Applied Linguistics).
Error analysis Examining the student's errors in order to classify them and to see what patterns of difficulties with the language system emerge. The teacher can then take action to help the student with these particular difficulties.
Error correction Situation where the teacher looks at the student's linguistic performance in detail and helps the student to make any necessary changes to deviant forms.
ESP English for Specific Purposes. This usually refers to specialised English language teaching such as English for Law or English for Military Personnel.
Executive student A business English student who already has job experience.
Extensive course A course where the student studies on a part-time basis, such as two evenings a week for ten weeks.
Extensive listening Listening for general understanding, not for detail.
Extensive reading Reading for general understanding, not for detail.
Extrinsic motivation Motivation which exists due to external factors, e.g. a student wants to get a promotion and needs to speak English to a certain level in order to be eligible for the job.

F

Fluency Being able to express yourself in a clear and confident way without seeming to make an effort. (*Macmillan English Dictionary for Advanced Learners*)
Feedback Giving the student comments about the overall success of his or her performance in a particular task.
Feedback sheet Sheet of paper on which the teacher makes notes on the student's linguistic performance, highlighting both good use of language and slips, mistakes and errors.
Fossilised error An error which is deeply ingrained, which results in the student making an incorrect form automatically and so having difficulty in using the correct form.
Framework materials Materials which allow the teacher to use the student's experience and knowledge by presenting the structure for a discussion, sometimes with key vocabulary on one page or less.
Function words Words which have little meaning on their own, but which contribute to the grammatical construction (such as prepositions, modals and pronouns).

G

Gap-fills Sentences with gaps which the students must fill. The blanks can be grammatical or lexical items.

Graded readers English readers which are specially written to cover only certain grammatical and lexical items, such as should be known by students of a certain level.

H

Homestay teaching Teaching a student in your own home.

I

Idiom An expression whose total meaning is different from the meaning of the individual words, such as *to have your feet on the ground* meaning *to be sensible.* (*Macmillan English Dictionary for Advanced Learners*)
Idiomatic Peculiar to a particular group, individual or style, e.g. *his English is correct but not very idiomatic* means he does not sound like a native speaker. *To speak an idiomatic English* means to sound like a native speaker. Compare *My feeling is good today* (grammatically correct) and *I feel good*/ I feel well (idiomatic).
Input Language which a learner hears or receives and from which he or she can learn. (*Longman Dictionary of Language Teaching and Applied Linguistics*)
Intensive course A course where a student studies on a full-time basis, e.g. a two-week course from 0900 to 1700 five days a week.
Intensive listening Listening to understand detail.
Intensive reading Reading to understand detail.
Intonation The way in which your voice rises and falls as you speak. (*Macmillan English Dictionary for Advanced Learners*)
Intrinsic motivation Motivation which exists due to internal rather than external reasons, e.g. a student learns English because of a love of British culture or a love of learning languages rather than because of a need to pass an exam. (See *Extrinsic motivation.*)

K

KISS principle Keep It Short and Simple.

L

Learning strategy A way in which a learner attempts to work out the meanings and uses of words, grammatical rules and other aspects of a language, for example by the use of generalisation and inferencing. (*Longman Dictionary of Language Teaching and Applied Linguistics*)
Learning style The way in which a student learns, e.g. a student needs to always write down a word before being able to pronounce it.
Lesson plan Detailed plan of a lesson, drawn up by the teacher before the lesson begins.

Lexical error Any kind of error connected with the use of vocabulary.
Lexis Vocabulary.
Liaison The linking of words particularly when the second word begins with a vowel (e.g. *at home*; *in a minute*). The sounds /r/, /w/ and /j/ can be inserted between words to improve liaison (e.g. l*aw and order*; *you are*; *she always comes*).
Listening strategy A strategy which helps the student to listen effectively (e.g. using visual clues to help decode what is being said; not trying to understand every word).

M

Mistake Situation where the student uses an incorrect form, but can correct himself or herself when the mistake is pointed out.
Mixed ability classes Classes where there is more than one level in the class.
Modal verbs May, might, can, could, must, have to, will, would, shall, should.
Monitor (language) To check the student's use of language during an output session such as a role-play or discussion.

N

Needs analysis The process of finding out what a student needs and wants to do during the language course.
Negotiated syllabus A syllabus based on the student's needs and wants, as opposed to a fixed syllabus which is imposed upon a student.
Nominalisation Forming nouns from other parts of speech, e.g. to sing = singer, singing.

O

Oral correction The teacher corrects the student orally rather than writing down the deviant language form.
Output Language a learner produces.

P

Passive vocabulary Vocabulary which the student knows passively but is unable to activate in speech or writing.
Pedagogical Referring to teaching, e.g. pedagogical methods = teaching methods.
Phrasal verbs Combination of words that is used like a verb and consists of a verb and an adverb or preposition, such as *give in* or *come up with*. (*Macmillan English Dictionary for Advanced Learners*)
Pragmatic error Production of the wrong communicative effect; e.g. through faulty use of a speech act or one of the rules of speaking. (*Longman Dictionary of*

Language Teaching and Applied Linguistics)
Pre-experience students Students who have not yet started full-time work.
Private lessons Individual lessons (i.e. one-to-one lessons).
Prominence Stressing syllables and words which the speaker wants to emphasise.

R

Readers (see **Graded Readers**).
Recycling activities Activities which repeat something already learned in order to help the student memorise the new language.
Redundancy Any words which are not necessary for expressing one's view. The degree to which a message contains more information than is needed for it to be understood. (*Longman Dictionary of Language Teaching and Applied Linguistics*)
Reformulation A technique whereby the teacher looks at what the student actually said or wrote, then reformulates the language into idiomatic English (i.e. something a native speaker would say).
Remedial grammar Helping the student improve grammatical knowledge according to his or her needs rather than according to a prescribed syllabus. Finding out the student's areas of grammatical weakness and then helping him or her to improve these, rather than teaching grammatical items with which the student does not necessarily have difficulties.
Role-play Drama-like classroom activities in which students take the roles of different participants in a situation and act out what might typically happen in that situation. (*Longman Dictionary of Language Teaching and Applied Linguistics*)
Rhythm The sequence of strong and weak elements in language; there are different views: some say rhythm refers to the occurrence of stresses, others say that it depends on strong and weak vowels.(*Pronunciation*: Christiane Dalton and Barbara Seidlhofer)

S

Scanning Reading quickly to find a specific piece of information.
Sentence stress Stress which falls in a sentence, and which is more important than the stress of the individual words in the sentence.
Slip The student knows the correct form but inadvertently makes a mistake.
Skimming = Reading for general meaning.
Socio-linguistic competence Ability to use language correctly in social situations.
Socio-pragmatic failure Failures which result from culture-clashes, from cultural differences of view concerning what is appropriate social (and socio-linguistic) behaviour in certain settings. (*Errors in Language Learning and Use*: Carl James)
Study strategies Any strategy which allows the student to study more effectively, e.g. noting down new vocabulary in a special notebook; knowing and implementing

all the uses of a dictionary.
SVO Subject – Verb – Object.
Syllable stress Stress on a particular syllable in a word (as opposed to 'sentence stress'); e.g. PRO-blem; de-STORY.
Syllabus List of the main subjects in a course of study. (*Macmillan English Dictionary for Advanced Learners*)
Syntax The study of how words combine to form sentences and the rules which govern the formation of sentences. (*Longman Dictionary of Language Teaching and Applied Linguistics*)

T

Tailor-made (programme) A programme which is designed to fit the student's particular needs and wants, as opposed to a 'one-size-fits-all' programme.
Top-down processing Situation in which the learner uses his or her non-linguistic knowledge to decode a speaker's message or a text, rather than relying on his or her linguistic knowledge. (See *Bottom-up processing.*)

W

Weak forms The 'little' words in speech (i.e. function words such as prepositions, modals and pronouns, which have little meaning of their own but which contribute to the grammatical construction) which are usually not stressed in spoken English.
Worksheets Exercises written to exploit the linguistic aspects of a piece of written or spoken text.

15

Bibliography

Books

Bartram, M. and Walton, R., *Correction* (Thomson Heinle, 2002)

Brieger, N., *The Teaching Business English Handbook* (York Associates, 1997)

Buck, Gary, *Assessing Listening* (CUP, 2001)

Council of Europe, *Common European Framework of Reference for Languages: Learning, teaching, assessment* (CUP, 2001)

Dalton, C. and Seidlhofer, B., *Pronunciation* (OUP, 1994)

Donna, S., *Teach Business English* (CUP, 2000)

Ellis, M. & Johnson, C., *Teaching Business English* (OUP, 1994)

Fried-Book, D.L., *Project Work* (OUP, 2002)

Grellet, F., *Developing Reading Skills* (CUP, 1981)

Halliwell, S., *Teaching English in the Primary Classroom* (Longman, 1992)

Harmer, J., *How to teach English* (Longman, 1998)

Halliday, M.A.K., *Spoken and Written Language* (OUP, 1985)

Hedge, T., *Writing* (OUP, 1988)

James, C., *Errors in Language Learning and Use* (Longman, 1998)

Kress, G., *Learning to Write (2nd edition)* (Routledge, 1994)

Lewis, M., *Projects in Britain* (LTP, 1993)

Macarthy, M. & O'Dell, F., *English Vocabulary in Use: Upper-intermediate and advanced* (CUP, 1994)

Moon, J., *Children Learning English* (Macmillan ELT, 2000)

Murphey, T., *One to one* (Longman, 1991)

Norrish, J., *Language Learners and their Errors* (Macmillan, 1983)

Parrot, M., *Tasks for Language Teachers* (CUP, 1993)

Phillips, S., *Young Learners* (OUP, 1993)

Ribé, R. and Vidal, N., *Project Work Step by Step* (Macmillan Heinemann, 1993)

Richards, Jack C., Platt, John and Platt, Heidi, *Dictionary of Language Teaching and Applied Linguistics (2nd edition)* (Longman, 1992)

Rixon, S., *Teaching English to Young Learners* (Modern English Publishing, 2005)
Reed, J., *Assessing Vocabulary* (CUP, 2000)
Underhill, A., *Sound Foundations* (Heinemann, 1994)
Ur, P., *Teaching Listening Comprehension* (CUP, 1984)
Wilberg, P., *One to One* (LTP, 1987)

Articles

Freebain, I. & Barker, C., Teaching young learners in *Arena*, issue 16 (ARELS Magazine)
Jackson, A., How to teach young learners in *Arena* Issue 33
Read, C., Towards whole learning in *IATEFL SIGs Newsletter in memory of Gillian Porter Ladousse*, Spring 2003

Books mentioned in the text

Barret, B. and Sharma, P., *The Internet and Business English* (Summertown Publishing, 2003)
Council of Europe, *Common European Framework of Reference for Languages: Learning, teaching, assessment* (CUP, 2001)
Brieger, N., *The Teaching Business English Handbook* (York Associates, 1997)
Collins CoBuild English Guides 9: *Linking words* (HarperCollins, 1996)
Cotton, Falvey and Kent, *Market Leader Intermediate* (Longman, 2000)
Dignen, B., *Down to Business Minimaxes* (York Associates)
Donna, S., *Teach Business English* (CUP, 2000)
Emmerson, P., *Business Builder Modules* (Macmillan, 1999)
Emmerson, P., *Framework materials* (CUP, 2002)
Gibson, R., *Intercultural Business Communication* (OUP, 2002)
Halliwell, S., *Teaching English in the Primary Classroom* (Longman, 1992)
Honey & Mumford *Manual of Learning Styles* (P. Honey, Maidenhead, 1992)
Laws, A., *Business Skills Series* (Summertown Publishing, 2000)
Lewis, M., *Projects in Britain* (LTP, 1993)
James, C., *Errors in Language Learning and Use* (Longman, 1998)
Moon, J., *Children Learning English* (Macmillan Heinemann, 2000)
Oxford-Duden *Pictorial Italian and English Dictionary* (OUP, 1995)
Redman, S., *English Vocabulary in Use: Pre-intermediate and intermediate* (CUP, 1997)
Richards, Jack C., Platt, John and Platt, Heidi, *Longman Dictionary of Language Teaching and Applied Linguistics* (Longman, 1992)
Schofield, J., *Double Dealing* (Summertown Publishing, 2004)
Utley, D., *Culture Pack: Intercultural Communication* (York Associates, 2000)
Watcyn-Jones, P., *Vocabulary Games and Activities for Teaching* (Longman, 1993)

Organisations mentioned mentioned in the text

IATEFL
ARELS

Examination boards, exams and tests mentioned in the text

BULATS (Business English Language Testing Service)
UCLES
LCCIEB
ARELS/Oxford exams
TOEFL
TOEIC
Oxford placement tests: two packs of tests for all levels from elementary to post-Proficiency
Dialang (Council of Europe diagnostic language tests)

Student Journals mentioned in the text

Business Spotlight
Modern English Digest
Spotlight

Websites mentioned in the text

www.bbc.co.uk
www.bbc.co.uk/worldservice/learningenglish
www.modernenglishdigeest.com
www.spotlight-verlag.de
www.englishlistening.com
www.h-p-a.org.uk
www.onestopenglish.com
www.crb.gov.uk
www.learnenglish.com
www.countryschool.com/ylsig
www.ajkids.com
www.longman-elt.com/young_learners
www.storyarts.org
www.enchangedlearning.com/Dictionary.html

www.lyrics.com
www.lyricworld.com
www.getlyrics.com
www.macmillan.czimg/readers.pdf
www.cambridge-org.elt/readers
www.puzzlemaker.com
www.geocities.com/esolscale/index.html
www.penpals.com
www.epals.com
www.teaching.com/KeyPals

Index